The Medical Transcription Workbook

Health Professions Institute
Modesto, California

The Medical Transcription Workbook
by Health Professions Institute

Published by:

Health Professions Institute
P. O. Box 801
Modesto, CA 95353-0801
Phone (209) 551-2112
Fax (209) 551-0404
Web site: http://www.hpisum.com
E-mail: hpi@hpisum.com
Sally Crenshaw Pitman, Editor & Publisher

Printed by:
Parks Printing and Lithography
Modesto, California

ISBN: 0-934385-23-8

Last digit is the print number: 9 8 7 6 5 4

In memory of
Vera Pyle, CMT

Acknowledgments

This book is primarily the work of Linda Campbell, CMT, Director of Education and Product Development at Health Professions Institute. Although the book has been written over a period of several months, *The Medical Transcription Workbook* has grown out of her experience in the medical transcription field over the past 20 years. Certainly she has been writing it mentally since 1987, when she began development of *The SUM Program for Medical Transcription Training*. For her, the book has truly been a labor of love, and her knowledge and skill are evident throughout.

Diane Heath, CMT, Associate Editor at Health Professions Institute, has contributed significantly to the book from her knowledge of medical transcription practices; her many hours of thoughtful writing, editing, proofreading, and making answer keys have greatly increased the value of the book.

Ellen Drake, CMT, former Director of Education at Health Professions Institute, and a noted author, editor, and medical transcription practitioner with many years of experience, contributed much of the material in the Style and Usage section. She has written many articles on medical transcription for students, teachers, and practitioners over the years, and her proofreading and editing contributed greatly to the book's accuracy and completeness.

John H. Dirckx, M.D., who has generously served as HPI's medical consultant since 1987, contributed many useful suggestions and corrections to the text, and as always, we appreciate his awareness of what medical transcriptionists *need*. We have borrowed liberally from three books he authored for HPI (*H&P: A Nonphysician's Guide to the Medical History and Physical Examination*; *Laboratory Medicine: Essentials of Anatomic and Clinical Pathology*; and *Human Diseases*).

To all the medical transcriptionists whose articles we excerpted and quoted in this book, we are truly grateful. We could not have produced this book without a lot of help from our friends and colleagues.

Sally C. Pitman, MA
Editor & Publisher

Preface

The Medical Transcription Workbook was written for both student and professional medical transcriptionists for the express purpose of helping them identify, learn, and test their knowledge of the most relevant and important topics in medical transcription.

It is hoped that upon completion of this workbook, students will have achieved an integrated understanding of the multifaceted world of medicine, and that practicing MT professionals will find this book has helped to fill gaps in their knowledge base. For both, it should greatly increase their understanding of the language of medicine and thus facilitate the preparation, taking, and passing of credentialing medical transcription examinations.

This workbook contains eight sections. Section 1, Professional Issues, contains many readings on dozens of important topics: editing, quality, confidentiality, employment issues, working at home, productivity, compensation, technology, and much more. Worksheets are provided at the end of each topic or related topics.

Section 2, Style & Usage, will serve as a primer for punctuation, grammar, and spelling rules for students, and as a necessary review for experienced MTs. Worksheets are provided to help students assess their understanding of the subject matter.

Sections 3 through 8 consist entirely of worksheets in anatomy and physiology, medical terminology, pathophysiology, surgery, laboratory medicine, and pharmacology. Each of these sections contains subsections which are laid out by body system or medical specialty. The contents of these sections should make obvious to any student or practitioner of medical transcription the depth and breadth of knowledge required in this profession. It is not likely that even the most experienced transcriptionist will be able to call to mind the answers to all of the exercises without referring to an anatomy text, a medical terminology book, a human disease text, a book on diagnostic and operative procedures, a laboratory reference, a pharmacology text, and English and medical dictionaries. This fact should also reinforce our recommendation that every practicing medical transcriptionist have access to an adequate reference library, both printed and electronic, and that these references be updated frequently in order to provide the latest information in a rapidly changing medical environment.

A special note about Section 5, Pathophysiology. The term *pathophysiology* was chosen over the more familiar name *human diseases* because its definition more closely defines what that section is: a study of order versus disorder in the human being. Included in the pathophysiology section are questions related to the history and physical examination, certain diagnostic maneuvers and procedures that are not usually classified as surgical, and, of course, human diseases.

The individual disciplines of anatomy, terminology, pathophysiology, surgery, laboratory, and pharmacology meld into a general fund of knowledge in medical transcription; it becomes impossible to clearly delineate each of these as courses separate and completely apart from one another. Thus, students and teachers will note the inevitable overlap of anatomy and medical terminology questions, anatomy and pathophysiology questions, pathophysiology and surgery, pharmacology with laboratory, and so on.

The style of question used was largely determined by the material. Some topics were conducive to the highly desirable multiple-choice format, while others could only be written true-or-false. Some worksheets contain fill-in-the-blank questions with a blank line long enough to write in an answer, but the length of the line has no bearing on whether the answer is long or short, one word, two words, or more. Matching exercises (matching words with definitions, matching diseases with symptoms) are provided for some topics. In the Style and Usage section, students may be required to circle an answer, punctuate a sentence, or correct the grammar. Infrequently, a question may be asked in one section and asked again, slightly rephrased, in another. Some abbreviations and medications may appear in more than one section because of the natural overlap of specialties; however, these redundancies have been kept to a minimum.

We at Health Professions Institute encourage and salute students and teachers in their pursuit of excellence in medical transcription. It is our hope that this book will be a means to that end.

Linda Campbell, CMT
August 1998

Contents

4 Medical Terminology *(continued)*

5 Pathophysiology

8 Pharmacology

Section 1.
Professional Issues

The Modern Healthcare Team

Through the years, the coupling of medical breakthroughs with improved health record documentation has produced the modern healthcare team. Today that team includes physicians, nurses, pharmacists, therapists, dietitians, technicians, technologists, health information managers, health educators—and medical transcriptionists (MTs). From the earliest inception of their identity as professionals, medical transcriptionists have sought recognition and validation of their role as members of the healthcare team. They want to be treated as professionals and to have a say in matters that pertain to the medical and legal accuracy of the patient's health record.

You've been reading the advertisements for medical transcription educational programs—those ads that tell you what a snap it is to learn medical transcription and promise that in no time you will be earning at least $50,000 a year. The ads tell you that if you can type, you can be a medical transcriptionist (and if you can't type, they will teach you). Remember that old maxim: "If it sounds too good to be true, it probably is."

Despite what these ads would have you believe, medical transcription is not easy to learn, nor is it possible to become a qualified medical transcriptionist virtually overnight. It is, after all, a profession, not just a job, and those who have reached the pinnacle of this profession have done so only with constant effort and a dedication to continuing education. Those who want solid information about the field should take time to speak with a variety of MTs working in the community in order to get a clear picture of what to expect.

While not as visible to the general public as other allied health professionals, the medical transcriptionist plays an important role in providing quality patient care. Because each dictated report represents a part of the patient's life, the medical transcriptionist must transcribe it with accuracy and care. The highest professional standards contribute to the medical transcriptionist's ability to interpret, translate, and edit medical dictation for content and clarity to produce a permanent health record document.

How is a medical secretary's job different from that of a medical transcriptionist? Medical typist? Medical word processor? Medical steno? What about a medical language specialist? In some facilities there may be no difference at all! *Medical secretary, medical typist, medical steno, medical word processor,* and *medical language specialist* are job titles that have all been used at one time or another to denote *medical transcriptionist.* In some job environments, however, there may a difference.

Physician offices, group practices, clinics, and large medical centers with individual specialty offices may utilize the *medical secretary* for duties other than (or in addition to) medical transcription:

The Modern Healthcare Team, Continued

answering phones, filing of patient records, office management, chart work, editing and revising medical documents, and so on.

Medical steno is a job classification that has evolved greatly over the years. This evolution is described in the gray box on this page. *Medical typist, medical word processor,* and *medical language specialist* are terms used to describe *medical transcriptionist* as we define it today.

Those who have relegated medical transcription to the "clerical" classification have a basic misunderstanding of the knowledge and skills required for this profession. Although medical transcription is performed using a keyboard—either a conventional computer keyboard or a steno (or court reporter) keyboard—it is not a keyboarding skill. It is a language skill.

The qualified medical transcriptionist (MT) must be fluent in the medical language, which means that the MT hears, understands, and translates dictation, employing medical language skills that are often equal to those of the physician or other allied health professional doing the dictation. The MT must understand basic anatomy and physiology, disease processes, laboratory medicine, and pharmacology in order to select and use appropriate terminology, since there are many soundalike words in the medical language.

The MT must also have a knowledge of virtually hundreds of medical procedures and a multitude of medical instruments and equipment. Further, in order to properly translate and document patient care records, the MT must employ a knowledge of English grammar, punctuation, and editing on at least a college level.

Basic and advanced knowledge of computers and related technologies is a necessity for individuals entering the medical transcription field. Knowledge of at least one major word-processing program helps students make the jump to other word-processing applications. Many hospitals and transcription services use proprietary word-processing software that has been developed for their particular needs.

Is Medical Transcription What I Do or What I Am?

After I moved to Massachusetts from Ohio, I went to the voter registration office and filled out a computer form. Occupation: Medical Transcriptionist. The gum-chewing clerk gave me a petulant look. "It doesn't fit in the boxes. What else are you besides this very long word? How about Secretary? How about Typist?

"No, I'm not a typist in the pure sense."

By this time she was out of patience and I was out of control.

"Pure or impure, what shall it be? Do you want to vote in this country or not?"

Yes, I surely did want to vote, so for the government, for the Commonwealth of Massachusetts, for God and the flag, I became a *MED SEC*. Now I fit in the boxes.

Ten years later the census office in my home town sent us a computer form. Our household is listed as "one retired male, one spayed dog, one neutered dog, one med trans." It took ten long years to move from *med sec* to *med trans* and the dogs got better billing.

Is a *trans* better than a *sec*? The next time I voted, one of the inquisitive election workers asked me what sort of medicine I transport and isn't it nice that women can be anything they want to be, even truck drivers.

Judith Marshall
Medicate Me Again

The Modern Healthcare Team, Continued

Knowledge of digital dictation technology is essential. Digital systems allow recording of voice files and transfer of those files to the transcriptionist without a need for analog (tape) recording. Most hospitals and transcription services use digital dictation systems, making it possible for MTs to work within a facility, at remote sites through use of telephone lines, and even over the Internet.

Medical transcription is an exciting and evolving profession that requires its participants to be knowledgeable in many areas. It is a place for those who are willing to make a major investment in learning, both in school and in experience. The individual interested in becoming a qualified MT must be willing to invest many months in academic learning and as an entry-level employee under the supervision of experienced transcriptionists. Because medicine is a rapidly changing and evolving field, no MT is ever finished learning.

Today's medical transcriptionists take pride in performing a vital task in a professional manner. They function with minimal supervision while producing maximum results that reflect integrity and skill. They take pride in the accuracy and completeness of their own work and gain satisfaction from a job well done, both in quality and quantity.

Medical transcriptionists demonstrate responsibility in their day-to-day working judgments by combining past experience, powers of deductive thinking, and a vast store of medical knowledge to produce an accurate health record. They demonstrate ethical values when dealing with confidential or personal information contained in the health record.

They demonstrate a disciplined work attitude with dedication to the needs of the patient before personal needs. They display a commitment to continuing education by adopting an attitude of lifelong learning, always questioning, reading, and studying in a never-ending pursuit of excellence in knowledge and skills.

Earn $50,000.00 or MORE in Your Spare Time Working from Home!

If you can type, you can be a medical transcriptionist! Earn the money YOU deserve while working from the comfort of your own home. Attend one of our seminars in your area to learn more about this exciting career option. Contact us at . . .

As to that advertised promise of $50,000 per year, it's quite possible to reach that income level—after a few years of full-time employment. The reality is that medical transcription is difficult, stressful work, but it is challenging and fascinating. The income possibilities are good, but only after a significant investment in education and experience.

Worksheet

Answer the following true or false questions by placing a T for true or F for false in the blank next to the question.

_____ 1. Medical transcriptionists work without close supervision.

_____ 2. Medical transcription is primarily a keyboarding skill.

_____ 3. Most medical transcription is done using typewriters.

_____ 4. "Medical language specialist" is another term for "medical transcriptionist."

_____ 5. Medical transcription can be learned with a minimum of effort in a brief time.

_____ 6. Medical transcription is a continuing education process.

_____ 7. The ability to take shorthand is an important skill for today's medical transcriptionists.

_____ 8. The medical transcriptionist is not as visible to the public as other allied health personnel.

_____ 9. An entry-level medical transcriptionist can expect to earn $50,000 per year.

_____10. Confidentiality issues are of concern to medical transcriptionists.

_____11. The medical transcriptionist functions as an editor of medical dictation.

_____12. The primary job of the medical transcriptionist is to see that patient records are filed appropriately.

_____13. The "clerical" classification is appropriately applied to the medical transcriptionist.

_____14. A medical transcriptionist must have the same level of medical vocabulary as the physician.

_____15. Most hospitals and transcription services use analog tape cassette systems to hold the bank of dictation.

_____16. Computer technology should be of concern to medical transcriptionists.

Technology—Tools of the Trade

No discussion of medical transcription would be complete without a brief overview of the technology that has influenced the phenomenal growth of this interesting and challenging career. To understand medical transcription as it is done today requires an understanding of methods that were used yesterday.

Who were the first medical transcriptionists? Although no one really knows for sure, it is quite possible that medical transcription has its origins as far back as ancient Egypt. It is not difficult to imagine a physician dictating medical findings to a scribe who carefully recorded them.

Transcription as we know it began in the 1950s, when machine dictation came into its own, displacing written shorthand as a method of recording physician notes. Utilizing such recording media as wax cylinders, plastic belts, and vinyl disks, physicians dictated their reports, and transcription was done using manual typewriters. Necessary copies—and in hospital work there were often three or more—were made using separate sheets of carbon paper. Reel-to-reel and cassette tapes (now referred to as "analog" dictation) came into use a few years later, along with electric typewriters. Toward the end of the 1960s, office workers everywhere were delighted with the advent of a remarkable innovation—the self-correcting electric typewriter.

Transcription continued its evolutionary path in the 1970s with the appearance of the word processor, which allowed production and storage of reports in an electronic environment. Recording was still done chiefly on magnetic tape, and many hospitals had central recording systems that featured endless loops of magnetic tape residing in huge "tanks," allowing dictation from workstations within the hospital environment and later from outside the hospital via telephone.

The cassette tape gained in popularity throughout the 1970s and remained the dictation medium of choice in hospitals and physician offices for years. Physician offices in particular utilized the handheld microcassette dictation machine, which allowed doctors to dictate anywhere, at any time. Such devices are still in use today. Management of cassette tapes by the dozens, however, presented a daunting task for transcription managers everywhere.

Electronic word processors gave way to personal computers with word-processing software in the 1980s, and a revolution in information processing began taking place, particularly in the field of medicine. While magnetic tape was still the most common method of recording dictation, transcribing machines were improving. Multi-tape dictation systems began making remote dictation and transcription common in every environment, even the small home office. The introduction of "telestaffing" units made it possible for transcriptionists to work in a variety of locations far away from sites of dictation. The development of sophisticated copying machines assured that transcriptionists would no longer have to deal with their old nemesis—carbon paper.

Technology—Tools of the Trade, Continued

The 1990s brought us digital dictation—dictation recorded directly into computers and managed by computers. Digital voice files can be stored, transferred, and manipulated totally by computer. The sound quality of digital recording is far better than that produced on analog tapes, making transcription easier and providing many more opportunities for remote transcription. Digital dictation can be transferred over telephone lines via computer modems, transcribed live or re-recorded for later transcription, and even transferred by WAV (waveform audio format) file. Using FTP (file transfer protocol), encrypted WAV files can be transferred between computers that are connected via the Internet, eliminating long-distance costs involved with telephone transfers.

In essence, a transcriptionist can live anywhere, even in extremely remote areas, and still work for a transcription service or medical facility using digital dictation technology. Editors and proofreaders can work from other remote locations, accessing transcribed reports and providing assistance and corrections on digitally produced documents, then transferring finished transcripts to a client. Of course, remote transcription requires transcriptionists who are not only highly skilled and experienced, but also very knowledgeable about computers and digital technology.

Digital technology has turned medical transcription into a global industry, allowing transfer of voice files to offshore locations such as India, Ireland, Jamaica, the Philippines, and the Bahamas. Many American transcription services doing business offshore or overseas have established transcriptionist training programs in the foreign locations, where labor costs are much lower and new transcriptionist jobs have the potential for improving the local standard of living.

Voice files are transferred to the foreign location via telephone lines or the Internet. Transcription is done by the trainees, and proofreading and editing are performed either by American MTs in the foreign country or by U.S.-based personnel. The completed transcription is then returned to the client, all within tight turnaround times. The client may not even be aware that the dictation left the city in which it originated.

As technology becomes more affordable, more dictated material may be forwarded to offshore locations for transcription. The greatest obstacle to successful offshore transcription will continue to be the foreign transcriptionist's difficulty in understanding idiomatic American English.

Other important tools of the trade include ergonomic keyboards, machine shorthand, abbreviation expander software, and speech recognition machines.

Ergonomic keyboards. While the conventional keyboard with the familiar QWERTY key layout is still the one most often used, a variety of alternative keyboards are available that are ergonomically designed to ease strain on the hands and arms. Many transcriptionists have found such keyboards to be helpful during long hours of continuous keyboarding.

Technology—Tools of the Trade, Continued

Machine shorthand. This is the method of transcription long practiced by court reporters. It uses "brief forms," or short phonetic forms, that represent whole words or phrases, employing a small keyboard, often referred to as a *stenotype machine.* The traditional stenotype machine in the past printed a long paper tape with phonetic symbols that were later transcribed into plain text by either the court reporter or a "scopist," who was familiar with machine shorthand and able to translate the symbols into printed form. However, the computer entered the world of the court reporter in much the same way as it has that of the medical transcriptionist. Many court reporters now utilize CAT (computer-aided transcription) systems, which translate the symbols created by the stenotype machine into clear text on the computer screen, all in "real time," or at the same time as the transcription is done. With only minimal editing, the court reporter is able to provide the finished transcript of a court proceeding or deposition without the lengthy delay that often resulted in the past when time elapsed between recording and transcription.

Many court reporters, particularly some who have become skilled in transcribing medical testimony, have chosen to transfer their skills to medical transcription. Because a skilled court reporter can transcribe at rates exceeding 200 words per minute—considerably faster than most transcriptionists using conventional computer keyboards, with much less fatigue—some have found their skills much in demand in a field where productivity is prized, resulting in increased income. Because they must provide their own equipment and often cannot interface with existing transcription systems, shorthand reporters may find it difficult to locate on-site transcription jobs.

The most significant drawback to use of machine shorthand has always been the length of time it takes to achieve a significant skill level. In order to qualify for certification as a court reporter, a student must achieve and maintain a consistent transcription level of over 200 words per minute or better. It is not uncommon for court reporting schools to advertise that students will be ready to work in the courtroom in only a year. However, the reality is that a "finished" court reporter is seldom produced in less than two years, and court reporting schools are often expensive.

Abbreviation expander software. Medical transcription has been affected significantly by the development and ongoing improvement of computer software that allows transcription in shorthand form. First developed for the DOS (a computer's **d**isk **o**perating **s**ystem) environment, these programs provide a number of brief forms for common words and terms (e.g., t=the, tp=the patient, yr=your, etc.), and the individual transcriptionist can customize the program by adding other abbreviations for the terms most frequently used in his or her own transcription. As the brief forms are transcribed, followed by either a space or a punctuation mark, they expand instantly into the words or phrases programmed, saving a significant number of keystrokes and allowing a higher rate of production.

While successful use of abbreviation expanders often requires memorization of the brief forms, more recently developed programs for computer systems include on-screen prompts that allow more rapid transcription. Both *WordPerfect* and *Word* have built-in abbreviation expanders, but their capacity is limited. Medical transcriptionists who become skilled in the use of abbreviation expander software are often able to meet or exceed the productivity achieved with use of machine shorthand, thus increasing their incomes in jobs where productivity determines compensation.

Speech recognition. One cannot approach the subject of medical transcription without a discussion of speech recognition, which many people predict will eventually "replace" the medical transcriptionist. The reality is that while speech recognition systems have been designed for use by the healthcare provider, there are forms of speech recognition currently being used by medical transcriptionists to enhance their transcription skills and increase their productivity. The medical transcriptionist "trains" the speech recognition program to recognize his or her voice by dictating to it, using common English and medical terms that are found in everyday dictation. After a reasonable training time, the transcriptionist is able to dictate to the machine while listening to medical dictation. As the transcriptionist redictates what he or she is hearing, editing as necessary, the words appear on the computer screen. At the completion of dictation, the transcriptionist is able to print out the finished dictation, all with only minimal use of the computer keyboard.

Transcriptionists currently using such technology claim that they are able to produce more finished transcription in less time using this method than they can on conventional computer keyboards, with the major drawbacks being the necessity for patience in training the machine and the possibility of voice strain through constant repetition of dictation. However, this technology has proven to be a great boon to transcriptionists who are no longer able to utilize a conventional keyboard due to repetitive strain injury such as carpal tunnel syndrome.

Speech recognition technology is being used by a number of physicians and even some hospital departments, most remarkably radiology and emergency departments, where a great deal of repetitive dictation is employed. Other forms of speech recognition providing "fill-in-the-blank" technology combine direct speech with technology that allows selection of terms by touching the computer screen.

By its very nature, speech recognition technology requires a fairly intensive level of training for the dictator. Not all systems are able to understand and translate discrete speech (speech delivered at a normal rate of speaking). A user must have excellent spelling and grammar skills in order to create an accurate and understandable document that is equal to that produced by the educated medical transcriptionist. It also supposes that the healthcare professional (physician, nurse, therapist) is willing to use time perhaps better spent providing patient care.

Will speech recognition ever replace the medical transcriptionist? It's difficult to say, but one thing is certain: This industry **will** continue to evolve, and only the best, brightest, and most computer-savvy medical transcription professionals are likely to find secure places in the transcription environment of the future. Individuals entering the profession at this time are encouraged to build and refine these marketable skills.

Worksheet

Answer the following true or false questions by placing a T for true or F for false in the blank next to the question.

_____ 1. Medical transcriptionists can use the Internet to download voice files for transcription.

_____ 2. Speech recognition machines are used by medical facilities rather than by individual medical transcriptionists.

_____ 3. Stenotype machines can be used in medical transcription.

_____ 4. Medical transcription is a local industry.

_____ 5. Medical transcription has existed since the 1950s.

_____ 6. Analog tape dictation came about in the late 19th century.

_____ 7. Abbreviation expanders can help seasoned medical transcriptionists improve their productivity.

_____ 8. Digital dictation has superseded analog dictation in most medical centers and hospitals.

_____ 9. A major advantage to using machine shorthand is the ability to set up the system in any environment.

_____ 10. The sound quality of analog dictation is superior to that of digital dictation.

_____ 11. The greatest obstacle to successful offshore transcription is the high cost of technology.

_____ 12. To successfully utilize speech technology, a great deal of time must be spent initially "training" the machine to recognize the dictator's voice.

_____ 13. More dictated material may be forwarded to offshore locations for transcription as technology becomes more affordable.

_____ 14. A "scopist" transcribes medical dictation and converts it to phonetic symbols.

_____ 15. Medical transcriptionists should hone their medical editing skills to prepare for changes in the MT industry.

The Patient Health Record

What exactly is the patient health record and what is its purpose? Simply stated, the health record is the chronological, documented evidence of a patient's medical treatment. It is used by the healthcare team to identify, evaluate, communicate, plan, treat, and document the best course of action for a patient.

The patient health record is "proof of work done" to meet federal, state, and other standards and regulations. It is used by insurance companies and the government to reimburse patients and healthcare providers. The health record is maintained for the legal protection of the patient, facility, staff, and physician. It is also used for research and compiling statistics.

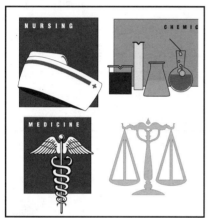

The health record is the property of the healthcare practitioner (or facility) that compiles it. Providers of care must keep records to support the services they render.

The fact that the provider owns the physical record does not prevent the patient from submitting a legitimate claim to access the information. Most facilities allow patients to review their own records and have copies made after a "release of information" statement is signed by the patient requesting the information. In some instances, mental health records are considered confidential and require a court order or subpoena to release them.

With advances in technology, words that were formerly used for some allied health concepts have changed. "Medical record" was the terminology that was utilized for over fifty years, but "health record" is used today to denote both illness and wellness. The medical record department has become the health information management (HIM) department, and the medical record director has become the health information manager.

In most medical facilities, patient health records are maintained in the HIM department. In the past, most HIM departments were headed by an RRA (registered record administrator) or an ART (accredited record technician). Assisting them were medical record clerks, coders, and technicians. In recent times, however, individuals with advanced degrees in business or public administration are often hired to head these departments. Health information management today is looked upon by some as a revenue-producing business that should be managed by business experts rather than record custodians.

In hospitals, the health record has its origin in the admissions department, outpatient registration (including laboratory and radiology), or the emergency department. Patients are either inpatients (hospital stay more than 24 hours) or outpatients (in and out of the hospital in less than 24 hours or seen in a brief visit to an outpatient clinic). In either case, a health record (also referred to as the patient's chart) is generated.

The Patient Health Record, Continued

The admitting department registers patients whose physicians have written orders for their admission to the hospital. Outpatient registration receives elective surgery outpatients and clinic patients. Emergency registration receives patients with acute conditions that need immediate medical attention.

The major role of all of these departments is to collect patient identification, as well as demographic and other pertinent information: name, address, next of kin, birthplace, Social Security number, occupation, sex, marital status, ethnic origin, and admitting diagnosis.

Financial entries include the patient's employer, job title, address of company, insurance company, person responsible for emergency notification and payments, type of coverage, insurance identification number, and type of payment plan.

Card Sharks

People do have strange names and we can usually verify them. Nicknames should be spelled by the physician and when they are not, we card them. We asked how to spell Brammie, Ivy, Lolly, Pudge, Nanook, Kip, and Pip. One day we heard a no-nonsense doctor recounting the clinic visit of little Hitler so-and-so. What? We had no chart or patient list. Could parents really name a child this name? They could and did, the response came back. (The family was visiting America from a foreign land.) Never assume a doctor is kidding with a name.

Judith Marshall
Medicate Me

These departments also have the responsibility for obtaining a patient-signed *conditions for admission statement*. This statement includes consent for treatment, outline of patient responsibilities (including payment), and the assurance that the patient's confidentiality will be protected. Additional informed consents for surgery, procedures, invasive diagnostic tests, transfer, etc., are obtained as appropriate.

The correct spelling of the patient's legal name and birth date are critical elements to determine positive patient identification. This information is utilized to assign a health record number that is maintained for all contacts with the facility during the lifetime of the patient and should be recorded on all transcribed reports. This information is recorded on an admission sheet as required by federal law, and this may be available in some format (either on paper or computer) to the transcriptionist to assist in patient identification.

Patients are admitted and treated only on the order of an attending physician. It is the physician's responsibility to communicate orders for diagnostic tests, medications, and appropriate therapy. From the physician's orders, healthcare workers generate requisitions (authorized requests) for any necessary diagnostic tests. These requisitions are sent to the appropriate department, whose personnel then perform the tests and document their results. Typical are laboratory tests, x-ray examinations, and EKGs, the reports of which may be generated by a machine or dictated by a physician for transcription. Orders for medication and treatment are generally handwritten on the chart and/or entered into the computer by the nurse or physician.

The Patient Health Record, Continued

Either before or shortly after admission to the hospital, the physician writes or dictates an admitting history and physical examination. Included are the patient's chief complaint (the patient's major problem), the history of present illness (history of the major problem), the patient's past medical and surgical history, family history, social history, review of systems (a brief overview of each body system), findings on the physical examination, an admission diagnosis, and a plan for treatment. This admitting history and physical (H&P) must be placed in the patient's health record as soon as possible after admission.

The physician may call in medical consultants as appropriate. A consultant carries out a comprehensive review of all of the available information in the health record and may perform either a limited or complete physical examination on the patient. A working diagnosis and treatment plan are then suggested. This document is most often dictated but is occasionally handwritten in the chart.

After a patient is admitted to the hospital, a nurse reviews the attending physician's orders, evaluates the patient, establishes a patient care plan based on the doctor's orders, and sets up forms for documentation of graphic information such as vital signs (temperature, pulse, respiration, blood pressure, weight). Diet, hygiene records, medication records, and the nurse's notes and observations become a permanent part of the health record.

If a diagnostic or surgical procedure is performed, the physician performing the procedure dictates a record of the procedure. This includes the preoperative and postoperative diagnoses, the name of the procedure and the names of any assistants, a description of the findings, operative technique, and outcome of the procedure. The anesthesiologist completes a preanesthesia and postanesthesia evaluation as well. In the past these anesthesia notes were handwritten, but recently many anesthesiologists have opted to dictate this information.

While the patient is hospitalized, many more entries are made into the health record. The physician writes or dictates progress notes that include all observations, findings, and pertinent plans. Physical, occupational, speech, vocational, and recreational therapists and social workers who might be asked to assist also document their visits. Dietary personnel, discharge planners, utilization review managers, and others participating in the patient's care write or dictate progress notes on each of their visits.

At the conclusion of the patient's hospitalization, the physician dictates a comprehensive discharge report (called a discharge summary or clinical resumé) that summarizes the patient's course of hospitalization. Included are a brief history, the results of laboratory and other tests performed, any complications or operative procedures, diagnoses and conclusions, discharge medications, and discharge instructions to the patient.

Patients evaluated and treated only in the emergency department have a condensed version of the inpatient health record, which includes demographic information, nursing assessment, physician's evaluation, treatment, and conclusions. A comprehensive visit might result in a dictated note. Diagnostic test results, consents, and instructions are included.

The health records maintained in physician offices include many, but not all, of the records and forms contained in the hospital health record. These often include the initial history and physical examination, progress notes, diagnostic test results, copies of acute hospitalization reports, letters to insurance companies, consultation letters, and so forth. These records have a higher percentage of handwritten notes, although many physicians do dictate a record of all contacts with their patients.

Worksheet

Choose the correct answer in each of the following multiple-choice questions. Write your answer in the space provided next to the number of the question.

____ 1. The main purpose of the patient health record is to:
   a. document evidence for lawsuits
   b. document patient care
   c. document changes in demographic information
   d. document signed consents

____ 2. Before or shortly after admission to the hospital, the admitting physician must write or dictate a:
   a. preanesthesia record
   b. progress report
   c. history and physical examination report
   d. report of consultation

____ 3. At the conclusion of a patient's hospitalization, the physician should dictate a comprehensive report that summarizes the patient's course of hospitalization. This report is called a:
   a. record of comprehensive visit
   b. report of operation
   c. progress report
   d. discharge summary

____ 4. An outpatient hospital stay is one that is:
   a. less than 6 hours
   b. less than 12 hours
   c. less than 24 hours
   d. less than 48 hours

____ 5. A patient is admitted to the hospital and treated only on the order of:
   a. the attending physician
   b. the emergency room physician
   c. the triage nurse
   d. the consulting physician

____ 6. The purpose of a physician consultant is to:
   a. take over the care of a patient if the attending physician is incompetent
   b. validate the attending physician's diagnosis
   c. ensure that the patient is ready to be discharged from the hospital
   d. render an opinion and recommend a treatment plan

____ 7. A patient health record is generated:
   a. every time the patient is seen in the hospital
   b. only when the patient is admitted to the hospital
   c. in all instances except in an emergency
   d. in all instances except for outpatient blood work and x-rays

Dictated Medical Reports

The transcribed medical report—a legal medical document—is essential to proper communication through the patient health record. Such reports are dictated by physicians in all medical specialties and even by oral surgeons and dentists. A check in the telephone Yellow Pages under "Physicians and Surgeons" would reveal a wide range of medical specialties and subspecialties in practice today.

Physicians in private practice frequently dictate office chart notes, letters, initial office evaluations, and history and physical examination reports.

Medical reports dictated in hospitals and medical centers are numerous in category; however, they invariably include dictations from the "**basic four**": history and physicals, consultations, operative reports, and discharge summaries. Emergency department reports, hospital progress notes, and diagnostic studies are often dictated as well.

Chart note. The chart note (also called progress note or follow-up note) is dictated by a physician after talking with, meeting with, or examining a patient, usually in an outpatient setting, although progress notes are occasionally dictated on hospital inpatients. The chart note contains a concise description of the patient's presenting problem, physical findings, and the physician's plan of treatment. It may also include the results of laboratory tests.

History and physical examination. The report of a patient's history and physical examination (H&P) includes information relating to the patient's main reason for admission. It includes two sections: the patient's history (history of the present illness, past medical and surgical history, family history, social history, review of systems), and the findings on the actual physical examination. The H&P forms the basis for several documents with different titles, among which are the admission history and physical examination, initial office evaluation, consultation, emergency department report, and discharge summary.

Initial office evaluation. Performed in the physician's office or clinic setting, the initial office evaluation is dictated after the physician sees a patient for the first time. It contains essentially the same information as the H&P, although the physical examination may be limited to specific areas of disease or trauma involvement.

Consultation and letters. Physicians frequently utilize business letters to communicate patient information to other physicians, insurance companies, and government offices. Thus, medical transcriptionists need to be familiar with various standard business letter formats. But such dictations are more than business letters—they are medical documents and as such should be transcribed accordingly. Medical consultations are often dictated in letter form. Consultations are dictated when one physician has requested the services of another physician in the care and treatment of a patient. A consultation report usually contains all of the elements of a history and physical exam-

Dictated Medical Reports, Continued

ination, including a very detailed history of the patient's illness that focuses particularly on the body system corresponding to the consultant's area of specialty, the consultant's findings, pertinent laboratory data, a working diagnosis, and a suggested course of treatment.

Emergency department report. An emergency department report is an abbreviated version of the history and physical examination and focuses most intensely on the problem that occasioned the emergency department visit. If the laboratory tests ordered are to be performed stat (immediately), the results may be included in the dictation. The course of treatment in the emergency department is also briefly described, along with the treatment and follow-up plan to be carried out after discharge. Sometimes the patient's condition is serious enough to warrant admission to the hospital, but more often the patient is seen, evaluated, treated, and then released to home.

Operative report. After a surgical procedure has been performed, a detailed description of the operation is dictated. The operative report contains such information as operation start and end times, anesthesia start and end times (and occasionally the type of anesthesia used), names of the surgical team, preoperative and postoperative diagnoses, title of the operation, a description of the operative findings, a narrative of the operative technique or procedure, and details regarding the estimated blood loss and condition of the patient at the end of the procedure.

Discharge summary report. By the time a patient is ready to leave the hospital, a variety of treatment modalities have been performed. The discharge report summarizes the patient's course of treatment, laboratory and other diagnostic studies performed, discharge medications, and the discharge plan (also known as *disposition).*

Radiology report. Radiology dictation includes a broad range of reports, from the simple negative chest x-ray to the complicated multistep magnetic resonance imaging (MRI) scan. Radiology is a field that is rapidly advancing with new technology and types of procedures, due mainly to constantly expanding capabilities of computers.

Subspecialty areas within the field of radiology include nuclear medicine, ultrasonography, computerized axial tomography (CAT), digital subtraction angiography, magnetic resonance imaging, positron emission tomography (PET), single photon emission computed tomography (SPECT), and others.

Pathology report. Pathology reports consists of two main types: the autopsy report and tissue specimen reports. Autopsies are dictated on deceased persons, while tissue specimens are also from the living. Both autopsies and tissue specimen reports contain a gross description, a microscopic description, and a diagnosis.

Dictated Medical Reports, Continued

Miscellaneous reports. Other report types may include psychiatric, radiation oncology, anesthesia, progress, respiratory therapy, physical therapy, occupational therapy, social services, workers compensation, and home healthcare.

Interestingly, many veterinary facilities, particularly those that carry out special surgical procedures and animal research, also employ MTs. The format of their reports will, of course, be somewhat different, but many similarities to human medical records do exist.

The Chart Note

Physicians in private or group practices dictate their findings after meeting with and evaluating a patient. If a patient is in for a brief visit, the format of the report is usually that of a **chart note** (also called *office note, progress note, or follow-up note*). These notes can vary in length from one or more pages to only a sentence, with the average note being two to four paragraphs in length.

Chart notes are sometimes dictated in an informal, staccato style using clipped sentences (see discussion on page 127). As a general rule, they can be transcribed verbatim, although the transcriptionist may at times edit for accuracy, completeness, and proper grammatical construction for clarity.

The chart note may consist of the following:

- Concise description of the patient's presenting problem
- Physical findings
- Results of any laboratory tests or diagnostic procedures
- Physician's recommended plan of treatment

A transcribed chart note might be printed on plain paper, on sticky-back paper which can be cut, peeled, and put into the patient's health record, or any number of ways. In addition, there are numerous formats for dictated chart notes. Some physicians like to dictate a simple, unformatted paragraph, while others prefer a more structured format.

The "**SOAP note**" is a chart note style used commonly by physicians in private and group practice. "SOAP" is an acronym for "subjective, objective, assessment, plan." The SOAP format is also used by many hospital dictators.

- *Subjective:* The reason the patient is being seen; the chief complaint.
- *Objective:* Results of the physical examination and any pertinent diagnostic studies.
- *Assessment:* The physician's conclusion or diagnosis.
- *Plan:* Recommended treatment, if any.

Some physicians follow a **history and physical**-type format when dictating an initial office evaluation (report of the patient's first visit). The dictator may include the patient's presenting problem, past medical history, the findings on physical examination, and a plan of treatment. A similar format may be used for annual physical examination visits.

A few physician offices have progressed to a completely computerized or "paperless" patient record in which all contacts with the patient are summarized chronologically in a continuous computer file.

Sample Chart Notes

The following chart notes contain the same information. The first is dictated and transcribed in SOAP format (subjective, objective, assessment, plan). The second is dictated and transcribed in regular paragraph format.

Name: Ima N. Payne   February 8, 1999

S: Mrs. Payne returned to see me today for follow-up of hypertension, which was noted on initial evaluation last month. She has had no physical complaints.

O: Exam today was unremarkable except for blood pressure of 180/106.

A: Suspect hypertension.

P: Will start her on captopril 25 mg. She is to check her blood pressure daily at the drugstore or as often as she can get over there. Return in two weeks, at which time we will evaluate the efficacy of the treatment regimen.

lc   ANNA PHYLAXIS, M.D.

Name: Ima N. Payne   February 8, 1999

Mrs. Payne returned to see me today for follow-up of hypertension, which was noted on initial evaluation last month. She has had no physical complaints. Exam today was unremarkable except for blood pressure of 180/106.

I suspect hypertension, so will start her on captopril 25 mg. She is to check her blood pressure daily at the drugstore or as often as she can get over there. Return in two weeks, at which time we will evaluate the efficacy of the treatment regimen.

lc   ANNA PHYLAXIS, M.D

Sample Initial Evaluation

INITIAL EVALUATION REPORT

Patient: Ima N. Payne   January 18, 1999
Chart #99-118

PRESENTING PROBLEM: Routine checkup.

HISTORY: Mrs. Payne is a 54-year-old white female who comes in today because her insurance carrier has changed and she needs to establish a new healthcare provider. She has not had a routine checkup for over 5 years with the exception of a yearly Pap and pelvic by her gynecologist.

She has no remarkable past history except for a T&A as a child. Usual childhood diseases. Childbirths were also unremarkable; no babies over 10 pounds. She takes no medication except for occasional OTC antihistamines for seasonal rhinitis. No problems on system review.

PHYSICAL EXAMINATION:
VITAL SIGNS: Pulse was 86, blood pressure 178/98; recheck was 180/106. Weight was 186 pounds, height 5'6".
HEENT: Unremarkable except for absence of tonsils.
NECK: No stiffness. No thyroid enlargement detected.
LUNGS: Clear.
HEART: Normal sinus rhythm. No murmur detected.
ABDOMEN: No rigidity, tenderness, or mass.
BACK AND EXTREMITIES: Unremarkable.
PELVIC AND RECTAL: Deferred.

IMPRESSION: Possible hypertension in an otherwise healthy-appearing woman.

PLAN: She is to take her blood pressure daily at the drugstore and record the findings. If blood pressures are still elevated, will consider antihypertensive medication when she returns in 2 to 3 weeks.

AP:lc   ANNA PHYLAXIS, M.D.
D&T 1/18/99

Worksheet

Answer the following true or false questions by placing a T for true or F for false in the blank next to the question.

____ 1. The history and physical examination forms the basis for several other documents.

____ 2. Veterinary reports are among the "basic four."

____ 3. Oral surgeons, dentists, and anesthesiologists may dictate medical reports.

____ 4. Physicians frequently use discharge summaries as the basis for consultation reports.

____ 5. Nuclear medicine is a subspecialty of pathology.

____ 6. An emergency department report is an abbreviated version of the H&P report.

Complete the following statements by filling in the blank with the correct answer. Some answers may require more than one word.

7. Two other names for the chart note are _____ and

_____.

8. List the four parts of a SOAP note.

_____   _____

_____   _____

9. The history and physical examination report is comprised of (number) _____ main parts.

10. The _____ report is dictated after the doctor sees the patient for the first time in the office or clinic setting.

11. Medical _____ are often dictated in letter form.

12. The _____ report is dictated after a surgical procedure or operation has been performed.

13. The _____ report provides a summary of the patient's hospital course and treatment.

14. Nuclear medicine, ultrasonography, MRI scans, CT scans, contrast media, bone, and soft-tissue study reports are categorized as _____ reports.

15. Autopsies and tissue specimen reports are types of _____ reports.

16. *Estimated blood loss* is a phrase that is used commonly in _____ reports.

The History & Physical

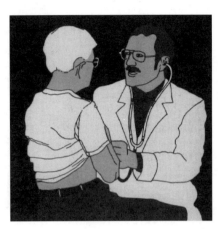

An important key to mastering dictation of the history and physical examination is understanding the repetitive nature of the key words and phrases used. In virtually every dictated H&P, the major headings vary little from report to report. Descriptions of the physical findings, while specific to each patient, are remarkably similar from transcript to transcript. Awareness of the similarities between dictated reports will help you learn to transcribe medical dictation more efficiently and with less effort.

Examples:

The patient is a well-developed, well-nourished, elderly Caucasian man appearing his stated age of 83. He is in no acute distress.

The patient is a 44-year-old black female in moderate distress from abdominal pain.

The patient is a 6-year-old Filipino female child, alert and cooperative but poorly developed, in no apparent distress.

This is a 27-year-old well-nourished, well-developed white male who appears to be in no acute distress.

To gain a better understanding of what the H&P is like from the physician's point of view, we'll go with fictitious patient Ms. Vernelle Johnson, a 47-year-old married African-American female, as she visits the office of Dr. Bill Body. She has had problems off and on with chest pain and is seeking advice from Dr. Body.

When Vernelle Johnson arrives at Dr. Body's office, she checks in at the front desk. After verifying her appointment, her health record (chart) is located and made available to the nurse or other healthcare professional who usually sees the patient first, and then the physician.

The nurse takes Ms. Johnson's vital signs (temperature, blood pressure, pulse, and respirations) and records them in her chart. Soon thereafter, Dr. Body makes his appearance, and he notes that her blood pressure was slightly elevated at 150/92. He is concerned that she has hypertension because this is the third time she has had an elevated blood pressure in three office visits over the preceding six months. Because of this, and because of the chest pain, Dr. Body decides to carry out a complete history and physical examination in the office. Dr. Body begins by taking the patient's history. He begins with her chief complaint—the reason she is seeking medical attention.

Chief Complaint. Generally, the Chief Complaint consists of one to several sentences, and in some instances, just a single word. It states, in the most concise way, the reason the patient is seeking medical attention. Of all the sections within the history and physical examination, the Chief Complaint is the one most likely to contain direct quotations from the patient.

The History & Physical, Continued

History of Present Illness. This section contains all historical details leading up to and in any way pertaining to the patient's current status. In an acute illness, the History of Present Illness may consist of just a sentence or two, but if the patient's current problem is the culmination of days, months, or years of chronic evolving illness, this part of the history may occupy a whole page or more.

Dr. Body begins this section with a brief description of the patient, including age, sex, race, and social status. Next is noted the time and nature of onset of the first symptoms. No matter what the initial or presenting symptom, Dr. Body will try to learn when it started, whether it came on gradually or abruptly, whether it has continued unchanged or waxed and waned, and whether Ms. Johnson can suggest any reason for it.

The duration of a symptom is of the utmost importance in analyzing its meaning. A two-hour history of constant, agonizing, left-sided chest pain could be indicative of an acute myocardial infarction (heart attack). A 15-year history of chest pain occurring off and on would not likely be due to an acute myocardial infarction.

Dr. Body next traces the progress of the illness. He will ask the patient about the appearance of any additional symptoms and their effect on her lifestyle and well-being, ask whether she has taken any medication or other treatment for the condition, and determine what event prompted her to seek treatment.

Past Medical History. The Past Medical History provides information about Ms. Johnson's past illnesses, injuries, surgeries, chronic diseases and disabilities, allergies, and immunizations.

Because most patients have difficulty recalling all of their prior illnesses, Dr. Body asks Ms. Johnson if she has ever had diabetes, tuberculosis, asthma, pneumonia, high blood pressure, heart attack or heart disease, stroke, epilepsy, ulcer, cancer, anemia, arthritis, kidney disease, nervous or mental disease. If she responds with an affirmative answer to any of these, Dr. Body will inquire further as to the date of the illness, severity, treatment, and complications.

Dr. Body will want to know if the patient is currently taking any medications and if she has any medication sensitivities or allergies. In Dr. Body's office, information about allergies is prominently displayed on the front of the patient's health record to prevent inadvertent administration of the offending medicine, and in the dictated record, allergies are listed on a separate line in all capital letters. In other physician offices, the policy might be to have allergies in bold typeface or underlined.

Family History. The tendency to inherit certain diseases can run in families, and so Dr. Body will question Ms. Johnson about any developmental abnormalities, hereditary diseases (genetically transmitted from parent to child), and familial diseases (occurring in some or all members of a family). For example, because this patient is of African-American descent, Dr. Body will want to know if and when she was tested for sickle cell disease. The complete Family History includes the age

The History & Physical, Continued

and state of health (or age at death and cause of death) of each member of the patient's immediate family, including parents, siblings, children, and occasionally other blood relatives.

Social History. This section includes any personal information about Ms. Johnson's past or present life that may have a bearing on her health. Although the Social History could include data on her birth, upbringing, academic record, marital history, present status, military service, past and present occupations, hobbies, foreign travel, residence, family structure, and living arrangements, Dr. Body simply does not have time to elicit all of this information. He limits his questioning to what he considers relevant history; in Ms. Johnson's case, it is her marital status, occupation, and foreign travel.

Habits. Under this heading comes information about the patient's lifestyle with respect to eating, sleeping, exercise, recreation, the use of caffeine, nicotine, alcohol, and illicit drugs. Upon questioning, Dr. Body discovers that Ms. Johnson used to smoke two packs of cigarettes per day for 10 years but quit 20 years ago. He records that she has a 20-pack-year smoking history (a pack-year is the equivalent of smoking one package of cigarettes a day for one year) but has not smoked for many years.

Dr. Body knows that people who abuse alcohol or drugs often lie about using them. The more questions are asked, the more likely these patients are to conceal or distort the truth about their drinking or drug use. Fortunately, Ms. Johnson reports that she quit drinking alcohol at the same time she quit smoking 20 years ago. He notes that her caffeine intake is limited to an occasional caffeinated cola beverage.

Review of Systems. The Review of Systems (not symptoms) is a brief overview of any relevant information about each major body system. Dr. Body begins by asking Ms. Johnson about any past or current problems with her vision, hearing, breathing, heartbeat,

Typical Standard Outline for History and Physical Examination Report

History
  Chief Complaint
  History of Present Illness
  Past Medical History (including Allergies)
  Medications
  Family History
  Social History
  Habits
  Review of Systems

Physical Examination
  General Appearance (including Vital Signs)
  Skin
  HEENT (Head, Eyes, Ears, Nose, Throat)
  Neck
  Chest (Thorax, Breasts, Axillae)
  Heart
  Lungs
  Abdomen (including Groin)
  Genitalia (or Pelvic)
  Rectal
  Back
  Extremities
  Neurologic (including Mental Status)
  Formal Mental Status (Psychiatric Exam only)

Laboratory Tests (when available)

Impression

Plan (or Recommendations)

The History & Physical, Continued

digestion, urination, bones and muscles, and mental state. Because of the patient's symptoms, Dr. Body questions her closely about any problems she has experienced with her heart or lungs. She reports that she has had a few brief episodes of burning chest pain in the past few years and at one point was diagnosed with a hiatal hernia. Dr. Body notes this in the chart. Often, however, the Review of Systems section in the transcribed report is very brief and is often stated to be "noncontributory" when all systems are negative.

The Physical Examination

Dr. Body carries out part of his examination while he is still questioning Vernelle Johnson about her history. Because the patient's blood pressure was elevated when the nurse first took it, he takes it again and notes that it is still elevated.

General Appearance. The general features noted by Dr. Body are Vernelle Johnson's body build (muscular development, proportions, skeletal deformities), nutritional status, apparent age, general state of health, skin color (unusual pallor, bluish or yellowish tinge, flushed appearance), alertness and responsiveness, mood, posture, gait, mobility, grooming and personal hygiene, quality and clarity of voice and speech, evidence of distress (problems with breathing, signs of pain or anxiety), abnormal odors of breath or body, and any other readily observable abnormalities (facial scars, absence of a limb). Her body posture, stance, mobility, and gait are of particular interest during orthopedic and neurologic examinations.

Head, Eyes, Ears, Nose, and Throat (often dictated as "HEENT"). When examining the patient's head, Dr. Body notes the size, shape, and symmetry of the skull, palpating for lumps or tenderness. The amount, distribution, texture, and color of scalp hair are observed, as well as any pattern of hair loss. Any tremors or involuntary movements of the head are additionally noted. A glance at the patient's face is enough to tell Dr. Body whether she is alert or sleepy, nervous or calm, angry or euphoric.

Dr. Body next checks Vernelle Johnson's pupils, sclerae (whites of the eyes), and conjunctivae (inside of eyelids) and performs a thorough eye examination with the aid of an ophthalmoscope, a handheld instrument with a light source and magnifying lenses. By visualizing the optic fundus, he can gauge the health of the retina, the optic disk, and branches of the central retinal artery and vein. Medical conditions such as diabetes, hardening of the arteries, and high blood pressure can damage these eye structures, and thus any changes can be readily observed with the funduscopic examination.

Visual acuity testing is usually performed with a Snellen wall chart to test far vision. The patient reads the smallest letters that can be seen on the wall chart from a distance of 20 feet, and the results are expressed as a fraction of normal. Thus, 20/20 vision indicates normal far visual acuity, while 20/40 means that the patient can see no letters at 20 feet smaller than those that a person with perfect vision can see at 40 feet.

An external examination of Vernelle Johnson's nose first checks for developmental abnormalities, trauma, enlargement, nodules, and skin lesions. The inside of each nostril is then viewed with a light source, noting any swelling, redness, ulcerations, discharge, blood, polyps, or tumors.

The sinus cavities, which are located within the bones of the skull but communicate with the nasal cavity, cannot be examined directly. To check if the sinuses are thickened or infected, Dr. Body places a small bright light inside the patient's mouth after darkening the room. If her sinuses are clear, a deep ruddy glow can be seen through the skin. If the sinuses are filled with fluid or infection, no light can be seen. This procedure is called *transillumination of the sinuses.*

With the use of a tongue depressor and with the patient's mouth open wide, Dr. Body can inspect her palate, inside of the cheeks (buccal mucosa), gums, tongue, teeth, throat structures, and odor of breath. He looks for ulcers, tumors, or white spots on the inside of the mouth or tongue.

Inspection of her throat (pharynx) is performed by having her say "ahhh," which raises her soft palate and opens her throat. The tonsils and the sides of her throat are checked for inflammation, swelling, or lesions, and with the use of a small angled mirror in the back of the throat, Dr. Body can look for tumors or other problems. He then palpates the patient's neck for enlarged lymph nodes, enlargement of the thyroid gland, intensity of neck pulses, and distention of the external jugular veins at the sides of the neck.

Chest. Dr. Body next notes the shape of Vernelle Johnson's chest wall. He observes to see if her breathing is even and regular. A patient with severe difficulty breathing may use the muscles of the neck and upper chest not normally involved in breathing (accessory muscles of respiration).

Breasts. The breasts are inspected for shape, symmetry, deformity, skin changes, scars, inversion of nipples, and discharge. They are palpated for masses or tenderness in both sitting up and reclining postures. The axillae (armpits) are felt to detect enlarged or tender lymph nodes. Dr. Body recommends that Ms. Johnson have a mammogram (a breast x-ray) to check for lumps or other abnormalities, since it has been over three years since her last one.

Lungs. Evaluation of the lungs is performed almost entirely by auscultation while the physician listens with a stethoscope. The passage of air into and out of the lungs produces a sequence of sounds that can be heard with the stethoscope. This technique is called *auscultation*. Disease or injury causes predictable changes in the quality and loudness of the breath sounds and can produce abnormal breath sounds.

To avoid hearing any extra sounds caused by breathing through her nose, Dr. Body asks the patient to breathe deeply with her mouth open. He listens at specific places on the front and back of her chest. Normal breathing in (inspiration) and out (expiration) produces a faint sighing or

The History & Physical, Continued

whispering sound called *vesicular breathing* that is reminiscent of a gentle breeze stirring the leaves of a tree. The inspiratory phase of vesicular breathing is normally slightly louder than the expiratory phase, but when the two are heard as being equal, it is known as *bronchovesicular breathing*.

Dr. Body checks Vernelle Johnson's lungs for abnormal sounds. He listens for rales (an irregular bubbling-fluid sound due to air passing through fluid), rhonchi (continuous sounds such as made by a whistle or horn), and rubs (a creaking or grating sound caused by two lung surfaces rubbing together). Although he rarely performs the percussion maneuver, during this exam Dr. Body places the palm of his hand with outstretched fingers against her chest and taps the back of his middle finger smartly with the flexed tip of his other middle finger. The tone produced by the tapping is called the *percussion note*. Any deviation from the normal sound might indicate a problem in the patient's chest or lungs.

Heart. Dr. Body then checks Vernelle Johnson's heart. By palpating her chest, he can locate the point at which the heartbeat is strongest (the point of maximal intensity, or PMI). Dr. Body's fingers can detect not only this point but also any abnormalities associated with the heartbeat, such as heaves of the chest wall (due to very intense cardiac contractions), thrills (due to passage of blood through abnormally narrowed valves), and shocks (from abnormally abrupt closure of valves in hypertension).

With the stethoscope he listens for her heart rhythm and rate, the intensity of her heartbeat, and the sounds of blood moving through her heart. Auscultation of the heart with a stethoscope provides more information than any other procedure. He listens for any alteration in the normal two sounds ("lub-dup," known as S1 and S2).

Dr. Body checks for a heart murmur by listening in four areas of the chest where the valves are best heard: the mitral area, the pulmonic area, the aortic area, and the tricuspid area. Dr. Body asks the patient to lean forward and then to lie on her left side so that he can adequately evaluate her heart sounds. He listens for murmurs (caused by abnormal flow of blood through a valve), clicks or snaps (caused by abnormal valve function), rubs, creaks, or grating sounds (caused by friction between the beating heart and an inflamed pericardium), and bruits (caused by passage of blood through a narrowed artery). All abnormal sounds are noted by name, but murmurs are graded by their intensity, with a grading scale of 1 to 6.

Abdomen. Dr. Body then turns his attention to inspection of the abdomen. He starts with light palpation of the abdomen to check for muscle tone and tenderness, then progresses to deep palpation to study the internal organs and search for masses. Ordinarily these organs must be enlarged before they can be felt. No part of the digestive tract can normally be felt, nor can the pancreas, gallbladder, or ureters. Percussion can be used to measure liver span, to distinguish between a solid organ or tumor, and to confirm the presence of ascites (from abnormal accumulation of fluid in the abdomen due to a disease process such as cirrhosis of the liver) by detecting a change in the percussion note (known as *shifting dullness*) as the patient rolls from back to side. Dr. Body uses auscultation to evaluate the bowel sounds and to listen for bruits. Because hypertension sometimes

The History & Physical, Continued

results from circulatory disorders of one or both kidneys, he listens carefully over the upper abdomen and flanks for bruits in the renal arteries.

Back and Extremities. Vernelle Johnson has had no problems with her bones, joints, or muscles, so Dr. Body carries out only a cursory examination here. He looks for any developmental or traumatic deformities and any evidence of generalized conditions such as muscle wasting or weakness, stiffness, or tremors. If she had complaints of arthritis or other pain, Dr. Body would have put her joints through passive range of motion (moving her arms and legs himself) and then have her put them through active range of motion (moving her own arms and legs). He would look for swelling, stiffness, tenderness, and instability of her joints.

Because the patient reports that she was told she had scoliosis as a child, Dr. Body carries out a more thorough examination of her back than he otherwise would. He checks for any spinal curvature or developmental deformities as well as any surgical scars. The heights of the iliac crests (pelvic bones) are compared as a rough test of leg length equality. He palpates her back for areas of tenderness and spasm and notes the range of spinal movements as she bends forward, backward, and to the sides.

Laboratory Tests

At the conclusion of Dr. Body's examination, he reviews any laboratory tests Vernelle Johnson has had recently and recommends others that he feels are necessary.

A routine urinalysis (examination of urine) done in his office was negative for any abnormalities. A complete blood count (CBC) done a week prior to her office visit showed a normal white cell count and normal red cells, a hemoglobin of 13.4, and a normal hematocrit of 40.

Dr. Body decides that he wants the patient to have a blood chemistry panel drawn to check her electrolytes (balance of minerals in the blood), glucose (blood sugar), cholesterol (a type of fat in the blood), liver, thyroid, and other functions. He also wants to send her for a routine chest x-ray and electrocardiogram (EKG) to check for any heart abnormalities. A preliminary EKG strip performed in Dr. Body's office was negative.

Because of her history of severe heartburn with associated chest pain, with a negative upper GI series in the past, Dr. Body recommends that Vernelle Johnson undergo an esophagogastroduodenoscopy as an outpatient. For this procedure a long, thin tube with a magnifying lens and light source is inserted into Vernelle Johnson's throat and advanced into her esophagus and stomach to check for abnormalities. It is usually done under I.V. anesthesia, with application of topical Xylocaine or a similar anesthetic to minimize the patient's gag reflex. Although some physicians schedule this procedure in their office, others prefer to use an outpatient surgery center.

The History & Physical, Continued

Neurological. Because the patient tells Dr. Body that she has had several severe migraine headaches recently, he carries out a neurological examination. He checks the functioning of her cranial nerves by asking her to demonstrate certain facial movements.

He taps her knee tendons smartly with a rubber reflex hammer to check her deep tendon reflexes. Because certain reflexes are seen only with upper motor neuron damage, Dr. Body checks the patient to see if she has a positive Babinski reflex (upward deviation of the great toe on stroking the sole of the foot), Hoffman (twitching of the thumb when the middle finger is snapped), and palmomental (twitching of the chin on stimulation of the palm of the hand). He checks for coordination by having the patient touch her nose with her eyes closed, run her heel up and down her opposite shin, and make rapidly alternating movements with her hands.

Throughout Dr. Body's questioning and examination, he does not detect any signs of a mental disorder. The patient's personal grooming, alertness, attention span, and ability to receive and process visual, auditory, and tactile stimuli are considered to be within normal limits. As he observes her, the patient's gait (walking motions), posture, and movements appear normal. Her awareness of time, place, and person are normal, which Dr. Body refers to as being oriented x 3.

Pelvic. Because she has not had a pelvic examination in several years, Dr. Body recommends that one be carried out today. In women, the pelvic examination is normally performed in the lithotomy position—with the patient on her back and the knees drawn up and out to each side. Dr. Body looks for abnormalities of the external genitalia such as swelling or inflammation. He tests for weakness of the pelvic floor by having the patient bear down while he observes for prolapse of her bladder (cystocele) or rectum (rectocele).

He uses a speculum to gain access to her cervix, where a Papanicolaou (Pap) smear is taken to check for cancer cells. He then carries out a bimanual examination (with one of his hands on her abdomen and two fingers internally) to detect any masses or tenderness in her pelvis. Normal ovaries and tubes can seldom be felt, and today's exam is negative for any overt signs of disease.

Rectal. Her rectal examination is not remarkable, but because Vernelle Johnson is over 45, Dr. Body recommends that she return to his office in a couple of weeks for a colonoscopy. The instrument— a long, thin tube with a light source—will allow Dr. Body to check for polyps, cancer, or any other abnormalities in the patient's lower colon.

Impression
At the conclusion of the history and physical examination, and after reviewing the available laboratory data, Dr. Body forms an impression of what may be causing Vernelle Johnson's symptoms. He must take everything into consideration—her smoking history, elevated blood pressure, current complaints of chest pain, her heritage, family history, current habits and exercise level, past history of chest pain and heartburn—and put everything into proper perspective.

The History & Physical, Continued

Plan

Dr. Body considers several courses of treatment for the patient and decides to begin treating her hypertension with oral medication. He gives her a prescription for a trial of nitroglycerin in case she has recurrent chest pain to see if that is effective.

After the results of the mammogram, chest x-ray, and EKG are available, he will consider sending the patient for a thallium treadmill exercise test to check her cardiac endurance. Because it is possible that her chest pain is due to her hiatal hernia, and she had a negative upper GI series in the past, Dr. Body gives her a referral slip to see a gastroenterologist, who will carry out the esophagogastroduodenoscopy in an out-patient surgery center. Dr. Body then has Vernelle Johnson make a follow-up appointment with him in three weeks.

After Dr. Body has seen his morning office patients and before he leaves for lunch, he dictates the results of his visits with each patient. He refers to the handwritten notes he had made on Vernelle Johnson and dictates a complete History and Physical Examination report on her. Even though Dr. Body has questioned the patient extensively and carried out a thorough physical examination, his dictation is fairly brief and reflects mainly the positive findings.

Sample History and Physical Report

The following history and physical examination was dictated for Vernelle Johnson's office chart. Because of the extensive nature of her checkup, Dr. Body dictated a complete history and physical examination rather than an initial evaluation report.

REPORT OF HISTORY AND PHYSICAL EXAMINATION

NAME: Vernelle Johnson
PATIENT #: 0178458

DATE OF VISIT: November 25, 2000
PHYSICIAN: William Body, M.D.

CHIEF COMPLAINT: Chest pain x 2 months.

HISTORY OF PRESENT ILLNESS: The patient is a 47-year-old black female who is seen in the office today for a complaint of worsening intermittent chest pain for two months. She states that the pain is burning in nature and lasts for 15 to 20 minutes each time. On a scale of 1 to 10, with 10 being the greatest discomfort she has ever experienced (childbirth), she rates the chest pain at 7.

She says that she does not experience diaphoresis, clamminess, or feelings of doom during these episodes. She has had a similar chest discomfort off and on for the past 15 years or so, but this is definitely worse, she states. There is no radiation of the pain into her arms or jaw, nor is the pain exacerbated by eating or exercise. She has no pain in her legs and denies claudication.

She reports that she has not experienced any significant episodes of shortness of breath since she stopped smoking nearly 20 years ago. She is taking Pepcid over the counter for what she believes is heartburn. She was diagnosed with a hiatal hernia in the past on upper GI series, but the study was apparently negative for gastroesophageal reflux.

PAST MEDICAL HISTORY: She had the usual childhood diseases but no other major illnesses except as noted above. No hospitalizations except for childbirth. She was treated several years ago with Tagamet for a suspected duodenal ulcer, although the upper GI series apparently did not demonstrate any pathology other than a hiatal hernia. She does complain of a feeling of fullness in her lower throat and, interestingly, states that she can swallow a pill, breathe normally, and then cough the pill back up because it "sticks at the bottom of my throat." She has no history of hypertension in the past. She did have a problem with chronic sinus infections in her twenties, but she states that when she moved out of the valley, things improved.

ALLERGIES: She is ALLERGIC TO PENICILLIN. Otherwise there are no known allergies.

MEDICATIONS: Pepcid over the counter. Maalox or Mylanta on occasion for heartburn. She takes no other medications.

HISTORY AND PHYSICAL EXAMINATION
Vernelle Johnson
Patient #0178458
Page 2

FAMILY HISTORY: Mother is living at 68 years of age and apparently carries the sickle cell trait. The patient herself has been tested on several occasions and was negative for sickle cell trait or disease. The mother reportedly had a heart attack in recent years but apparently recovered nicely. Father is deceased from prostate cancer at age 71; he apparently had hypertension and what sounds like rheumatoid arthritis. The patient has two younger siblings, both of whom are healthy.

SOCIAL HISTORY: As stated above, the patient has a 20-pack-year history of smoking but quit 20 years ago. She does not drink alcohol or coffee at this time. She is a sociologist and works part-time for the county. She is married in a monogamous relationship.

REVIEW OF SYSTEMS: Not remarkable except as noted above.

PHYSICAL EXAMINATION:
VITAL SIGNS: Blood pressure was 160/98 when taken by the nurse, 164/92 when I repeated it. Pulse was 78 and regular, respirations 16 and regular, temperature 98.2. She is 5'4" tall and weighs 172 pounds.
GENERAL APPEARANCE: The patient is an alert, cooperative, 47-year-old black female in no apparent distress.
HEENT: Head was normocephalic. Ears, nose, and throat were essentially negative. Sinuses transilluminated well. Eyes: PERRLA. Funduscopic examination was carried out, and no pathology was noted.
NECK: Supple. No masses. No thyromegaly noted. No bruits heard.
CHEST: The chest is symmetric with equal respiratory excursions. No thoracic deformity or tenderness.
BREASTS: Pendulous breasts and slightly lumpy but without discrete masses or tenderness.
HEART: No visible or palpable precordial activity. Normal S1 and S2. No S3 or S4. The cardiac rhythm is regular with a rate of 72. I did not appreciate any murmurs, gallops, or rubs.
LUNGS: The lungs are clear to A&P. No rales, wheezes, or rhonchi were heard.
ABDOMEN: Abdomen was somewhat obese but without organomegaly or tenderness. Normal active bowel sounds.
PELVIC: External genitalia unremarkable. BUS glands normal. No tenderness to cervical motion. On bimanual examination, uterus was noted to be anteverted, anteflexed. No adnexal masses detected. Rectopelvic examination was essentially unremarkable.
BACK AND EXTREMITIES: Back exam revealed no problems; no evidence of scoliosis. No cyanosis, clubbing, or edema of the extremities.

Sample History and Physical Report, Continued

HISTORY AND PHYSICAL EXAMINATION
Vernelle Johnson
Patient #0178458
Page 3

LABORATORY: An EKG strip was taken in the office today to rule out acute infarction and was negative. Urinalysis and CBC were unremarkable.

IMPRESSION:
1. History of intermittent burning chest pain, worsening over the last 2 months. Rule out myocardial infarction (MI). Rule out angina.
2. History of heartburn with possible duodenal ulcer in the past. Rule out gastroesophageal reflux as the cause of her chest pain.
3. Essential hypertension.

PLAN:
The patient will be sent for an electrocardiogram, chemistry panel, and mammogram. Pending these results, we will consider sending her for a thallium treadmill exercise test. She was given oral nitroglycerin to try in case she has a recurrence of the chest pain. She was also started on Zestril 10 mg and HCTZ 25 mg daily for control of hypertension; instructions given. Referral given to see Dr. Jones for possible EGD. Return to see me in 3 weeks.

WILLIAM BODY, M.D.

WB:abc
D&T 11/25/00

Worksheet

Write out a brief definition for each of the following.

1. Chief Complaint _____

   _____

2. History of Present Illness _____

   _____

3. Past Medical History _____

   _____

4. Family History _____

   _____

5. Social History _____

   _____

6. Review of Systems _____

   _____

Examine each of the dictated sentences below and indicate whether it would be found in the *Chief Complaint, History of Present Illness, Family History, Social History, Habits,* **or** *Past Medical History* **section.**

Dictation	Report Section
1. The patient reports vomiting blood three times in the last 24 hours.	_____
2. He has a 30-pack-year history of smoking cigarettes.	_____
3. "I am having chest pains."	_____
4. His father died at age 50 from a stroke; mother is also deceased.	_____
5. Previous surgeries include a total hysterectomy and a tonsillectomy.	_____
6. He denies exposure to asbestos or toxic fumes.	_____
7. The patient admits to drinking two six-packs of beer each weekend.	_____
8. Allergies: Penicillin.	_____
9. She is married and has two children.	_____

Worksheet Continues

Worksheet, Continued

Dictation   *Report Section*

10. The patient noticed the gradual onset of fever, anorexia, and nausea. _____

11. Acute abdominal pain. _____

12. She reports sensitivity to sulfa drugs, which causes a rash. _____

13. He works 6 days a week as a longshoreman. _____

14. She has had the usual childhood illnesses. _____

List the four vital signs.

15. a. _____

    b. _____

    c. _____

    d. _____

Surgery and the Operative Report

Not long ago, the majority of people in the United States lived and died without ever having undergone a surgical procedure. This has changed dramatically as newer diagnostic methods and minimally invasive procedures have improved the quality of life, not to mention increased longevity.

Let's check in on a typical patient about to undergo surgery. Dr. Mavis Davis has recommended that Mr. Jonas Waile, an otherwise healthy 56-year-old Caucasian male, undergo a procedure to remove his gallbladder. The patient recently had six episodes of severe right upper quadrant abdominal pain lasting approximately one hour each. An ultrasound examination was performed and demonstrated several "acoustical" shadows that are believed to represent numerous gallstones.

Dr. Davis has recommended that the patient undergo a laparoscopic cholecystectomy—that is, removal of the gallstones and gallbladder through tiny openings made in the abdomen. Dr. Davis explained to Mr. Waile that before 1990 this procedure would have required severing the omentum and abdominal oblique muscles, resulting in a large scar, major postoperative pain, a four- to six-day hospital stay, and six weeks of recovery time. With the laparoscopic procedure, the patient can expect to have minimal scarring, a manageable amount of postoperative pain, an overnight stay in the hospital, and a two-week recovery period.

Before surgery. Jonas Waile arrives at the hospital two and a half hours before his scheduled surgery. His history and physical examination were done yesterday by his family physician, and a copy of the dictated report is already in his hospital chart. The results of routine preoperative laboratory tests are also available in the chart.

After Mr. Waile checks in through the admitting department, he is taken to a hospital room where he changes into a hospital gown. After he is situated, a nurse comes in to take his vital signs, listen to his heart and lungs to make sure there are no problems, and answer any questions he has about the surgery. She also takes this opportunity to ask if he has any health problems or allergies they should be aware of.

The anesthesiologist also visits before the surgery. Because Mr. Waile did not have a preference for an anesthesiologist, he has agreed to use one of the anesthesiologists assigned to work for the hospital that day. This doctor asks the patient about any previous anesthesia reactions and describes what the anesthesiologist's role will be during surgery.

Dr. Davis used to routinely order a preoperative sedative by injection, but recently she has eliminated this from the preoperative routine. Some physicians order a preoperative injection of a sedative or antihistamine one hour before surgery.

Surgery and the Operative Report, Continued

A half hour before the scheduled surgery time, attendants come to the patient's room to take him to surgery. While lying supine (face up) in his own hospital bed, he is wheeled by the attendants to a holding room before surgery. Because the operating room is fairly chilly, he is covered with several warm blankets to keep him comfortable.

Mr. Waile's bed is soon wheeled into the operating room, and with some help from the operating room personnel, he scoots from his bed onto the operating room table. As the patient looks up into the glare of the brightly lit operating suite, the faces of his surgeon and anesthesiologist offer some comfort. He feels a prick on the back of his left hand as the anesthesiologist inserts an intravenous (I.V.) needle into a vein. The anesthesiologist asks the patient to count backward from 100. Jonas Waile reaches 92 before the lights begin to spin and then fade as he slips into unconsciousness.

The information contained in Mr. Waile's operative report is essential to the completeness of his health record. Like any other medical document, the operative report may be required to justify the fee charged by Dr. Davis for the operative procedure, and, in cases of litigation, the operative report supplies evidence in court on such matters as the indications for surgery, the choice of procedure performed, the names of persons who participated in or witnessed the operation, and the exact nature and sequence of techniques employed.

The information in the operative report is also crucial to Jonas Waile's future medical and surgical care. Exactly what condition was found by the surgeon at the time of the operation? Which of various possible techniques were used, and why? Were grafts, implants, or other foreign materials left in the patient, and, if so, what was their nature, origin, and exact placement? Were any unusual problems encountered in the course of the surgery, and, if so, how were they dealt with? If this information was not recorded, other physicians could only guess at what exactly took place on the day of surgery when, later on, they may be called to diagnose and treat delayed complications or a recurrence of the condition for which surgery was performed.

Identifying Data. In the past, operative reports were transcribed on preprinted forms with carbon packs, and the transcriptionist was expected to type in all pertinent information. Today, with the advent of word processing programs, Jonas Waile's operative report form is generated by the computer, and his demographic information is electronically supplied from the mainframe computer database. The transcriptionist adds other information that must go on the report of operation, such as the names of the surgeon, the assistant, and the anesthesiologist.

Name of Surgeon. Since Dr. Davis was the person who performed the operation and dictated it as well, her name appears as the principal surgeon. In some cases, the name of the person dictating the operative report is not the person who did the surgery, and this must be noted in the record.

Dr. Davis, the principal surgeon, conducts the operation, makes all important decisions, and personally performs the essential procedures. Under Dr. Davis' direction, the assistants hold retractors to provide optimum exposure of the operative site, apply sponges or suction to the operative field to keep it free of blood, help to clamp and ligate bleeding vessels, and may close the surgical wound.

Surgery and the Operative Report, Continued

If the patient were undergoing a cardiac procedure, there might be as many as four assistants, all with advanced surgical training. If the patient were to undergo a very long, exhaustive surgical procedure, two or more surgical teams might work in relays.

Name of Assistant. In addition to the principal surgeon, there may be one or more surgical assistants who are usually physicians but not necessarily surgeons. The first assistant for routine abdominal surgery is often the patient's family physician. Surgeons in training, medical students, nurses, physician assistants, and others may serve as assistants in certain circumstances. In some institutions, nurses and technicians assisting in the operating room (the scrub nurse, the circulating nurse, etc.) are also identified in the dictated report. Jonas Waile has requested that his family physician, Dr. Joe Bleau, act as assistant surgeon, and Dr. Bleau is in attendance.

The scrub nurse or scrub technician helps the surgeon and any assistants put on sterile gowns and gloves as they enter the operating room. It is the responsibility of the scrub nurse to arrange the sterile supplies and instruments on tables in the operating room, to ensure that all instruments, sutures, sponges, and other articles used during the procedure are kept sterile, and to stand ready to hand them to the surgeon or assistants as they are needed.

Because the scrub nurse cannot handle anything unsterile, the circulating nurse or technician assists the scrub nurse by handling and opening unsterile outer wrappings or containers of sterile supplies and instruments as needed. The circulating nurse also adjusts lamps, suction machines and other unsterile equipment, telephones other departments for supplies or test results, delivers specimens to the laboratory, picks up blood from the blood bank, and takes telephone messages for members of the surgical team.

Name of Anesthesiologist. An anesthesiologist is a physician who specializes in the induction of surgical anesthesia, monitors the patient's vital signs, and gives other drugs as needed. In some instances, a qualified nurse anesthetist administers anesthesia, essentially carrying out the same functions as an anesthesiologist.

Indications/History. In her dictation, Dr. Davis briefly reviews the reasons that led to Jonas Waile's surgery. This part of the operative report is not to be confused with the full clinical history contained elsewhere in the health record and dictated by the patient's attending physician.

Preoperative Diagnosis. Here, Dr. Davis names the disease or condition that is the principal reason for the surgery.

Postoperative Diagnosis. A more definite diagnosis is established at the end of the operation. In many instances the postoperative diagnosis is more precise than the preoperative diagnosis. In some cases, however, the postoperative diagnosis is exactly the same as the preoperative diagnosis, or it also might add more detail than the preoperative diagnosis. When the preoperative diagnosis and the postoperative diagnosis do not differ, the dictator often gives the name of the preoperative diagnosis but simply says "same" for the postoperative diagnosis. All dictated abbreviations in the diagnoses should be translated by the transcriptionist for clarity in the patient's health record.

Name of Operation Performed. The type of operation performed is listed under this heading. In addition, Dr. Davis may dictate a code number for insurance and statistical purposes.

Operative Technique or **Operative Procedure**. Under this heading, Dr. Davis makes a single statement about the type of anesthetic used, in this case, general endotracheal anesthesia. Additional information on dosages and monitoring under anesthesia is recorded by the anesthesiologist. Dr. Davis mentions the position of the patient on the operating room table, and if bolsters, sandbags, or other supports were used, she would mention those as well.

Scrubbing of the skin is usually a routine procedure carried out by an assistant or technician. Dr. Davis mentions the name of the disinfectant soap used and any special procedures used for sterile draping. She records the anatomic location, landmarks, and orientation of the incision through which access to the operative site is achieved.

Dr. Davis always gives a step-by-step narrative of an operation, from beginning to end. This may be brief (two or three paragraphs) or quite lengthy (three to four pages), depending on the type of surgery she performs. Although sections of the operative report may be quite routine, each operation varies in some details from others, and a thorough and accurate report will reflect this uniqueness.

Dr. Davis takes care to mention any foreign objects or materials she leaves in each patient, including grafts, artificial cardiac valves, artificial joints, orthopedic fixation devices, pacemakers, shunts, mesh, screws, wires, and cement. The brand name, chemical nature, size, shape, and exact anatomic location of such materials are an essential part of the operative report.

The repair of the incision is described. Each layer of the body wall is closed separately, often with a different type of stitch and a different suture material for each layer. The skin may be closed with metal clips or adhesive strips. Drains or packing materials may be temporarily placed in or on the patient at the conclusion of the operation. Since they must later be removed, recording their presence is of critical importance. Splints, casts, and suction devices for removing blood from the operative site are also reported.

If Jonas Waile was having surgery on his arms or legs, the number of minutes during which blood flow to the extremity was shut off by a tourniquet would be recorded. Any tissues or foreign materials removed from the patient during surgery would be recorded and submitted to the pathology department for study.

Surgery and the Operative Report, Continued

In an open procedure, it is standard practice for sponges, needles, and other materials used in surgery to be counted before surgery is begun and again just before the surgeon begins to close the incision. Usually two persons perform the counts together for greater security. The surgeon does not begin closure of the incision until the sponge and needle counts are reported as correct.

Various methods are used during the operation to monitor blood loss, including close observation of blood absorbed by sponges and measurement of blood in a suction machine. Intravenous fluids and blood administered during the procedure are often recorded in the operative report as well as in the anesthesia record.

Dr. Davis reports the patient's condition after surgery and before he has left for the recovery area. In her dictations, she usually reports that the patient left the operating room in satisfactory condition, but if this is not so, she records any significant problems as a result of the surgery or anesthesia. These include any accidental injuries to healthy organs or tissues, extensive hemorrhage, or adverse reactions to anesthesia.

Postoperative Plan. Dr. Davis here records her intentions for Jonas Waile's postoperative care, and since the plan is to release him from the hospital the following day, she mentions this also.

Sample Operative Report

The following operative report reflects the findings of Jonas Waile's surgery. This is the report that Dr. Davis dictated.

NAME: Jonas Waile
PATIENT #354657

DATE OF OPERATION: 7/13/01
ATTENDING: Joe Bleau, M.D.
SURGEON: Mavis Davis, M.D.

REPORT OF OPERATION

ANESTHESIA TIME: 7:45 AM - 9:00 AM
OPERATION TIME: 8:00 AM - 8:50 AM

PREOPERATIVE DIAGNOSIS: Cholelithiasis; recurrent, intermittent biliary colic; chronic cholecystitis.

POSTOPERATIVE DIAGNOSIS: Cholelithiasis; recurrent, intermittent biliary colic; chronic cholecystitis.

OPERATION PERFORMED: Laparoscopic cholecystectomy.

OPERATING SURGEON: Mavis Davis, M.D.
ASSISTANT: Joe Bleau, M.D.

ANESTHESIA: General endotracheal.

INDICATIONS: The patient presented for evaluation of recurrent, intermittent biliary colic. Ultrasound revealed multiple acoustical shadowing. Laparoscopic cholecystectomy is indicated for definitive treatment.

PROCEDURE AND FINDINGS: After satisfactory general anesthesia was established, a nasogastric tube was placed for decompression of the stomach. The anterior abdominal wall was sterilely prepped and draped.

A curvilinear infraumbilical incision was made and the fascia grasped with two Kocher clamps. Two #1 PDS sutures were placed to assist with retraction of the fascia, and the Hasson trocar was placed in an incision in the fascia. The placement of the Hasson was preceded by digital examination of the peritoneal cavity to ensure that there were no periumbilical adhesions to the anterior abdominal wall. Pneumoperitoneum was established, and the camera was placed through the Hasson retractor for placement of the other trocars under direct visualization. A 10 mm epigastric port was placed, and two lateral 5 mm ports were placed in the subcostal plane.

REPORT OF OPERATION
Jonas Waile
Patient #354657
Page 2

Graspers were placed through the lateral ports and used to retract the fundus of the gallbladder over the edge of the liver and to retract the body of the gallbladder to facilitate dissection of the hilar structures. Before this could be accomplished, some thin, filmy adhesions between the omentum and the gallbladder were taken down bluntly with the dissector. Attention was then directed to dissection of the hilar structures. The cystic artery and cystic duct were isolated, doubly clipped proximally and doubly clipped distally, and then divided with the parrot scissors.

Dissection commenced with the cautery, and the gallbladder was removed from the hilar structures to the fundus. The camera was moved to the epigastric port, and the gallbladder was removed through the Hasson umbilical port. The gallbladder was inspected and indeed found to have all the clips in the appropriate places. There were numerous stones in the gallbladder about the size of chocolate chips.

The Hasson retractor was replaced in the umbilical port and the camera was replaced through this. Inspection of the right upper quadrant revealed the hilar clips to be in good position. The right upper quadrant was copiously irrigated with saline and aspirated. Of note, there was no spillage of stones during the case; however, one of the graspers had disrupted the gallbladder wall early in the case, and there was some minimal spillage of clear yellow bile. All of this was irrigated and aspirated at the conclusion of the case.

The lateral ports were removed and revealed no bleeding. The epigastric port was removed and also revealed no bleeding. The Hasson retractor was withdrawn and pneumoperitoneum evacuated. The PDS sutures at the umbilical fascia were approximated to close the fascial defect, and an additional #1 PDS suture was placed to completely close this fascial defect. All skin incisions were closed with a running subcuticular 4-0 Vicryl suture. Steri-Strips and Band-Aids were applied.

The patient tolerated the procedure well. Estimated blood loss was nil. He was taken to the recovery room in good condition.

POSTOPERATIVE PLAN: If there are no untoward complications, the patient can go home tomorrow afternoon.

Worksheet

Fill in the blanks below with the correct answers. Some answers may require more than one word.

1. Surgical anesthesia is administered and supervised by the _____ or a qualified nurse _____.

2. The surgeon always describes the anatomic location of the _____ through which access to the operative site is achieved.

3. The operating surgeon always dictates a _____ diagnosis and a _____ diagnosis.

4. Scrubbing of the skin and sterile draping of the patient might be dictated: "The patient was _____ and _____ in the usual sterile manner."

5. When a _____ is used on the patient's arms or legs, the amount of time the extremity was devoid of circulation should be noted by the surgeon.

6. It is the responsibility of the _____ nurse or technician to arrange sterile supplies and instruments in the operating room

7. The _____ nurse or technician is not "sterile" in the operating room.

8. Weighing of used surgical sponges and observation of the contents of the suction machine are two methods used to monitor _____ .

9. The surgeon's first assistant is often the patient's own _____.

10. The _____ and _____ times are often recorded at the beginning of the operative report.

11. The surgeon does not begin closure until the count of _____ and _____ is reported as correct.

12. The patient is taken to the _____ following completion of the operative procedure.

Reference Books

Experienced medical transcriptionists value their reference books. They know the right references can save time and increase productivity, and productivity may mean higher compensation.

There should be a basic set of reference books on every transcriptionist's desk. This basic set should include the latest edition of a good medical dictionary, a reliable and up-to-date pharmaceutical reference, an English dictionary, a surgical reference book, quick-reference medical spellers, a laboratory medicine reference book, and an abbreviations book. Other specialty reference books should be available as needed.

Dictionaries. A reputable medical dictionary, one that is well-suited for medical word research, is essential for the accurate transcription of dictated medical reports. Such a dictionary should provide a wealth of words with definitions, pronunciation, and etymology of main entries. **Dictionaries written for and utilized by nurses and hands-on healthcare professionals are not appropriate for medical transcription**. Standards in the industry include *Dorland's Illustrated Medical Dictionary* (from W. B. Saunders) and *Stedman's Medical Dictionary* (Williams & Wilkins). Check with experienced MTs to see what dictionary or dictionaries are the most useful and well-regarded in your community.

Although there are numerous brands of English dictionaries available, a *Merriam-Webster* (not just *Webster*) collegiate dictionary contains the most widely acceptable word spellings and definitions. An unabridged dictionary, though oversized and heavy, is quite helpful in locating words that do not appear in standard English dictionaries.

Glossaries. A glossary is a book that lists difficult or specialized words with short but not necessarily complete definitions. A glossary written specifically for medical transcription should be updated at least every two years. Vera Pyle's *Current Medical Terminology* is the most popular glossary used by medical transcriptionists.

Word books/spellers. Word books, or spellers, abound in the medical transcription field today. These books give only the spelling of words, sometimes with word division and pronunciation aids; there are no definitions or indications for use unless the words are categorized by specialty. Word books definitely have their place on the transcriptionist's bookshelf, as they are a quick reference source for word finding.

Word books may be limited to one specialty or to related specialties, which makes using them easy. Because they contain no definitions, they are small and easy to handle, and word searching is quick. They do have some disadvantages, however. Most do not differentiate between preferred and alternative acceptable spellings. There is usually no indication that a word may have a sound-alike word or homophone; thus, the transcriptionist may choose the wrong medical word if he or

Reference Books, Continued

she does not verify the correctness of the chosen word with a dictionary. This is especially true for less experienced transcriptionists or trainees.

There has been a proliferation of word books compiled from databases without input from experts in medical transcription. Some books, even by authors in the medical transcription field, have been hurriedly compiled, poorly edited or proofread, and not well researched. It is important to make sure that the word books you buy are reputable and come highly recommended from others who have used them.

Textbooks. Textbooks are generally used by transcriptionists and students to gain a better understanding of a disease or surgical process. Textbooks can be kept on the bookshelf rather than on a transcriptionist's desk, as they are consulted less frequently than other references. They are usually not updated as often as reference books and may not be written with the medical transcriptionist as the intended audience, but they can still be invaluable.

When selecting reference books, it is important to consider these factors:

- **Publisher:** Does the publisher produce multiple medical references? Are they well regarded in the medical transcription industry?

- **Author:** Is there an author or editor listed? Some books are compiled from dictionary databases with no input from knowledgeable medical transcriptionists. Does the author or editor have experience as a medical transcriptionist? Other medical experience? If there is no author, is the book published by a company that specializes in medical transcription references?

- **Copyright:** Some specialty areas change more rapidly than others (e.g., pharmacology, radiology, and surgery), while others are relatively stable (anatomy and laboratory procedures). The copyright date should be recent, especially in areas that are changing rapidly (one or two years old), but may be as much as five years old in areas that do not change as rapidly. Dictionaries are seldom revised more frequently than every five to seven years.

- **Contents:** Check the preface or foreword for the purpose of the book and the intended audience. Read the sections on how to use the book. Look at the table of contents. Does the book seem to serve the purpose you have in mind? Are there extensive subentries and cross-references? Is it easy to use? Are phrases included?

It is amazing how many times a medical transcriptionist may use a medical dictionary over the years without ever having read the preface and introductory pages! This part of a dictionary holds a wealth of material for students and practitioners alike. Read the preface and introductory pages of each dictionary in your MT library. Notice in particular what that dictionary says about its pronunciation guides, definitions of main entries and subentries, methods used to alphabetize entries,

Reference Books, Continued

use of cross references, and other information contained in each word entry such as word origin, plural form, and preferred spellings.

Finally, answer the following questions about the references in your MT library.

- Which words are included and which words are not included in this reference, and why?

- How often is this reference updated? If annually, why? If not annually, why not?

- How does the reference address current issues such as the use of 's (apostrophe and s) with eponyms? Does the reference present itself as a definitive source on this question?

In the short term, selecting and using the right reference books will increase your knowledge base and the accuracy of the transcribed reort. In the long term, they will increase your productivity and income.

Word Research Techniques

Not only does transcription itself take time, but so does the preparation involved before sitting down to work. Before you begin transcribing, check to see that your equipment is in proper working order. Assemble your references and other supplies. Isolate yourself from frequent interruptions, if possible. Then, pace yourself. Get in the habit of pacing yourself so that you don't "burn out" early. Needless errors are made when quantity supersedes quality.

Make sure that what is transcribed makes sense in relation to the report. What you think was said is not always what was dictated. And never type any word that cannot be verified. Transcribe each report carefully, and stop as often as necessary to look up new or unfamiliar words for spelling and meaning.

If you are unable to decipher a word the first time it is used in the dictation, don't spend an inordinate amount of time trying to figure it out. Leave a temporary blank and continue with the transcription assignment. You may find that the dictator repeats the word in question later, or you may get a clue from the context of the report.

You may encounter a dictation that seems too challenging for you at the moment. If you find yourself becoming too frustrated or discouraged after an honest attempt at transcribing a particular report, skip it for the time being and return to it later.

Your medical language foundation will build as you master each dictation. Plan to transcribe each report more than once, if possible, until you become thoroughly familiar with its terminology. Some English words may have a different meaning or nuance when used in the language of medicine. For example, the word "complaint" in English may mean a formal accusation, whining, or nagging; in medicine it may simply refer to a patient's stated medical problem: "The patient has complaints of abdominal pain."

One of the most common frustrations shared by working MTs and MT students alike is difficulty finding a word in available resources. Although this may be a legitimate problem for the person who is working without the appropriate reference books, it may actually be that she/he is *hearing* the word wrong.

If you fail to locate a word in your reference materials, it could be that the word in question has an initial letter other than the sound you hear. For instance, the phonetic pronunciation of *v* sounds very much like that of *f*. The letter *m* may sound like an *n*. Some letters share the same sound. The *z* sound you hear may actually be an *x* (as in *xiphoid*), and the *k* may be *ch* (*ischemic*). Medical words that contain silent letters (*euthyroid, pneumonia*) also present a challenge.

Word search first under main entries. This produces a higher percentage of fruitful searches. Make sure you understand which word in a phrase would be the main entry in a dictionary. For exam-

Word Research Techniques, Continued

ple, to find *Q fever,* look first under the noun *fever;* to locate *transhepatic cholangiography,* look first under the noun *cholangiography.*

Recognize that the second word of a phrase is not always the noun that represents the main entry. Example: *caput medusae.* In this Latin phrase, *caput* (head) is the main entry and *medusae* ("of the Medusa" in Latin) is the subentry. The definition for *calcium carbonate* would be found under *calcium.*

In the Latin phrases *in vitro* and *in vivo,* the word is alphabetized under *in* and not under *vitro* or *vivo.* This is different from English in which the preposition *in* would not be considered in word-searching. Be sure to look under both the Latin and English main entries of these words: *musculus, muscle; fissura, fissure; ligamentum, ligament; arteria, artery; vena, vein.* When tendons are named, those names are often based on the muscles to which they are attached. For tendons not listed under the main entry *tendon,* look under *muscle* and *musculus.*

Know when to select an alternative main entry to continue word-searching. If the phrase you want is not under *disease,* look under *syndrome.* If the phrase you want is not under *sign,* look under *test.* If the phrase you want is not under *operation,* check *procedure.*

Another important skill involves dealing with new or coined medical terms that originate from time to time. You need to know that nouns and adjectives can be transformed to be used as verbs; for example, *Bovie* becomes *bovied, convex* becomes *convexed.* This is called *back formation.*

What do you do when you simply cannot find a word? Depending on your situation (if you are on the job or a student in the classroom), the answers may vary, but here are several options:

1. Get a second opinion from another transcriptionist.
2. Refer to the patient's health record, if available.
3. Contact the dictating physician to ask what was dictated.
4. Leave a blank in the report and attach a note for the dictator (this is called *flagging* the report) so that he or she may insert the correct word or return it to the transcriptionist for insertion.
5. Ask the person in charge what action to take.

As you gain experience utilizing available resources, you will become familiar with the techniques of differentiating soundalikes and efficient in locating the appropriate terms. You should never be ashamed to leave a blank when you have made every effort to locate an unfamiliar term. A blank simply means, "I don't know."

Worksheet

Answer the following true or false questions by placing a T for true or F for false in the blank next to the question.

_____ 1. Quantity should supersede quality.

_____ 2. New and unfamiliar terms should always be checked.

_____ 3. Some English words have different meanings when used in the language of medicine.

_____ 4. The initial letter of an unfamiliar term may be different from what you think you are hearing.

_____ 5. When attempting to research an unfamiliar phrase, look first for the adjective.

_____ 6. Latin phrases are constructed similarly to English phrases.

_____ 7. The term you are researching may have an alternative main entry.

_____ 8. Never bother another transcriptionist for assistance with an unfamiliar term; just leave a blank and finish the report.

_____ 9. There should be a set of reference books on every transcriptionist's desk.

_____ 10. A glossary contains difficult or specialized terms with exhaustive definitions.

_____ 11. It is essential that transcription references be updated on a regular basis.

_____ 12. It is necessary for the transcriptionist to differentiate between soundalike terms.

Fill in the blanks below with the correct answers. Some answers may require more than one word.

13. List four types of reference books in the medical transcription reference library.

    a. _____

    b. _____

    c. _____

    d. _____

Flagging Medical Documents

When transcriptionists are unable to interpret a term or section of dictation, or when dictation is completely unfamiliar and cannot be referenced, they are responsible for seeking the assistance of other MTs or appropriate supervisory personnel. If the question cannot be resolved with assistance, or if assistance is not available, the document should be "flagged" in order to alert the originator to the area requiring attention.

To "flag" a transcribed medical report is to attach a note or marker of some kind to indicate that there is a blank, discrepancy, or inconsistency.

The MT should provide as much information as possible to assist the person making additions or corrections, jogging the dictator's memory with reminders of context or a phonetic rendering of the missing word or phrase.

Flagging is carried out according to established policies or standards of the institution or business for which transcription is being done. If a printed document is being sent to the originator for review and signature, a removable "sticky" note may be affixed directly to the document. In some transcription environments, a preprinted note is filled out and affixed to the document to direct the originator to an area requiring attention and completion.

If computerized documents are referred to editing or quality assurance personnel, the flagging may be done electronically, marking the document with an appropriate code. Blanks can then be filled in and copies of completed dictation returned to the MT for future reference. Electronic flagging may also be used in a system where the dictator retrieves the computerized document to the screen, reviews it for completeness, and affixes an electronic signature.

Sample Preprinted Flag

Dear Dr. (Name)_____:

The attached report contains:
❏ Blanks where the dictation was obscured or cut off
❏ A possible dictation error
❏ A possible transcription error
❏ Missing patient demographic information:

_____

Please:
❏ Fill in the blank(s):
Page ___, Paragraph ___ Sounds like

_____
Page ___, Paragraph ___ Sounds like

_____
❏ Redictate the following sections:

_____
_____
_____
❏ Read the following paragraph to check for accuracy: _____

_____
_____

Then:
❏ Return this report with attached note to (transcriptionist) at (facility).
❏ Return to _____.

Flagging Medical Documents, Continued

The following are examples of appropriate flagging:
- The report begins with information about the *right* leg and later mentions the *left* instead (or some other reference to the wrong body part).
- A medication is not consistent with the history or diagnosis.
- The dosage mentioned is not consistent with the medication dictated.
- A male patient's name is dictated, but the dictation is about a female.
- A lab value is improperly expressed.
- Physical findings are not consistent with the diagnosis (i.e., "the breast exam shows no masses" in a patient whose diagnosis is "left breast mass").

Samples of possible discrepancies:
- Missing or incorrect patient name
- Missing or incorrect patient identifier (e.g., hospital number)
- Missing dates (e.g., dates of admission, discharge, operation, consultation)
- Missing sections of a report (e.g., history and physical without the physical examination)
- Missing diagnoses or names of procedures

Attaching notes is not without risk. Post-it notes or paper notes clipped to reports can fall off. Communication in writing is much more difficult than speaking, and notes must be worded in a tactful manner. The person to whom the note is directed can take offense when none is intended. Since leaving notes must be done with great tact, it may in some instances be best handled by the supervisor or lead transcriptionist.

Proofreading and Editing

Most of us have been conditioned to think of physicians as smarter and more all-knowing than we are, but we fail to recognize that the areas in which they are most proficient are medicine in general, and their own medical specialties in particular. Few of them were English majors in their undergraduate studies, and most will frankly admit that they have neither time nor inclination to carefully consider the structure of their sentences, even assuming that they are adequately educated in this regard. The dictation of patient records is usually their least favorite part of medical practice, and it is often left to the end of the day when they are tired and perhaps even a little out of sorts. It is a rare physician who does not admit to being grateful for the assistance provided by an experienced transcriptionist in putting thoughts into coherent form.

It is important to develop good proofreading habits from the start, but proofreading is easier said than done. Proofreading takes a different type of concentration than is used for transcribing. For medical transcription students, proofreading is the reading and re-reading of every word of every document transcribed, both on the screen and in printed copy. Research indicates that it is much easier to miss errors on a computer screen than on a sheet of paper. Beginning students should check first for accuracy in content while listening to the dictation, then read again for spelling, grammar and punctuation, style, and format. If time allows, the report should be re-transcribed (not just retyped) without referring to the previous attempt.

What about experienced MTs? On the job, it is simply not feasible to expect the transcriptionist, working in a production-oriented environment, to proof word-for-word against dictation. However, it is important that each report be read for accuracy on the screen. If a printed copy of the report is available, it too should be read.

An excellent way for students to develop good proofreading habits is to have them read and compare their own transcribed reports against an accurate master transcript key. This not only facilitates the acquisition of proofreading skills, but it also provides immediate feedback to keep error perpetuation down. It is much easier to learn something correctly the first time than to learn it wrong, unlearn it, and then learn the correct way.

Sometimes it is beneficial to have a second pair of eyes check a transcript. Many transcription facilities utilize QA (quality assurance) reviewers, whose job it is to check a percentage of each MT's work against dictation. If the QA reviewer discovers that quality is continually sacrificed for quantity, the MT's job may be at stake. If it is discovered that the MT is lacking in certain skills, further education or training may be required.

It is not uncommon, when listening through a dictation during the proofreading process, to discover that a word or even a whole phrase was left out. Because MTs concentrate intently during

Proofreading and Editing, Continued

the transcription process, it is easy to miss parts of dictation that are quite clear on a second listen.

Obviously, these are serious errors that must be corrected before a report can be considered complete, and an inadvertent omission happens to even seasoned professionals. The most accomplished, experienced, and qualified transcriptionists make mistakes because **no one is immune from error.**

Physicians and other healthcare providers are busy people whose main concern is patient care. Their dictation is often done when they are tired or hurried, and it may contain errors in syntax. MT students and practitioners encounter incomplete and run-on sentences, subjects and verbs that do not agree, and dictated punctuation that is inappropriate. These kinds of errors can be easily edited without changing the dictator's style; simply apply the appropriate rules of grammar and punctuation to the medical document.

Students should never rephrase dictation. Even experienced MTs should tread the editor's road carefully, since it is easy to change medical meaning without intending to. When physicians communicate with the transcriptionist through the dictated report, the dictation can be highly technical, abstruse, or complex in nature, and the potential for transcribing errors is high.

Editing Tips

1. Always communicate any problems with any report that you are responsible for, and I emphasize *you* are responsible for it. I attach messages constantly: "Doctor was cut off." "Sounds like." "Couldn't understand." I do not include snide remarks like, "When you dictate from an aviary, the birds really make it difficult." "Must you eat and dictate at the same time?" Or even, "The jets at the airport where you dictated are responsible for your report looking like Swiss cheese."

2. Keep your ego in check. Dictating is not easy.

3. Be aware of your responsibility to make editing changes where they will enhance but not change the meaning. Don't be afraid to ask questions or leave blanks.

4. Above all, don't lose your sense of humor.

Jean Harrell
Excerpt from *Journal of AAMT*

What about spellcheckers and abbreviation expanders? Beginning students should not use them. Many medical terms sound alike, and it is necessary to search out definitions in order to make proper choices. Students need to develop important reference book skills early on; they need to learn the meaning of words, not just their spellings; and they must develop good proofreading skills. However, spellcheckers and abbreviation expanders *are* important tools for advanced MT students. Their appropriate use is necessary to balance quality and quantity, and to prepare for the workplace.

Physicians do not dictate as they would write. (Neither would we if we had to dictate.) Most editing is done so unobtrusively that the majority of dictators never suspect that their dictation has undergone revision, or that it needed it. Those who do discover that dictation has been edited usually appreciate the improvement.

Proofreading and Editing, Continued

The final transcribed report is a vastly different document from its source, the original dictation. Gone are the "um's" and "ah's," the long pauses, the page rattling, the ICU beeps, the screaming child, the dictator's chewing. The abbreviations have been interpreted, the grammatical errors corrected, the inconsistencies usually resolved, the dictation fit into format.

As the physician is the author of a particular document, we are the editors. We have reworked the dictation, we have corrected, we have honed, we have sharpened, we have clarified, but we have not changed content. As conscientious editors, we have preserved the integrity of the physician-author's style.

Barbra Ellis
Excerpt from *Journal of AAMT*

Vera Pyle tells this story: "I was transcribing the manuscript of a textbook by a physician for whom I had worked in the past. He is a well-educated, extremely literate person. He is a published poet, a musician, a composer, a teacher—a real Renaissance man. So it was with some trepidation that I presumed to suggest changes. I transcribed the page the way he dictated it, and then I gave him my version as well. He read it and beamed. 'This is a tremendous improvement,' he said. 'You know, Vera, together we could rule the world!' "

The goal of medical transcription is, or should be, the communication of medical information about a patient as clearly, concisely, and accurately as possible. On the most basic level, this requires constant decision-making regarding syntax, punctuation, and grammar. At the phonetic level, producing an accurate document involves discriminating among sounds which convey meaning and those that don't (background noises, asides, and the like), analyzing dialects and accents, and constantly choosing between various soundalikes and near-soundalikes. Producing a quality medical document becomes most difficult when dictation is garbled, unclear, incomplete, or medically inaccurate. And it is this latter area that creates the greatest controversy in editing.

It is nearly impossible to transcribe dictation without inadvertent editing. The omission or addition of articles, prepositions, and other minor words represents only a small part of the unconscious editing that takes place everywhere at all times. Recognizing the necessity and inevitability of altering the dictated document makes thoughtful, purposeful editing much more logical and desirable.

The number of variations heard (several of which may be acceptable) for a given dictated expression is often proportional to the number of pairs of ears listening. Did the dictator say "adnexa were thickened, nodular" or "thick and nodular"? Some may hear, "She has some dorsal asymmetry in the nose"; others hear "There was some dorsal . . . " These examples illustrate variations that make little or no difference in meaning.

There are times when you transcribe a phrase that seems correct, but on listening again you discover you've made a grave error. An experienced MT transcribed, "I wondered if she continued to drink, she would certainly die from end-stage liver disease." Because the context of the sentence did not quite make sense, the MT listened again and finally realized what the physician had actually said: "I **warned** her that if she continued to drink, she would certainly die from end-stage liver

Proofreading and Editing, Continued

disease." It is important to make sure that a sentence makes sense within the context of the report. If it does not, go back and listen again!

It is shocking that there are still supervisors, attorneys, and risk management personnel who direct transcriptionists to "type exactly what the doctor says." Editing is necessary to good risk management, which is discussed in another section.

Speaking to a meeting of medical transcriptionists, an attorney wanted to emphasize how important quality transcription is. She held up a large poster board with an excerpt from a medical report that contained a typo magnified in eight-inch letters and said, "When you make a mistake, this is what we make it look like in court."

Indeed, attorneys for the plaintiff in a lawsuit make as big an issue as possible of anything that will make the defendant look bad. If typos can influence a jury in a malpractice or liability case, then grammar errors, garbled sentences, and, most damaging of all, medical content errors should be avoided at all costs. The medical transcriptionist is expected to:

- insert silent letters.
- analyze dialects and accents to select appropriate spellings.
- recognize and correctly transcribe mispronounced words.
- differentiate between preferred and less preferred spellings.
- remember medical words that change spelling as they change form.
- choose the appropriate spelling from among sound-alike words.

Adventures in Thought Transference

By choosing to dictate a document rather than write it out, the dictator not only sidesteps many of the mechanical tasks associated with composition, but implicitly delegates these tasks to the transcriptionist. No dictators have such perfect powers of concentration that they never accidentally repeat themselves, never inadvertently substitute one word for another, never leave a sentence unfinished. Sooner or later, the most alert and cautious dictator makes each of these mistakes, and others besides. Clearly, these normal human lapses ought not to be reproduced in the transcript, and just as clearly the duty of identifying and correcting them devolves on the transcriptionist.

The transcriptionist performs various analytic and interpretive functions and modifies the record by a complex series of deletions, additions, and alterations. . . . The editing process is done with a constant mental awareness based upon a solid foundation of medical and grammatical/stylistic knowledge. As such, medical transcription is both an art and a science.

John H. Dirckx, M.D.
Excerpt from *Perspectives on the Medical Transcription Profession*

Soundalikes cause many of the errors made by both experienced and inexperienced transcriptionists. Choosing the wrong word is not editing; it's a transcription error and should be studiously avoided. Is it *peroneal* or *perineal*, *breech* or *breach*, *Buerger disease* or *Berger disease*? When the physician dictated *malignment* (libel), was *malalignment* (out of alignment) intended? Quality-conscious transcriptionists should study lists of English and medical soundalike words and learn the most common.

Proofreading and Editing, Continued

In editing dictation, we do not go charging in, doctoring up reports in an aggressive way, in an intrusional way. It has to be done so subtly, so delicately, so carefully, that we get a favorable response from the dictator. . . . We must be so involved with what we are transcribing that we know what is going on and can detect something that is dictated that does not make sense, that does not flow, that does not add up. We must listen with an educated ear, with an intelligent ear, so that we can produce an accurate, intelligent, clear document, always remembering the fine line between editing and tampering.

Vera Pyle
Current Medical Terminology

A transcriptionist should never type a word whose meaning is unfamiliar, even if certain of the spelling. One inexperienced transcriptionist had to be threatened with being fired before she would give up her favorite word book. The book listed many sound-alikes as well as less preferred spellings, and she was forever choosing the wrong word or the less preferred spelling because she was too lazy or in too much of a hurry to check unfamiliar words in the dictionary. Naturally, the wrong word or less preferred spelling seemed to be the one that appeared first alphabetically.

Even these routine functions, often undertaken unconsciously by the transcriptionist, may have significant impact on the meaning of the report. Physicians sometimes dictate non-words, especially by using an incorrect prefix or suffix. For example, a physician who dictates *nonsensible* may mean *nonsensical* or *insensible* (a major difference in meaning). If *varicoces* is dictated, the physician might mean *varicocele* or *varices*. The transcriptionist must use the context of the report to determine which word is intended. A common dictation error of this type is the dictation of a word like *nonavoidable* (not in any dictionary) for *unavoidable*. Some non-words are actually mispronounced words, such as *reoccur* (recur), *reoccurence* (recurrence), *recannulization* (recanalization).

Punctuation. Although some physicians dictate punctuation, most do not. The transcriptionist must determine if dictated punctuation is correct and alter it if it is not. Punctuation not dictated must be supplied. There are times when it may be difficult to tell if a clause or phrase belongs at the end of a preceding sentence or the beginning of the next one. The transcriptionist must analyze the context of the report and determine the position and punctuation associated with that phrase.

A physician who dictated punctuation at one hospital was especially fond of semicolons. Almost every sentence he dictated included at least one and many included two, three, and sometimes more. Transcribing the punctuation as dictated made his reports difficult to read and understand, often requiring the re-reading of a sentence several times. Changing many of his dictated semicolons to periods or commas contributed to the clarity of his reports.

While punctuation is very important in correct transcription, students often make the mistake of spending way too much time pondering the proper placement of commas, the use of semicolons, exceptions to rules, and so on. It is important that punctuation dilemmas do not overshadow or delay the real goal: the learning of the language of medicine.

Proofreading and Editing, Continued

Grammar. Agreement errors frequently cause problems, particularly for the foreign dictator, and subject-verb agreement errors are probably the most common dictation error corrected by transcriptionists. These errors are often due to separation of the subject from the verb by prepositional phrases or intervening clauses. The transcriptionist must catch in real-time proofreading what the ear of the dictator does not catch as he talks. When the physician dictates, "The edema in both legs have not yet responded to diuretics," the transcriptionist should correct the verb to *has*. Another example: "There do not appear to have been any associated eye blinking or other automatisms" should be edited to "There does not appear" to make the verb agree in number with the subject "eye blinking."

Another common dictation error is the lack of agreement between pronouns and their antecedents and the failure to have an easily identifiable antecedent for a pronoun. For example, a physician dictated, "The dog was removed from the house with no change in his symptoms." Is it the dog's symptoms the physician is concerned with or the patient's? "His" should be edited to "the patient's" for clarity.

Foreign physicians sometimes misplace modifiers by putting them in the position they would occupy in the physician's native language; for example, "The patient tolerated well the procedure." While the meaning of this sentence is abundantly clear, the physician looks much more knowledgeable (and, to some, competent) if the transcriptionist moves the adverb to the end of the sentence.

Minor editing of content. Decisions made by transcriptionists that do not affect meaning include the following:

- deleting redundancies
- differentiating between brief forms and slang
- translating slang forms
- correcting inconsistencies in grammar and punctuation

A blank is an honorable thing; it means you don't know. If you have tried everything you can try to fill in that blank and can't, leaving a blank is preferable to guessing. Guessing is bluffing. . . A blank is entirely legal and entirely acceptable.

Vera Pyle
Current Medical Terminology

These types of changes are necessary for clarity and conciseness. Slang, especially, should be translated into acceptable forms, as slang may make the dictating physician appear careless, sloppy, and unprofessional. Differentiating between brief forms and slang may include some gray areas, but, in general, acceptable brief forms are taken from the beginning of the word they represent and are easily recognizable (*basos, polys, segs*). Slang forms, while sometimes taken from the beginning of a word, may also be taken from the middle or end of a word and may not be easily recognizable ("crit" for *hematocrit*, "lytes" for *electrolytes*).

Inconsistencies, such as *left/right* discrepancies, gender discrepancies, and inconsistencies in lab results or medication dosages, should be investigated. If it is possible to determine what is correct, that is what should be transcribed. If the discrepancy cannot be resolved, or if it constitutes a major problem, the report should be flagged and a note written to the dictator.

Editing of medical content. Editing medical content requires a superior fund of knowledge in the areas of medical terminology, anatomy and physiology, pharmacology, laboratory medicine, surgery, and pathology. Editing of medical information should be done only when the transcriptionist can give a sound explanation of the reason behind the change and support that reasoning in medical reference books. As stated previously, this type of editing should not be made by beginners unless approved by the teacher or supervisor.

The greatest controversy in editing involves the substitution of a different word based on contextual meaning and the substantial editing of medical content. Following are examples of word substitution:

Clear Communication

The ultimate goal of medical transcription is clear communication.

Accurate transcription of confusing dictation is an ongoing challenge for MTs. The dictating physician is counting on the transcriptionist to know and spell all medical words, including drugs, and to be familiar with their proper expressions.

Books on transcription style and format provide guidelines; nevertheless, the experienced transcriptionist should use common sense when transcribing potentially confusing dictation. For example, a physician dictated the following statement:

"The patient was placed on Tylenol three one to two three times daily."

If one followed the accepted rules of transcription style, the result would read:

"The patient was placed on Tylenol No. 3 1-2 3 times daily."

How confusing it is to interpret this statement! *Since the goal of the medical document is clear communication, it is acceptable to modify an accepted guideline for purposes of clarity.* The alternative expressions below are much easier to read and more clearly convey the dictated meaning:

The patient was placed on Tylenol #3, 1-2 three times daily.
The patient was placed on Tylenol #3, one to two, 3 times daily.
The patient was placed on Tylenol No. 3, 1-2 tablets three times daily.
    (The word *tablet* was added.)

Remember, flexibility is the key when it comes to transcription techniques and procedures.

Proofreading and Editing, Continued

Dictated: Vitamins are given to *supply* a deficiency.
Transcribed: Vitamins are given to *correct* a deficiency.

Dictated: In *lieu* of the patient's high fever, antibiotics were continued.
Transcribed: In *view* of the patient's high fever, antibiotics were continued.

If "forced ventilatory capacity" is dictated, editing to "forced vital capacity" could be justified because that is the name of the test. However, if there is any doubt as to the exact intended meaning, no editing should be attempted, and the dictation in question should be brought to the attention of the supervisor or dictator for clarification.

It is unlikely that there will ever be unanimous agreement on what is or is not tampering. Perhaps that's good, because as long as people disagree, they can never become complacent. Editing will never be a routine, mindless task as long as the discussion about what's right and what's wrong, what's proper or not, is open.

Worksheet

Fill in the blanks below with the correct answers. Some answers may require more than one word.

1. The ultimate goal of medical transcription is clear _____.

2. If a portion of dictation is not clear and cannot be ascertained with the assistance of a supervisor or another MT, it is appropriate to _____ the document to draw the attention of the originator.

3. The transcriptionist has a responsibility to make editing changes that will enhance but not alter medical _____.

4. Hospitals and transcription services often employ _____ personnel to proofread transcription and help with skill-building.

5. The transcriptionist chooses the _____ of a report using guidelines established by the employer or client.

6. According to Dr. John Dirckx, medical transcription is both _____ and _____.

7. Errors in _____ agreement are probably the most frequent grammar corrections a transcriptionist must make.

8. Foreign dictators often misplace _____.

9. _____ should be translated into acceptable forms, as its inclusion in a report can appear sloppy and unprofessional.

10. An appropriate blank is an honorable thing; it simply means, "_____."

List five examples of inconsistencies or discrepancies that would require calling the dictator's attention to a transcribed report.

11. _____

12. _____

13. _____

14. _____

15. _____

Quality Assurance

Quality assurance (QA) is the process by which medical transcription achieves its primary goal: effective communication. It should be a teaching/learning process, rather than a punitive one.

The quality assurance process begins with the individual medical transcriptionist, who must have access to current reference materials and equipment. If an employer does not choose to purchase reference material, it is the responsibility of the medical transcriptionist to provide and maintain his/her own reference library. Without sufficient references, quality will suffer.

In implementing the quality assurance process, the medical transcriptionist is responsible for:

- appropriate use of reference materials

- skillful and efficient use of transcribing equipment

- verification of all patient and dictator information

- application of appropriate format

- application of rules of English grammar and punctuation

- appropriate editing

- visual proofreading and use of spellchecking software

- referring all inappropriate dictation to proper supervisory personnel

- meeting established deadlines

- protecting patient confidentiality

QA personnel should be qualified medical transcriptionists. In some employment environments, specific personnel are responsible for completing the QA process by checking completed transcription for missing or incorrect information, improper grammar and spelling, and overall accuracy. Copies of all transcription reports edited or corrected should be returned to the medical transcriptionist along with discussion of rationale for any changes made. This helps to fulfill the QA objective of teaching/learning by providing appropriate feedback.

Quality Assurance, Continued

Unfortunately, some employers unfairly utilize QA as a means of fear and punishment, withholding compensation and threatening loss of employment when quality standards are not met. QA may also be unfairly tied to quantity standards. Because quality assurance can be very subjective, rather than objective, this is entirely inappropriate. While every medical transcriptionist, new or experienced, should make every effort to produce quality documentation, while at the same time adhering to productivity requirements, productivity should not be allowed to override the need for quality. Of course, if an MT fails to respond to QA by improving the quality of her/his transcription to acceptable levels, it would then be appropriate for an employer to set a time limit for improvement as a condition of continued employment.

The consistent application of appropriate quality standards serves to protect the ultimate medical transcription "customer," the patient.

Quality

What I believe "quality" refers to in medical transcription is the excellence of the medical content within the document. When the anatomy, the physiology, the combining forms, and the difficult terms all appear within their correct medical context in the report, we have quality.

What about correct spelling and neat-appearing reports? Isn't that considered quality too? In a sense, yes, and it is important, but only secondarily so. These factors fall into the category of accuracy, which I consider a measure of typewriting skills. Quality as I have defined it is the measure of medical transcription.

Medical transcriptionists who have learned to spell medical terms by rote, without knowing the meanings, will transcribe what they think they hear, not necessarily what the dictator expects them to hear.

When I can find transcriptionists who have a good knowledge of the human body and its functions, the depth of medical knowledge to detect medical inconsistencies and know which sound-alike word to use, the curiosity to question and the tenacity to research, and who consider the problem-dictator a challenge to their capabilities, then I know I have quality.

Sue Covel, CMT
Journal of AAMT

Transcribing for the ESL Dictator

As more foreign-born physicians and other allied health professionals for whom English is a second language become a part of the American healthcare scene, medical transcriptionists are faced with an increasing number of ESL (English as a second language) dictators. This is a scary experience for newcomers to the MT profession, and even seasoned MTs often find transcribing for ESL dictators to be a major challenge.

Successfully translating the dictation of those who are foreign-born requires one to become familiar with the speech patterns of various nationalities, bearing in mind that English is a very difficult language that has few hard-and-fast rules. One must give credit to those ESL dictators who do their best to communicate clearly in what is essentially two languages rolled into one—English/medical.

The syntax in many foreign languages is entirely different from what is found in English, and ESL dictators often have difficulty wrapping their tongues around sounds that are not common in their own languages. For example, there is no *p* sound in Arabic, and for many healthcare professionals whose native language is Arabic, a *p* sound may be converted to a *b* sound. A transcriptionist who worked for a time in Saudi Arabia reported that she was confused by the request from a resident physician for what sounded like a *boberglib*, and it was only after much discussion that she was able to determine that the young man was seeking a paper clip.

Foreign Accents Revisited by Susan Dooley, CMT, and Ellen Drake, CMT

Foreign-accented dictation seems very daunting at first. Approach it as a challenge. Believe it or not, the accent that seems totally unintelligible at first will eventually become second nature. Remember—the more versatile and capable you are as a transcriptionist, the more valuable you will be in the employment market.

Sometimes it helps to make a game of it. Perhaps a dictator will sound like Roseanne Roseanna Danna, Ricky Ricardo, or Crocodile Dundee to you. Relating an accent to a familiar character from TV or the movies can, silly as it seems, help get your ears "into the rhythm" of the accent of a foreign dictator. It may help you to listen ahead; the dictator may repeat the word in question more clearly, or context clues may help you to choose the correct word.

It is a good idea to keep your own list of foreign pronunciations of English words. In your notebook, write the word phonetically the way it sounded to you, write the word correctly spelled, and note the nationality of the dictator if you know it. This practice will increase your awareness of pronunciation variants and improve your ability to understand foreign dictators.

Transcribing for the ESL Dictator, Continued

General Anomalies

Often, in an attempt to be clear in dictation, the speaker may pronounce final consonants so that it sounds like there is an added syllable at the end of a word, like *chestah* for *chest*. Sometimes, *ed* endings are made into separate syllables; the word *explained*, for example, is pronounced *ex-plain-ed*.

It's also very common for speakers to place emphasis on the wrong syllable of a word, like *ba-SI-tra-cin* instead of *ba-ci-TRA-sin* (bacitracin), or *ter-EE-ter-EE* for *TER-i-tor-ee* (territory). Additional examples are *deb-BRISS* for *debris*, *per-i-TON-eum* for *per-i-to-NE-um* (also, *peri-TON-eal*), *rezi-DOO-al* for *re-SIJ-oo-al* (residual), *cap-PI-lar-ees* for *CAP-i-lar-ees* (capillaries), *ce-fo-TOX-i-ME* for *cefotoxime*, *ce-FIX-i-ME* for *cefixime*, *obi-SI-ty* for *obesity*, *vera-PAM-il* for *verapamil*.

Sometimes several words may sound like one word because the dictator does not pause between them. Conversely, one word may sound like several words, or pauses may occur so that syllables from one word appear to be part of the following word, as in *intap*[pause]*ering* dose for *in tapering dose*. When all else fails, try to write out the sounds you hear, syllable by syllable. Once the sounds are on paper, you may more readily see that several words are involved.

Watch for interchange of personal pronouns—sometimes the dictator refers to the patient as *he* for *she* or may use the possessive *his* and *her* for the opposite sex in the same report.

In some languages, there are no articles; thus, when translating to English, the speaker may drop *a*, *an*, or *the* preceding a noun. In languages where an article precedes every noun, the speaker may add articles when translating into English. These articles may occasionally sound like part of the trailing word rather than a separate word. If the word you are hearing has an initial vowel sound, you may want to drop off the initial sound and determine if what is left is a complete word.

Word endings such as *-s*, *-ed*, *-al*, and *-ive* may not be pronounced. The transcriptionist should use the proper noun, adjective, or verbal form of a word called for in the sentence, even if the dictator did not. Also, the final sounds of some words ending in *m* may be dropped—for example, *spaz* for *spasm*, *neoplaz* for *neoplasm*. Internal syllables may be omitted as well, thus *trans-luminal* may become *transminal*.

A *schwa* (∂, like a soft short *e*) sound may be added in the middle of a word, creating an extra syllable. Examples: *ad-∂-van-tage*, *ad-∂-ven-ture*, *ad-∂-vance*. Some dictators may use word endings not used in English—*abdomens* for *abdomen*, *feets* for *feet*, or *childs* for *children*.

Foreign physicians may choose an incorrect word that is similar in meaning to the one intended but does not exactly fit. For example, they may say *look* for *see*, *prolonged* for *extended*. One gastroenterologist consistently dictated on a colonoscopy report that the scope was "slided up" the colon. This could be edited to *slid*, but a better edit might be *advanced*.

Transcribing for the ESL Dictator, Continued

Unfamiliar words and expressions may be used that the transcriptionist thinks must be a mistake but are not. One Indian physician dictated, "Please *vide* (VI-DEE) the anesthesia record," the word *vide* a Latin term meaning "see."

Many Spanish dialects add an *eh* sound before words that begin with the letter *s*, so that *skin* becomes *eskin*, *spine* becomes *espine*, *stone* becomes *estone*, etc. *Eh* is often used by foreign dictators the way Americans use *uh*, as a filler when thinking.

Pronunciations That Cannot Be Categorized

An East Indian physician pronounced *trivial* as *tri-gal* or *tri-ger*, both syllables receiving equally heavy accent. *Basically* was pronounced *vesi-CA-ee*. One physician pronounced a patient's name like *Fuller*, spelled what sounded like *F-O-W-E-R*; the patient's name was *Fowler*. A phrase sounding like *double-up pain* (a somewhat logical and reasonable-sounding expression for a foreign dictator) was actually *developed pain*.

Punctuation

The punctuation mark *comma* (,) may be pronounced *KO-ma*, which sounds just like the medical word *coma*. Sometimes foreign speakers use the term *point* to indicate a *period* (.), *two points* to indicate a *colon* (:), *dot* to mean a *period* (.), *stop* or *full stop* to mean a *period* (.). For European speakers, *stop* can also mean a *comma* (,). East Indians often say *perrid* with the rolled *r* for *period* (.).

Note: When the word *period* is dictated, it does not always signify a punctuation mark; it may be that you are to type the word. For example, "The patient denied any new complaints during this period." You might also hear *new line* for *new sentence* or *new paragraph*.

Both native and foreign speakers of English frequently dictate the wrong punctuation. You should edit for correctness. Foreign dictators tend to place adverbs and adjectives according to their native syntax, not ours. For example, a Spanish speaker might say, "A polyp, large, was in the colon," instead of "A large polyp was in the colon," or "tolerated well the procedure," instead of "tolerated the procedure well." Edit them to the correct English syntax.

Prepositions can also be a problem for foreign dictators. "Patient agreed for the discharge," should be edited to "The patient agreed to the discharge." *In* and *on* are also frequently confused. Remember that when one learns a new language, one tends to use the rules of syntax from one's native language, whether they are correct or not. For this reason, always be prepared for grammatical errors and know how to correct them.

Transcribing for the ESL Dictator, Continued

Sounds to Listen For

- The sound of *a* is frequently pronounced *ah*, like *vahgus* for *vagus*, *ah-CEE-tus* for *ascites* (which also contains the *ee* sound for *i*), *ah-mine-o-FI-lee* for *aminophylline*, which illustrates the dropping of the ending sound as well.
- *Ch* at the beginning of a word that may be pronounced as *sh* in English will often be pronounced as a hard *ch* (as in *cherry*) by Hispanics. For example, *Chevy* ("shevy") will sound like *tshevy* (as in *chair*).
- The final *d* sound of a word is sometimes pronounced *t* or *dt*; thus, *sound* might become *soundt*. The word *the* frequently sounds like *de* or *ze*.
- At times, the *g* sound is replaced by the *k* sound, so a word like *tingling* becomes *tinkling*. *G* and sometimes *j* may also be pronounced as an *h*, as in *au-dino-FA-hia* for *odynophagia* and *HI-mee* for *Jamie*, *hu-hu-lo-way-nus* for *jugulovenous*, the *v* being pronounced as a *w*, as explained below.
- The short *i* sound becomes *ee* when *distress* is pronounced *dee-stress* and *rib* is pronounced *reeb*. At the beginning of a word, a short *i* may sound like a short *a* or *uh*, as in *uh-skemia* for *ischemia*.
- The pronunciation of *j* as a *wha* sound as in *Juanita* and *Juan* is familiar to most of us, but *wule* for *joule* may throw us.
- Speakers of British English may use the *k* sound of *c* for certain words that Americans usually pronounce with the *s* sound, such as *kephalic* for *cephalic*.
- *L* may be substituted for *r*, as in *lelief* for *relief*, *bleathe* for *breathe*, *plesant histoly* for *present history*. Some words, like *chloride*, are especially tricky because of the combination of problem sounds: *ch*, *l*, and *r*, thus *krolide*. *L* may also be substituted for *n*: *leoplas* for *neoplasm* (note the dropping of the final sounds as well).
- *N* may be substituted for *l*, as in *inuum* for *ileum*.
- *O* may sound like *au* as in *au-dino-FA-hia* for *odynophagia*. Note: Here the *g* is pronounced like an *h*.
- *Qu* frequently is pronounced *k*, that is *frekent* for *frequent*.
- *R* may be substituted for *l*, like *breed* for *bleed*. *R* from Hispanic speakers may be inadvertently "rolled," as it is in many words in their native language. When this is combined with other anomalies, it may take some detective work to arrive at the correct word. For example, x-ray may sound like *esrrra*.
- Sometimes speakers can't pronounce the *shr* sound, so a phrase like "The patient is allergic to shrimp" comes out "The patient is allergic to *seerimks*."
- The speaker may be unable to make the *th* sound and may substitute *t* or *s*, like "I *sink sa* patient has a . . ." instead of "I think the . . ."
- *U* at the beginning of a word may be replaced by *yoo* as in *YOOM-bi-LI-cus* for *umbilicus*. The final *us* sound may be pronounced as *oose*—*vagus* becomes *vagoose*.
- *V* may be pronounced *b*, like *bery* for *very*. *V* may also be pronounced as a *w*—*womiking* for *vomiting*, *walwular* for *valvular*, *waig* for *vague*, *woices* for *voices*, *wile* for *vile*, *woid* for *void*.
- A *y* at the beginning of a word might be pronounced *u*, with *Yvonne* pronounced *U-won*.
- Spanish speakers also frequently pronounce *x* as *s*, like *espire* for *expire*, *esamination* for *examination*.

Worksheet

Answer the following true or false questions by placing a T for true or F for false in the blank next to the question.

_____ 1. There are only a few ESL physicians in today's healthcare facilities.

_____ 2. Allied health professionals who are foreign-born find it easy to speak the medical language in English.

_____ 3. A transcriptionist should look upon the mastery of ESL dictation as a challenge that will make him/her more employable.

_____ 4. Learning to "think phonetically" will help the MT to understand foreign dictators.

_____ 5. ESL dictators often refer to patients in the wrong gender.

_____ 6. The MT should transcribe ESL dictation as dictated, rather than editing for proper grammar and syntax.

_____ 7. ESL dictators often use different terms for punctuation than are used by American-born dictators.

_____ 8. Those who speak English as a second language often confuse the parts of speech.

_____ 9. There are as many differences in pronunciation as there are differences in languages and dialects.

_____ 10. One should respect ESL dictators' efforts to speak correct English; it is not easy because there are no hard and fast rules to assist them.

_____ 11. According to Sue Covel, quality is the measure of medical transcription.

_____ 12. The person in charge of quality assurance should be a registered nurse.

_____ 13. Inappropriate dictation should be referred to proper supervisory personnel.

_____ 14. Some employers may use QA as a means of fear and punishment.

_____ 15. Productivity should not be allowed to override the need for quality of transcription.

_____ 16. Quality assurance is an objective review process.

_____ 17. It is the responsibility of the medical transcriptionist to purchase medical references if the employer does not provide them.

Patient Confidentiality

Medical transcriptionists are pledged to protect the privacy and confidentiality of the individual health record. They must never acknowledge or disclose that they are privy to personal, medical, or social patient information. Even if a patient is a relative, friend, or celebrity, the details of every report must remain absolutely confidential. This is true in every work setting.

A privately owned medical transcription company once ran an ad in several allied health publications picturing a home-based medical transcriptionist in her bathrobe, gossiping on the telephone to her friend, with a crying baby nearby in a playpen. The caption read, "Madge, you won't believe what I just found out about your neighbor!" The implication was, of course, that a medical transcriptionist working at home is more likely to breach confidentiality than one who is working in an office or within the confines of a hospital. Is this a valid conclusion?

In the past, medical transcriptionists who "came up through the ranks"—that is, those who were trained and then practiced medical transcription solely in the hospital or clinic environment—were often directly involved in some way with patients' medical records. This may have included accessing patient charts to find specific information or even "charting" transcribed reports (physically placing transcribed reports in patient charts). The need for confidentiality of the patient health record was well understood within this environment.

Today there are many practicing medical transcriptionists who have never set foot in a hospital health information or transcription department. Having learned their craft in a college setting or private company, they have gone on to work in transcription services or at home and have never worked directly with patient charts. These transcriptionists may have signed confidentiality agreements in which they commit to hold all patient information in the strictest confidence. But merely signing a confidentiality agreement does not necessarily mean that they truly understand all that the term "breach" encompasses. Because breach of confidentiality is one of the few areas in health information management where the transcriptionist can be held liable, its importance cannot be overstated.

The following are true case histories that describe encounters with health information. Which are breaches of confidentiality?

1. A transcriptionist sees the name of a friend on a hospital inpatient roster. He phones the patient's room and says, "I heard you're in the hospital. Would you like a visitor this evening?"

2. A transcriptionist overhears two lab technicians discussing a patient by name. Because she transcribed the patient's operative report earlier, the transcriptionist is familiar with the patient's history. As she listens to their conversation, she realizes they have inaccurate information. "You've got it wrong," she interjects. "The woman in 413 had a therapeutic abortion, not just a D&C."

Patient Confidentiality, Continued

3. You are an employee in the medical transcription department of a hospital. A registered nurse who works on the surgical floor is a friend of yours. She calls you on the phone and in a hushed voice says, "You've got to come up and see the tattoo on this woman. It starts on her tummy and goes all the way down to you know where! She won't know you're not a nurse."

4. A physician admits an Elvis impersonator for facial plastic surgery. The medical transcriptionists on the evening shift eagerly locate the chart after the patient is discharged to look at the "before" and "after" pictures.

5. A patient is admitted to the radiology department for x-ray of a foreign body in an embarrassing location. The radiologist makes a joke about it, which the transcriptionist later relates to her husband.

6. Your mother has had quintuple bypass surgery. You are a medical transcriptionist working at home, and you want to help your mother better understand her medical condition. You call your friends in the health information department of the hospital where she is a patient and ask them to make photocopies for you of any report they transcribe on your mother.

7. A transcriptionist was scheduled to have breast augmentation at a nearby hospital but did not want to use her real name, fearing that everyone she knew would get a look at her chart and photos. To protect her privacy, the physician dictated a false name. In the confusion that ensued in trying to get the report correctly identified, a co-worker who knew the patient discovered her real identity. Word got back to the facility where the patient worked, and rumors flew about the nature and purpose of her surgery.

8. You are transcribing a psychology dictation on a married couple with a sexual dysfunction. As you are transcribing the report, it dawns on you that you are acquainted with the couple.

9. A transcriptionist employed by a private company transcribes what she believes to be a sexual abuse case. The physician fails to report the case to the proper authorities. The transcriptionist contacts state authorities and relates the incident.

10. You transcribe at home for a private practice physician. He uses your call-in line and frequently dictates from his cellular phone, where he isn't bothered by office noise or children at home.

11. A medical transcription service owner in a large metropolitan area is interviewing job applicants. One applicant proudly shows the service owner samples of work she has transcribed at a different facility in the same town. The service owner observes that patient names appear on the reports.

Patient Confidentiality, Continued

Case Review

1. The transcriptionist is breaching confidential patient information by contacting his friend in the hospital. It doesn't matter that the transcriptionist avoided telling his friend where he got the information—the patient has the right to privacy. This incident indicates either inadequate education regarding the extent of confidentiality, or lack of professionalism on the part of the transcriptionist.

2. It's certainly possible that the transcriptionist felt it was all right to set the record straight with fellow workers; however, it was not her prerogative to do so under these circumstances. The information did not promote patient care and could even be construed as gossip. Knowledge obtained from transcribing a report should not be discussed with co-workers and must never be related to anyone other than those with a valid need to know.

3. The nurse in this case has violated the patient's right to privacy by divulging information that might embarrass or humiliate the patient. In addition, the nurse invited an unauthorized person to the surgical floor and, beyond that, encouraged her to masquerade as a member of the nursing staff.

4. Curiosity does not justify the violation of confidential patient information.

5. The radiologist violated confidentiality in joking about the case, even within the radiology department, and the transcriptionist was in the wrong when she discussed the case with her husband.

6. The home worker is not utilizing proper channels to obtain report transcripts on her mother. The health information sought might be legally obtainable, but it must be procured in accordance with regulations. Even if the patient is a relative or friend, the details of every report must remain absolutely confidential; thus, the appropriate action on the part of hospital staff would be to deny the request.

7. It is apparent that the patient went out of her way to remain anonymous. The physician, in attempting to protect her privacy, actually compromised it by dictating a pseudonymous name, since it was necessary for the health information department to correctly match the report with the patient. It is not clear how the patient's identity got back to her place of employment, but it does appear that a health information department employee who knew the patient was involved.

8. No breach of confidentiality has occurred here. However, the transcriptionist must never reveal to anyone her knowledge of this couple's situation, her awareness that they are having problems, or her part in documentation of their health record.

Patient Confidentiality, Continued

9. This is a very serious breach of confidentiality. Even where state laws mandate the reporting of suspected child abuse, that reporting is the responsibility of the hospital or the examining physician, not the transcriptionist. (What actually transpired in this incident is that the transcriptionist was in error about the validity of the child abuse, and she was successfully sued for violation of confidentiality.)

10. The physician and the transcription company owner may be unaware of the fact that cellular phones are not secure. These transmissions can be intercepted by anyone with inexpensive eavesdropping equipment. The dictation should be done only on traditional phone lines and not from cars, portable phones, or airplanes.

11. The applicant not only violated patient confidentiality by taking documents from a facility, but she left the patient names intact. The service owner who spoke with this applicant advised her that showing work samples was inappropriate since the sample documents could have been someone else's work. Furthermore, the service owner stated that he would not hire the applicant under any circumstances because she had blatantly violated patient confidentiality by not removing or obscuring the names in the documents.

During World War II there was a popular slogan that was printed and posted prominently: "Loose lips sink ships." In other words, the slightest breach of confidentiality may cause irreparable damage. There are several steps that you as the transcriptionist can take to promote the confidentiality of the patient healthcare record.

- Use document shredders to dispose of discarded health information sheets, photocopied documents, or other printed matter containing confidential health information data that is no longer needed.

- Clarify standards for the use of demographic information which is computer-downloaded to other settings.

- Adhere to the length of time that documents can be retained in computer hard drives by employees or outside contractors and the means by which confidential information is deleted.

- Verify guidelines for archiving, and adhere to security measures that must be taken when modeming, faxing, or using other unsecured communication lines.

- Use passwords and encryption methods where appropriate.

- If you are working in an environment that is not secure from prying eyes, whether at home or in an office, use privacy screens. These prohibit anyone from reading the monitor who is not sitting directly in front of it.

Patient Confidentiality, Continued

- Never leave your desk with confidential information on the monitor screen.

- Make sure that your environment is secure from intruders. A hospital in California went to great expense to implement state-of-the-art computers networked to their satellite facilities, running sophisticated software programs, then neglected to provide adequate locks and alarm systems. A resulting break-in resulted in the theft of millions of dollars' worth of computer equipment—and an untold amount of confidential patient information—when the thieves just walked out with computers in hand.

Finally, understand that the penalties for violation of confidential patient information will probably include immediate dismissal or termination of contract and legal liability for violations. In other words, you can be fired *and* sued.

Worksheet

Choose the correct answer in each of the following multiple-choice questions. Write your answer in the space provided next to the number of the question.

_____ 1. If the transcriptionist discovers through a dictated medical report that a close friend has been hospitalized, the MT should:
a. do nothing
b. call upon the friend's pastor to make a hospital visit
c. contact the health information manager to get permission to see the chart
d. get permission from the family before visiting the patient

_____ 2. When discarding old copies of health records, they should be:
a. archived
b. shredded
c. sealed in a plastic bag
d. put onto microfiche

_____ 3. Under normal circumstances, who has the right to breach a patient's confidentiality?
a. the clergy
b. the health information manager
c. the patient himself/herself
d. the psychiatrist

_____ 4. An "on-call" physician who is having dinner in a crowded restaurant is "beeped" and told that he needs to dictate a "stat" (immediate) preoperative history and physical on a patient who is about to have surgery. The physician should dictate the report:
a. on a cellular phone from his car
b. over a citizen's band radio
c. from a pay phone in the restaurant
d. on a handheld dictating unit on the way to the hospital

Answer the following true or false questions by placing a T for true or F for false in the blank next to the question.

_____ 5. Transcriptionists working at remote sites are not covered by the same rules relating to the maintenance of patient confidentiality as those who work on site.

_____ 6. If your home office is in your living area, your computer screen should not face outward where it can be seen by others entering the room.

_____ 7. No one should access a patient health record who does not have a legitimate need for the information contained therein.

_____ 8. It is unfair for an employer to fire you because your son logged onto your computer and disseminated to a friend some confidential patient information that he found there.

Risk Management

Risk management is the reporting, analyzing, and tracking of atypical things that happen in a hospital. In medical transcription, risk management may involve identification of inconsistencies within a report, inflammatory or derogatory remarks by the dictator, or the mention of an *incident* that may not have been reported. Dictations containing potential risk management problems should be routed through the transcription supervisor and department head to the risk management team.

Transcriptionists should bring to the attention of the department head, service manager, or client any reports that contain the following:

- Mention of any incident, even though the dictator states an incident report was completed.

- Derogatory statements referring to another physician, a hospital employee, or the hospital.

- Comments regarding injury to a body structure during the performance of an operative procedure or untoward complications as a result of anesthesia or the procedure.

- Procedures or operations that were aborted due to inadequate preparation of the patient or difficulties performing the procedure.

- Report of hospital-incurred incidents such as drug overdose, wrong drug administered, or patient injury.

- Inappropriate comments about the patient.

- Comments about patient dissatisfaction with personnel or treatment.

- Tests performed or drugs administered that were not ordered by the physician.

- Positive test results that may not have been on the chart or which the physician failed to note prior to the patient's discharge.

Incident

Any action or occurrence that causes harm or has the potential to cause harm to the patient or a staff member is called an *incident*. In addition, any occurrence that prevents the safe or professional conduct of staff members is also an incident. Should an incident occur, one or more of the team members involved personally, or as a witness, should submit a description of the incident in writing to a member of the staff designated by the hospital to receive such reports. The purpose of the *incident report* is to accurately describe the occurrence in the event legal or disciplinary action is subsequently taken. Incident reports must be completed regardless of the implications they carry. It is grossly unethical for any staff member to ignore occurrences that have harmed or could harm the patient or staff members.

Joanna Fuller
*Surgical Terminology:
Principles and Practice*

Risk management begins even before the first line of a report is transcribed. It begins with meticulous attention to the correct spelling of the patient's first and last names, entering the correct patient number in the report, correctly spelling and entering the physician's name on the report,

Risk Management, Continued

and entering the correct dates of admission, discharge, or procedure. While technology makes retrieving this information and inserting it into the report easier, it also introduces new ways to make mistakes. Lack of attention while performing what may constitute an "automatic" procedure could mean incorporating a "Jr." when the report is really on "Sr.," or a mother's number instead of a daughter's when their names are the same, or even the name of someone completely unrelated to the patient.

Transcriptionists should be alert to names that may be either first or last names and should check for both in the master patient index when in doubt. For example, the physician may dictate a name like James Dean, when the patient is actually Dean James. It is not inconceivable that both names could appear in the master patient index because they are two different people. Social security number (if known), birth date (if given), date of admission, age, and admitting physician should be checked whenever there is a question concerning the patient name.

Hyphenated names (e.g., Smythe-Jones), nicknames (e.g., Meg or Peg for Margaret), soundalikes (e.g., Ellen and Helen), and foreign names (e.g., Hasus and Jesus) can all be sources of error carried on indefinitely in the patient's health record. Unusual first names (such as Syphyllis, Ranellen, Princess, Doc) need to be verified as to spelling and authenticity (real first name or nickname?).

It is not unusual for a transcriptionist to find multiple entries with different patient numbers but with the same or only slight variations in spelling, and on closer examination, dates of birth, gender, and other demographic data that appear to be the same. These should be reported and an effort made to determine whether they are indeed the same patient or different people.

Slang or vulgar terms used disparagingly to refer to patients should be removed from the record. Physicians may utter such comments in anger or frustration, but they really do not intend for offensive or off-color remarks to be entered in the patient's record and preserved permanently. One physician had to be urged to cease his constant sarcastic references to every obese female as "that porker" (Judith Marshall, *Medicate Me*).

Neither should disparaging remarks referring to nursing or allied health staff members, management, or other physicians be allowed to remain in a record. One internist who performed history and physical examinations on patients in the eating disorders unit of a hospital would frequently question the judgment of the psychiatrist who was in charge of the unit, and more than once called him a "fat slob." He seemed to feel that it was intolerable that an overweight physician should be responsible for an eating disorders unit.

While most MTs would not think of transcribing "fat slob" or the like, administrators and risk managers may never know of that physician's attitude—a dangerous attitude if both physicians were named in the same malpractice case—toward another medical staff member unless such dictation is reported. This is not gossip but, properly reported, is looking out for the best interests of the hospital and even the offending physician.

Risk Management, Continued

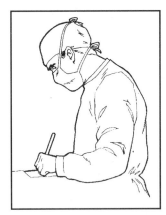

Another physician who frequently dictated the admitting history and physical within earshot of his patients was dictating about one patient's anxiety and altered mental state in the patient's presence, and recommended a psychiatric consult. Within 10 or 15 minutes of completing the report, the physician came on the dictation lines again, dictating a "correction" to the previously dictated report and asked that the references to the patient's mental state be removed. The patient had become quite angry at the physician's implications that the patient was "crazy"and demanded that a new report be dictated. At the second dictation, the transcriptionist could hear the patient complaining angrily in the background.

One transcriptionist received considerable criticism because a patient had received a copy of a report in which she was consistently referred to as "he." The patient took immense offense and felt that the report was implying that her sexual orientation was equivocal. The patient actually threatened a lawsuit. The physician dictator had been foreign, and foreign doctors often confuse feminine and masculine pronouns. The patient's name was one that could have been a male or female, and the transcriptionist either had not noticed that the gender was inconsistent within the report or had not checked the health record to be certain of the gender.

An older physician at a small rural hospital was reluctant to adapt to new practices and procedures, and his nemesis became the PRO (Peer Review Organization). Almost every surgical procedure and discharge summary contained some kind of defamatory remark about the PRO. If he was not lambasting the PRO, it was the UR (Utilization Review) Committee. He would make remarks like, "I wanted to perform [a certain] procedure, but the PRO would not approve it, so I had to perform another procedure which I did not feel was in the patient's best interest," or "This patient really needs to be in the hospital another few days, but the UR committee insists on discharging the patient, even though I have repeatedly stated that the patient is not ready for discharge." These types of inflammatory comments are inappropriate and could increase the hospital's and physician's risk of a malpractice judgment should the case end up in court for any reason.

The transcriptionist is expected to remain alert throughout the entire transcription of any given report in order to detect inconsistencies within the report, but access to the patient's chart is needed to verify and correct most inconsistencies. When the transcriptionist can access the patient's pharmacy and laboratory records via the appropriate databases on the mainframe, many inconsistencies can be avoided. If one of these routes is not available, the report should be "flagged" to the attention of the physician to make the necessary corrections. In some cases, the areas of inconsistency within a report may be widely separated. The original statement at the beginning of the report (for example, the patient was admitted with pain in the left knee) may not be contradicted until the very end of the report (Discharge Diagnosis: Dislocation, right knee).

Risk Management, Continued

The following are excerpts from actual physician dictation. Each contains an inconsistency.

1. This patient developed a persistent lesion on the inner aspect of the left upper lip. This lesion was at the junction of the vermilion and mucous membrane. A punch biopsy was obtained of this 1 cm lesion and was read as a probable verrucous squamous cell carcinoma of the lower lip.

2. He was referred to our office for evaluation recently and was noted to have a normally positioned urethral meatus but a persistent ventral hood with deficient ventral penile foreskin. Testes were bilaterally descended. He is to be admitted on an elective basis at the convenience of his parents' schedule. The plan is for removal of the dorsal hood, artificial erection to rule out chordee, and circumcision.

3. The patient is approximately one week prior to the onset of her menstrual period. The ultrasound shows a complex cystic ovary on the right side. Left ovary is deep into the cul-de-sac area, but is essentially normal with a small 1.5 cm follicle. Pelvic examination reveals the uterus to be retroverted, mobile. Both adnexal areas reveal no masses or thickening. The right adnexal area is slightly tender. Cannot appreciate the complex cystic ovary on the left side on bimanual examination.

In the first example, the physician dictates *upper lip* in the first sentence and *lower lip* in the last sentence. In the second example, the patient is said to have a *ventral hood* and later a *dorsal hood*. In the final example, the ultrasound report notes a cystic ovary on the *right* side, but on physical examination, the physician states he cannot appreciate the cystic ovary on the *left* side.

Transcriptionists are also expected to detect erroneous or incomplete drug dosages, laboratory values, and other measurements and to correct these (if the correct value can be clearly ascertained) or to flag the report to the attention of the physician for further clarification. Should charts with inaccurate or incomplete information end up in court, the opposing attorneys could have a field day. The following examples of actual physician dictation contain such errors.

1. The patient's physical examination revealed a 2 x 1 x 1 mass in the right upper pole of the thyroid.

2. Lasix 20 q. day, Micro-K 10 q. day, Zantac 150 p.o. b.i.d.

In the first example, it cannot be known whether the measurements are in millimeters or centimeters or even inches. The report should be flagged, asking the physician to clarify. In the latter example, the measurements are again omitted, but consultation with a suitable pharmaceutical reference would provide the usual units used for each of these medications—milligrams (mg) for Lasix and Zantac, and milliequivalents (mEq) for Micro-K.

In some cases, risk management involves recognizing when the dictation is not an error, is not slang, is not inflammatory, and letting the work remain as dictated. Each of the following excerpts contains dictation that a transcriptionist might mistakenly believe was an error.

Risk Management, Continued

1. She gives a history of shooting crank. Since that time, the left antecubital space has been infected.

2. The blistering is typical of strep. I would go ahead and give her 2 million q.6h. of the penicillin and modify therapy according to culture report.

3. The patient underwent an intravenous pyelogram to rule out obstruction caused by tumor or stone. The urogram was negative.

In the first example, a transcriptionist might think *crank* should be *crack*, but *crank* is a different street drug from *crack*. In the next example, 2 million (units) of penicillin may seem excessive to an inexperienced transcriptionist who might think the physician meant milligrams or milliliters, but it is a standard dose for the problem indicated. In the last example, *pyelogram* and *urogram* are correctly used interchangeably.

At times, the physician must indicate that the results of a procedure cannot be found, or that an unusual test result was artifactual in nature or the result of an error in the testing process. These remarks should not be edited as they form an important part of the record with legal implications. These excerpts demonstrate remarks that should never be deleted. They should, however, be reported to risk management to see if the problems noted can be resolved.

1. EKG showed sinus bradycardia with no acute ischemic changes. Repeat EKG showed a right bundle branch block with first-degree AV block. The pattern on this EKG was so different it may not have actually been the same patient.

2. Chemistry panel showed a BUN of 26 with a creatinine of 1.6, a calcium of 11.7, SGOT of 271, LDH of 690, alkaline phosphatase of 69. Urinalysis on admission cannot be found in the chart.

Remarks regarding the administration of an overdose or an unprescribed drug are important to the health record in that the patient's subsequent treatment may be affected by the incident and the information should never be deleted from the report. Failure to include the report of such incidents in a document could also appear to be an attempt to hide incriminating material from the court should the situation result in litigation.

The actual incident in the transcript below might have made the 6 o'clock news. To remove all documentation of the incident from the report would definitely look like a cover-up.

This 6-month-old child presented to the emergency room with a history of being listless. [History, lab, and physical examination are then given in the report.] As the child's insurance was through the employee's union, the child could not be admitted. We were told that at that time there was no surgeon available, but if we were able to find a surgeon in the area we might be able to transfer the patient. The child continued to get worse. The child was here from 1410 to 1845, a delay of $4^{1}/_{2}$ hours. We tried our best to get permission to have the child admitted and operated on here, but we were refused. As it happened, the

Risk Management, Continued

child was transferred after about 4$^1/_2$ hours of stay here, and after the child was admitted to [another hospital], the child could not be treated there because of absence of a surgeon. The child was subsequently transferred to [another facility] where the child was operated on.

When it comes to risk management, a medical facility cannot afford be too conscientious, and MTs, whether students or experienced, should be aware of their role in risk management.

Worksheet

Answer the following true or false questions by placing a T for true or F for false in the blank next to the question.

____ 1. The medical transcriptionist need not be concerned with issues of risk management.

____ 2. "Incidents" have the potential to create legal liability.

____ 3. It is essential that meticulous attention be given to entry of correct patient identifiers within every report.

____ 4. Slang and derogatory comments should not be preserved in the permanent patient record.

____ 5. Reporting negative physician attitudes expressed in dictation constitutes "gossip" and should be avoided.

____ 6. If a report incorrectly identifies the patient's gender, it is not the transcriptionist's responsibility to correct this error.

____ 7. Dictated mentions of injury to the patient during an operative procedure should be reported by the transcriptionist to supervisory personnel.

____ 8. Remarks in a dictated report concerning the medical judgment of physicians or nursing staff are simply the dictator's opinion and do not constitute a risk to the hospital.

____ 9. Inflammatory comments in dictated reports increase the risk of a malpractice judgment.

____ 10. If a dictated report includes mention of an accidental needle stick by a member of the hospital staff, the report should be brought to the attention of supervisory personnel, even though the dictation states that an incident report was submitted.

____ 11. Incident reports must be completed regardless of the implications they carry.

____ 12. The medical transcriptionist who identifies a dictation that contains potential risk management problems should bring it to the attention of the attending physician.

____ 13. Remarks regarding the administration of an overdose or an unprescribed drug are important to the health record and should never be deleted from the report.

Work Environments

After the appropriate level of education and training, and having demonstrated competent skills in transcribing authentic physician dictation in a variety of specialties, the fledgling transcriptionist is ready to go to work. It is time, then, to determine which work environment will provide the experience, income, and challenge that will best suit the individual.

Medical transcriptionists work in a variety of settings—hospitals, multispecialty clinics, solo physician practices, transcription companies, home offices, radiology clinics, pathology laboratories, tumor boards, law offices, and even veterinary hospitals. Some work as employees; others prefer the independence of being "freelance" MTs. Qualified MTs may eventually become supervisors, managers, and teachers, while others may establish their own transcription companies.

Hospitals and medical centers. In the not-too-distant past, medical transcriptionists employed by hospitals worked under the direct supervision of a medical record director (now known as a health information manager). Today, it is common for a hospital's transcription staff to be centralized in its own department, in some instances physically remote from the health information management department.

Most modern hospital transcription departments are headed by transcription supervisors who may or may not be medical transcriptionists. This supervisor may work under the auspices of the health information manager or may report directly to a hospital administrator. However, MTs who perform specialty transcription, such as radiology or pathology, may work within or adjacent to those departments.

In large teaching hospitals, some medical transcriptionists function as secretaries/transcriptionists in the offices of physicians who act as department heads for the various medical specialties within the institution.

Hospitals may offer competitive salary and benefit packages, particularly larger hospitals in metropolitan areas. In addition, many offer some type of incentive pay plan that has the potential to increase income for productive MTs.

Hospitals offer opportunities for advancement into supervisory positions for motivated employees. Hospital transcription provides a wide range of dictation types, covering all medical specialties and challenging areas of interest to transcriptionists. Facilities and equipment are often state-of-the-art.

Traditionally, hospital employment has offered job security and stable work schedules. In addition, some hospitals include in their benefit packages the payment of professional membership dues and/or registration fees for continuing education events such as conventions and seminars.

Disadvantages of working in the hospital setting may include lack of autonomy, inflexible scheduling, lower wages, a sterile environment, supervisory personnel who are unfamiliar with or unsympathetic to the needs of transcriptionists, and the frustration of dealing with hospital bureaucracies. With the advent of managed care and its associated cost-cutting, more hospitals are looking toward outsourcing their medical transcription to transcription services or simply reducing the income and benefits of those MTs who work in-house.

Physician offices and clinics. The small office environment can be decidedly more personal, often providing a family-like atmosphere. Employees in such environments may enjoy medical and retirement benefits and a predictable income, although with the decline in physician income due to managed care, some offices no longer offer benefits to their employees.

Physician office/clinic hours may more readily accommodate the needs of MTs with school-age children, seldom requiring weekend work. In addition, transcriptionists may enjoy the direct contact with physicians, who may be more appreciative of their work, more accessible for questions, and more willing to take the time to teach and offer feedback—a real advantage to the new MT.

While the transcriptionist in a physician's office or clinic may become more proficient with practice, there are less likely to be opportunities for advancement in this environment, and the dictation will offer less of a challenge to the MT hoping to increase his/her knowledge and skills.

Transcription services. Employees of transcription companies often enjoy competitive pay rates of pay. Because they transcribe a variety of dictation from different accounts (physician offices, clinics, hospitals), their skills are continually challenged. Transcriptionists working in a service's office usually enjoy a comfortable environment, and there may be greater flexibility of work schedules.

Disadvantages of working for a transcription service can include absence of immediate feedback concerning questions about dictation. Compensation may be based entirely on production, so that a day of poor-quality dictation, lack of dictation available for transcription, or personal illness can wreak havoc with the transcriptionist's income. Benefit packages may not be as comprehensive as those offered by a hospital, and health insurance is often unavailable. However, a number of transcription services are responding to the shortage of qualified transcriptionists by offering attractive benefit packages.

At-home employees. Many hospitals and transcription services employ home-based workers who transcribe exclusively for those employers, using the employer's equipment and working under the employer's direction. Such employment may offer medical and retirement benefits as well as a predictable income.

Work Environments, Continued

Disadvantages of at-home employment, however, may be the same as those experienced by freelance medical transcriptionists working from home.

Freelance transcriptionists. These transcriptionists function as independent contractors, most often working from home, although some prefer to maintain offices outside their homes. Because they are solo workers, few of them can individually handle the volume of a hospital account, but some transcribe hospital overflow (the excess of dictation that cannot be handled by a hospital's in-house transcriptionists).

Advantages of freelancing include a sense of accomplishment and independence, high self-esteem, pride in entrepreneurship, and the opportunity to work flexible hours. For those who choose to work at home, the advantages also include decreased costs for transportation and office wardrobe, as well as the possible elimination of child-care costs.

For the freelance MT, disadvantages can also include the burden of having to handle all areas of a business, including bookkeeping, arranging for pickup of dictation and delivery of finished work to each client's office, and the need for finding other MTs to cover during times of overload, vacation, or sickness. Also, a disadvantage is the unpredictable level of income, difficulty with financial planning, lack of affordable medical benefits, and the necessity for complying with the IRS and other regulatory agencies.

The transcriptionist working from home must be prepared to practice self-discipline and deal with distractions created by family members, neighbors, solicitors, and the telephone. Some at-home MTs complain that they are never able to "get away" from their work, household chores, or family concerns that demand their attention. Finally, there is often a sense of isolation, and the inability to ask questions or network with other transcriptionists and physicians can prove frustrating.

Other employment settings. Medical transcriptionists are often employed by insurance companies or government facilities. Others combine their transcription skills with clinical skills to function as medical assistants. Still others work in medical research facilities or tumor registries. In law offices that specialize in personal injury or medical malpractice cases, medical transcriptionists may be employed to analyze discrepancies in health records and translate medical language in a chart into lay language for attorneys.

Within all of these settings, MTs may also perform transcription, or they may act as supervisors, managers, or quality assurance experts. In addition, many are called upon to teach medical transcription within hospitals, in community colleges, at vocational/technical schools, or in court-reporting schools. A few MTs have found alternative job pathways in dictating reports for physicians, as well as serving as researchers, editors, consultants, and authors in the areas of the publishing industry that service medical transcription.

Working at Home

Many who express an interest in medical transcription as a career do so with the idea of working at home, often because they have young children and would prefer not to work outside the home. Others just have a strong desire to leave the hurly-burly of the corporate world. Still others deal with physical disabilities that make working outside the home difficult. Some may even be experienced MTs who are tired of dealing with the politics of healthcare facilities. Whatever the reason, working at home seems to be a goal of both novice and experienced MTs.

Articles and advertisements in popular magazines describe medical transcription as an ideal way to earn significant income while remaining at home. Unfortunately, the popular magazines and the advertisements for educational programs do a disservice to the aspiring transcriptionist by emphasizing the advantages of working from home, while at the same time de-emphasizing the complexity of the work that is done by professional medical transcriptionists.

The truth is that medical transcription *can* be done at home, and it *does* in fact have the potential to provide a good living. However, in order to perform quality medical transcription in any environment—hospital, physician office, transcription service, clinic, insurance company, radiology center, or home office—an aspiring MT must be willing to invest time (and money) in an appropriate educational program, followed by at least one year of additional education/experience under the supervision of qualified medical transcription professionals in a healthcare facility. After establishing this base of education and experience, the new transcriptionist *may* be ready to work at home, assuming that some form of mentoring or minimal supervision is available to assist in resolving the problems and questions that will inevitably arise.

Quality medical transcription cannot be performed from the kitchen table—at least not for long. The home transcriptionist must have sufficient space for a desk and a chair and any other office equipment that may be needed. Ideally, this space will be in a separate room with a door that closes the work area away from the remainder of the living space. If a separate room is not available, the work area should at least be outside the flow of normal family traffic.

There are good reasons for this, the primary one being that medical transcription requires a high level of concentration in a reasonably quiet environment free from frequent interruptions. It is also essential that confidentiality of all patient information be strictly maintained, requiring that the computer screen be shielded from the eyes of family members or visitors and that materials having to do with patient medical records are secure at all times. If the computer is used by other members of the family, all files pertaining to medical transcription should be locked, thereby maintaining confidentiality while preventing accidental or deliberate alteration or deletion of records.

Working at Home, Continued

Employers and/or clients of home-based MTs often impose stringent productivity requirements, and most expect regular and rapid turnaround of completed work. The home-based MT must be prepared to provide quality transcription within those parameters or face the loss of job or clients. This requires imposing upon oneself a regular work schedule, and it may well mean avoiding the temptation to do just one more household chore or take time out to watch a favorite movie, chat on the phone, or run an errand.

Ideal working conditions are not often found in the midst of an active family, and the home-based MT parent is frequently found working late into the night in order to take advantage of the quiet hours when other family members sleep. Many home-based MT moms or dads find it necessary to seek at least part-time daycare for active toddlers in order to minimize interruptions.

The seasoned home-based transcriptionist is often amused by the advertisements of educational programs that emphasize the benefits of working from home—spending time with family, going out to lunch with friends, taking part in children's activities, setting one's own working hours. Yes, these are benefits of working at home. However, to be successful, the home-based MT must be disciplined, setting the priorities and schedules that contribute to quality work.

Unless the home-based MT is working as an employee for a facility or business that furnishes all computer equipment, software, and resource material, he/she must be willing to make a considerable financial investment in these items. In addition to the necessary expenditure for a state-of-the-art computer, monitor, and printer, funds must be allocated for purchase (and regular updating) of appropriate reference material, both printed and electronic, covering many medical specialties, since there will be no one to assist with difficult dictation or unfamiliar terms. A spellchecker will not suffice! Excellent reference sources and supportive colleagues can also be found on the Internet, but Internet access, while it can be quite valuable, will create additional expense (and sometimes unwise distraction).

Medical transcription is physically and mentally stressful, and the MT may spend long hours at the keyboard. This necessitates purchase of a sturdy, well-designed chair and a desk that is the right height for optimal use of both monitor and keyboard. Installation of proper lighting will also help to prevent fatigue and improve quality of work. While good used office furniture may be available at reasonable price, shortcuts in these purchases can represent false economy if they have the potential to affect the health of the MT.

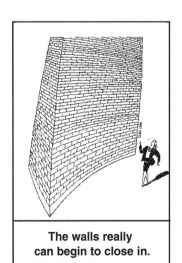

The walls really can begin to close in.

Other purchases may be required, depending on the needs of the employer or client. These might include one or more transcribers, modem, fax machine, copier, computer disks, file cabinet, bookcases, extra phone lines for incoming/outgoing dictation and/or fax messages, and call-in dictation system. The list often seems endless.

Working at Home, Continued

Working at home can be very isolating. While it may at first seem wonderful not to deal with office politics or an unpleasant boss, the home-based MT may begin to feel somewhat out of touch with the world. He/she may yearn to take part in office birthday and holiday celebrations and to keep up with what is happening in the lives of working friends. The walls really can begin to close in. Working at home can intrude on family and social lives, since the workload often spreads to include weekends and evenings. The home-based MT may need to schedule the work to allow for a regular day or afternoon off. Family support and cooperation are essential, and it may be necessary to establish with employer or clients clear boundaries between business and family lives.

Having considered the pros and cons of working at home, keep in mind this quote from a veteran home-based MT: "Working from home is still *work.*"

Worksheet

Fill in the blanks below with the correct answers. Some answers require more than one word.

1. Name five major MT work environments.

    a. _____

    b. _____

    c. _____

    d. _____

    e. _____

2. The medical record director is now known as the _____

    manager.

3. _____ dictation is the most varied and challenging.

4. Freelance medical transcriptionists often function as independent _____.

Answer the following true or false questions by placing a T for true or F for false in the blank next to the question.

_____ 5. There is a glut of qualified medical transcriptionists.

_____ 6. Employees in physician offices often enjoy higher rates of pay.

_____ 7. Because setting up a home-based medical transcription business requires so little investment of time and money, it is appealing to those who are not qualified to do transcription work.

_____ 8. An advantage to working for a medical transcription company is flexibility in work scheduling.

_____ 9. There are several alternative career paths for the medical transcriptionist.

_____ 10. One disadvantage to being a freelance medical transcriptionist is the unpredictable level of income.

_____ 11. Working at home is never isolating because family members are frequently around.

_____ 12. With the advent of managed care, more hospitals are outsourcing their medical transcription work.

Practicums (AKA Externships)

A medical transcription practicum is supervised "on-the-job" experience offered as part of an educational program. The practicum is placed near the end of the program and should consist of at least 240 hours working in a healthcare facility, physician office, or transcription business under the supervision of a qualified and experienced medical transcriptionist. Let's be specific, though: the practicum is meant to hone and refine medical transcription skills that have already been learned. It is **not** designed as a beginning medical transcription class.

Practicum

A school or college course, especially one in a specialized field of study, that is designed to give students supervised practical application of previously studied theory.

The practicum is a result of cooperation between a school or individual and the medical community. Facilities willing to take students into a practicum are usually identified by the medical transcription instructor or program director. Students in independent self-directed study who are interested in taking a practicum are responsible for arranging their own practicum sites.

The practicum gives the student an opportunity to experience the "real world" of medical transcription and helps with skill-building. In today's production-oriented transcription environment, employers are often unwilling to hire new graduates who have not had at least minimal experience, and a well-designed practicum is often accepted by employers as qualifying experience. Students who do well in their practicum experience often find it easier to get a foot in the door when seeking their first transcription jobs. Indeed, a student who demonstrates good potential will sometimes receive a job offer from the facility in which they serve a practicum.

Most facilities do not compensate students at all, although a few facilities offer at least minimum wage during a practicum. The student should view the practicum as a career investment. If the practicum is well structured, it will be time well spent.

The practicum is not meant to provide the supervising facility with cheap labor; it is meant to be a learning experience for the student and a contribution to excellence in the medical transcription profession. Although the structure of the practicum depends upon the facility in which the experience is offered, the ideal design is one that offers the student at least four hours a day doing actual transcription under direct supervision.

Some facilities place the student at a workstation in the same area as the working MTs; others choose to have the student work in a separate area. The hours available for practicum supervision vary. Some facilities may require that students come in only during the evening hours, because vacant transcriptionist work stations are not available during the busy daytime shifts.

Productivity demands should not be placed on practicum students initially. Some facilities have students practice on dictation that was previously transcribed by experienced MTs; others may assign a lead transcriptionist or supervisor to check original transcription work performed by the practicum student before it is completed. Depending on the student's progress, current dictation

Practicums (AKA Externships), Continued

could be introduced toward the end of the practicum, allowing the student to experience entry-level production requirements.

The practicum experience provides little benefit to either student or facility if the student is simply consigned to a corner and told to transcribe. A supervising MT should be available to the student during the practicum to answer questions and provide expert guidance and continuous feedback. All transcription should be carefully proofread and discussed with the student, and rationale should be provided for all changes and corrections.

The student MT should have ready access to reference material. If a spell-checker and abbreviation-expander software are available, it is helpful for the student to learn how to use these transcription aids. If transcription production is measured in the facility, either for staffing requirements or compensation, detailed information about these standards and how they are measured is extremely valuable.

Because they have access to confidential patient information, students should be asked to sign confidentiality agreements, placing them under the same obligation as MT employees to maintain patient privacy and the confidentiality of all information that they process.

Medical Transcription Program
Student Practicum Application (Sample)

Student: _____ ID No. _____

Address: _____ Phone

(day): _____ Phone (eve): _____

I will commit to _____ training hours per week (minimum 12) at the practicum site.

My preferred training days are (circle):   M   T   W   Th   F

My preferred training hours are: _____

My current typing speed is approximately _____ net words per minute (corrected speed).

Number of days absent from school or work in last year: _____

Date available to begin training: _____

I understand that there is no guarantee that my preferences as noted above will be accommodated and that there is no guarantee of a job at the end of my training.

I understand that I (will, will not) be paid during the training period.

I agree to submit to further testing for consideration of a training position.

Signature _____

Attach a resumé, copy of school transcript, cover letter, and two letters of recommendation (one from your medical transcription instructor). Include any awards or honors that you have received. Optional attachments may include samples of your work, a list of specialties studied, and even a list of types of reports transcribed.

Resume' Preparation

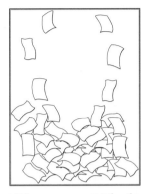

Preparing a resumé is not difficult, and there are many books in the library and in bookstores that provide information on resumé design. Employers are not interested in fancy formats or expensive paper. They want to know four things:

• Who you are.
• What skills you have that will benefit their business.
• How and where you learned those skills.
• What experience you have in exercising those skills.

Who are you? The heading of your resumé should tell an employer your full name, your current address, your home phone number, and a number where you can be reached during the business day. If you have a fax number and/or an e-mail address, include this information.

Even though you may use a post office box for your mail, your resumé should include a street address as well. This indicates to the employer that you are not a transient but have a permanent address. If you are currently employed but do not wish to receive calls at work, you may leave off your current business phone number.

It is not necessary (or advisable) for you to include your date of birth or Social Security number on a resumé, although the employer will ask for that information once you have been hired.

What skills do you have? List those skills which will be most appealing to the employer of medical transcriptionists. Example:

• Excellent knowledge of medical terminology, including anatomy and physiology, disease processes, pharmacology, and laboratory medicine

• Excellent English grammar and punctuation

• Knowledge of both PC and Macintosh

• Windows 95 and Windows NT

• WordPerfect 5.1 for DOS

• WordPerfect for Windows

• Microsoft Word for Windows

• Lotus and Excel

Resume' Preparation, Continued

Keyboarding speed (or copy typing speed) is a useless number to the medical transcription supervisor or department head because it doesn't necessarily correlate with transcription ability. Nevertheless, human resource departments may require a keyboarding certificate. Since many facilities no longer give timed typing tests, you should have your keyboarding speed documented at an appropriate facility. Community colleges and temporary employment agencies often provide this service. To your potential employer, emphasize instead your knowledge of medical terminology and your ability to quickly reference unfamiliar dictation through efficient use of printed medical transcription resources.

How did you learn these skills? Provide the name of the educational program you have completed, how many hours of transcription practice time you had, what specialties you learned, and what types of dictators you encountered (accented, male, female). If you have had additional training or education in medical transcription, be sure to list that as well. List other post-secondary education, including name of the educational institution, the dates you attended, and the degree or certificate that you earned.

What experience do you have? If you are a young student who has very little work history, you may wish to summarize that history in a well-worded paragraph. Examples:

> During my high school years, I worked part-time at both Burger Haven and MacDoody's, where I gained valuable experience in customer service. I also worked as a file clerk in the office of Dr. Rufus Fawlen, a family practice physician, from June through December of last year, while attending Hard Knox College to learn medical transcription. For a reference, you may contact Mrs. Dawn Gloaming, Dr. Fawlen's office manager, at 555-7575.

An older person who is about to enter the workforce for the first time, or re-enter after many years away, should emphasize past work experience, volunteer work, and any other positions of responsibility.

> Following graduation from high school, I worked for two years as a legal assistant in the offices of Campbell and Company in Honolulu. I then married and raised a family of five children. During that time I held a number of responsible teaching and administrative positions in my church, and I served as an officer in several community organizations.

A student who is entering the medical transcription field after many years of significant work experience should list past positions in a more detailed fashion, beginning with the most recent employment and working backward, always emphasizing those skills which have a direct bearing on current employment needs (keyboarding, computers, scheduling, organization, meeting planning, etc.). Obviously, any experience in allied health fields should be emphasized.

Appearance of the resumé. The resumé should be neatly presented on good paper. Format of the resumé should be a simple one that allows the eye to follow quickly down the page. If possible, the

94

Resumé Preparation, Continued

resumé should be no more than one page in length, with a note at the bottom that references and additional information will be furnished upon request.

Nothing will "turn off" a prospective employer as much as misspelled words or poor grammar. The resumé should be proofread by at least three people who are good spellers and able to recognize correct grammar and punctuation. After all, this resumé is the applicant's first (and perhaps only) introduction to the employer, and first impressions often are the most important. And **do not** assume that a professional resumé preparer will not make mistakes! Be sure to proofread any resumé prepared for you. Photocopies of a resumé are acceptable if produced on a quality copy machine.

Cover letter. Unless you have been previously introduced to the person with whom you will interview, your resumé should be accompanied by a cover letter that indicates the position for which you are applying, how you learned of the position, and/or the way in which you gained an interest in the business to which you are applying, be it hospital, physician office, or transcription service. Follow with a short paragraph on the duties you are qualified to perform and the benefits you feel you can bring to the business. End with thanks for time spent in considering your qualifications and offering to come for an interview or provide further information as necessary. The cover letter should be short and to the point, since all other pertinent facts will be found in your attached resumé.

If your goal is to obtain clients for a home-based business, submission of a resumé is not an appropriate approach. When seeking clients, you are not asking for a job—you are offering a service. Material submitted to a potential client should emphasize the services you offer and the benefits you can provide. A manager may request a resumé after considering your marketing material, but this should not be your primary contact with the client.

No matter what your experience or education, a carefully prepared resumé may very well make the difference between getting that job—or not.

Worksheet

Answer the following true or false questions by placing a T for true or F for false in the blank next to the question.

_____ 1. A medical transcription practicum is designed to serve as a class for beginning students.

_____ 2. A practicum introduces the student to the "real world" of medical transcription.

_____ 3. Students participating in a practicum should be closely supervised.

_____ 4. A resumé should be typed on very expensive paper in order to impress potential employers.

_____ 5. A medical transcription job applicant should obtain documentation of his/her typing speed prior to beginning job interviews.

_____ 6. Cover letters should be extremely detailed and as long as necessary in order to inform a potential employer of everything the applicant has done.

_____ 7. Both resumé and cover letter should be carefully proofread and spellchecked by at least one person.

_____ 8. An independent contractor seeking clients should use marketing materials rather than a resumé.

_____ 9. During the practicum period, all transcription should be carefully proofread by a supervisor and discussed with the student.

_____ 10. Practicum students should be required to sign a confidentiality agreement.

_____ 11. On your resumé, under the category "Job Experience," it is best to list your most recent job experience first.

_____ 12. Photocopies of your resumé can be distributed if the copy quality is good.

_____ 13. Professional resumé preparers make mistakes.

_____ 14. Most facilities do not pay practicum students.

_____ 15. When preparing your resumé, it is preferable to list a post office box rather than your street address so that you can always be contacted.

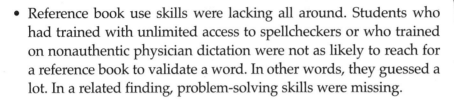

What Employers Look For

A survey of medical transcription supervisors and business owners—the very people who will decide whether or not to hire you—turned up some interesting observations. It was uniformly felt that with classroom-trained transcriptionists, certain essential skills were missing.

- Reference book use skills were lacking all around. Students who had trained with unlimited access to spellcheckers or who trained on nonauthentic physician dictation were not as likely to reach for a reference book to validate a word. In other words, they guessed a lot. In a related finding, problem-solving skills were missing.

- Editing skills were lacking, including recognition of inconsistencies, catching errors in dictation, and correcting errors without altering the physician's meaning or style.

- Students did not know when to ask a question.

The following essay written for medical transcription instructors by a potential employer or supervisor may offer some unique insights.

Would I Hire Your Students? by Judith Marshall, MA

Would I hire your students? Maybe, maybe not. Let me take you through the crucial phone call, resumé, cover letter, interview, and transcription test. Then I will tell you what attitudes, preconceptions, and skills I am seeking.

Tell your students to flee—yes, flee—from any social intercourse whatsoever with human resources departments of hospitals and aim instead for the health information manager or transcription manager or supervisor.

Tell your students that when they respond to a newspaper ad, do not make a phone call with a babe in arms or any small children in the same room, preferably not in the same house. Tell your students to change those gosh-awful phone messages that have children babbling and making cute little beeping noises. I am not only unimpressed, I am truly annoyed.

Applicants should have a current resumé and know how to write a reasonable cover letter. I believe in a one-page resumé with a statement of career goal. I often will ask people to send these when I am unsure of whether to give them a shot at testing. More and more companies are requesting resumés to be faxed, as we have, since this is very efficient and cuts down on extraneous phone calls.

Past lives, former lives, children, husbands, lovers, pets, hobbies, political views, schedules of one-car families—I don't care. Criticism of former employers sets off alarms for me as well. Women who are already working 20 hours someplace and maintaining a residence (which is all of us), married or not, children or not, already have two jobs. If they come to our company with the idea that they can fill in another 8, 10, or 12 hours, I tell them candidly that I do not want the crumbs of their lives.

This is a demanding profession, not something to be taken lightly, not something to do after the regular job and the duties and responsibilities of modern life. I want their full attention, I want them body and soul. I want a commitment of not less than 20 hours, or about 7,000 lines a pay period of two weeks. It never fails to amaze me that instead of negotiating for better wages, people simply go out and get another job, creating patchwork quilts of time where nothing gets priority and everything is tugging at them.

Candidates should have a very good idea of their place in the profession and the nature of transcription as an element in the health information sector of patient care. I want a healthy interest in our company, how we got started, what our policies and goals are, do we encourage telecommuting and certification. Applicants should have an understanding of production pay versus hourly or salary. What equipment or phone lines do we provide, if any?

They should have a basic knowledge of what digital dictation is and what a standard cassette is or a microcassette. For the last class I taught at a local college, I took in three different types for show and tell. Students should understand the nature of these systems as opposed to analog tapes and how we can access and manipulate voice files. This is not new technology. No tapes, no printing, no paper—none of this is new in transcription. They should know about medical transcription associations, JCAHO, the difference between an RRA and ART, and a bit about the history of the business of medical transcription.

Please, no portfolios. Some correspondence schools make quite too much of this. Are we dress designers or graphic designers or architects? If so, then bring a portfolio. Otherwise I have no desire to see any reports. They could have been copied from a book, but more than that, they reflect nothing to me. Formatting is taken care of by computerization. I would hope they know how to set up a letter, though. I am more interested in seeing if they understand what a basic heading is in one of the Basic Four reports (H&P, consultation, operative report, and discharge summary).

I live in hope that each candidate who arrives for an interview is not dressed for a hoe-down or cleaning the garage. In this age of casual dress, the dressing down of America, something is lost. I miss hats and gloves, but I will settle for something decent, and no jeans for women. I always appreciate a thank-you note, too. There is a lot of class in that. Call me old-fashioned.

When I test applicants, I give them a tape, all the books they want, and tell them I am not timing them but I want at least four pages of solid typing, discharge summary and operative report. I tell them to name the file with their last name, put their name and the date on the first page. Only one of four listens to me. I say, if you don't understand something, leave a blank—not a question mark, underlining, parentheses, or asterisks—and only one of four listens to me.

What Employers Look For, Continued

I realize the testing is on a piece of equipment they are not using daily. Please—no whining or apologetic spasms. I hope and pray they know . . .

- Never guess at anything.
- Never trust a doctor's spelling. Any doctor, anywhere, ever.
- Never rely on spellcheck, ever, anywhere.
- Know our role as medical editor. Know what verbatim transcription is and why people who practice it should be forced to bathe in nuclear waste.
- A blank is an honorable thing, as Vera Pyle has taught us so well. It means we don't know.
- Know basic labs. Normal body temperature is 96 to 99.6. WBCs are increased at what, 11,000, 12,000? EKGs and enzymes are used to rule out myocardial infarctions.

I am seeking staff whose knowledge is integrated. If a patient eats raw shellfish, the threat of hepatitis exists and I expect to hear about elevated liver function tests. This is not complex medicine. I care about informed and interested people, lively people. Are they reading? Are they using more than 200 words in their own vocabularies? My golden retrievers know more words than that. We have to spell in front of them and they learned that, too!

Does the applicant know that the *Physician's Desk Reference* (*PDR*) and the dictionary may not be the last resources to use? Do they know there are word books by medical specialty? Do they know how to recognize lab tests, to use an abbreviation book, and other references?

The persons I hire must convince me I can trust them. I want them to be flexible, mature, intelligent, and confident. Do they know anything about how healthcare delivery impacts on all of our lives? Have they been patients? Do they know anything about the economics of Medicare and Medicaid? Do they know that there is no such thing as the big bad transcription company and the warm, loving, caring hospital? Each employer is a little of both. Do they truly understand the benefits of pay based on production versus salary?

An important overlooked requirement is fast, accurate typing. I have had lovely women interview and test who pass a written medical test with ease, but who cannot type more than 40 words per minute and do not know how to go home and practice because they have no computer and no transcriber and have no idea of what tapes to use. I tell them to come up to 80 or 90 + and then I will see them again.

Well, it seems like I want a lot. Yes, I do. We are about to invest a lot of money in an individual. The best in patient care is what we are about as well. Like marriage, it is not to be entered into lightly. I want that person who says, "After the first time I did this, I was so excited I couldn't sleep." "I love books." "I love words." "I can't believe people actually get paid to do this. This is fun." "This is great. What a challenge!"

If the keyboarding skills and medical knowledge are there, welcome on board.

Job Searching

An oft-heard lament from students and entry-level transcriptionists is that it is very difficult to break into the medical transcription field. How does one get a job as a medical transcriptionist with no experience?

Transcriptionists work in virtually every large clinic and hospital, and many more are employed by small private physician practices, surgery centers, radiology offices, pathology offices, physical therapy centers, and tumor boards. So when you're starting out, be flexible; consider all job options in medical transcription if you have mastered the medical specialties involved. The following guidelines are offered to help you not only get a job, but also to help you assess your own abilities.

1. Be prepared to deal with Human Resources (the personnel department) before you get to talk with transcription department personnel. If you are applying for a job at a medical facility, you most likely will have to deal with them first. Come to the appointment with a carefully prepared resumé in hand. There are many sources of information to help you prepare a resumé; make sure it appears professional and is specific for the position for which you are applying. Make more than one copy so that you can present it to more than one department.

   Include a cover letter to accompany your resumé (no more than a page long) in which you indicate the type of job you are seeking, why you are suited for the job, and your availability for an interview. If you have not already done so, get the name of the transcription supervisor and make sure you send a copy of your resumé and cover letter directly to that person. Even if Human Resources is not interested in you, the supervisor might be.

   You may need to fill out the facility's application even though you have prepared a resumé. Fill it out completely and ask that your resumé and cover letter be attached. Be prepared to take a copy-typing speed test. Although copy typing is a skill seldom used in medical transcription, many job descriptions require a minimum typing speed, usually 60 words per minute or faster. It is also possible that a literacy test, spelling test, reading test, or other type of written test will be given to applicants. If you have good spelling and English skills, you should have no problem.

   You may have to convince Human Resources that you are an appropriate candidate for a medical transcription position. If you are told that a minimum of two years of experience is required for the position, as is often the case, be prepared to equate your medical transcription educational practice with on-the-job training if your training included transcribing authentic, original physician dictation from a variety of dictators. For example, if you spent 480 hours in medical transcription practice of authentic physician dictation consisting of chart notes, letters, H&Ps, consults, and discharge summaries, you have the equivalent of three months of clinic transcription experience. If you spent another 480 hours transcribing surgical dictation, add three months of hospital-level experience. Although six months falls short of the two years Human Resources is requesting, it indicates that you do have some experience and that you are serious about being considered for the transcription position. Your goal is to get past Human Resources so that you can speak to the medical transcription department head. Insist upon an appointment with that supervisor.

2. Be diligent and persistent in your job search. Write a follow-up letter after the interview and check back in person or by telephone frequently until the job is filled. Transcription supervisors are often willing to take a chance on a less-experienced person if you demonstrate that you are serious about working and committed to doing a good job.

3. Be prepared to demonstrate your transcription ability. Chances are good that you will be asked to take a transcription test. It is only in this way that a supervisor can truly assess your abilities, your strengths and weaknesses. It is really not necessary to bring in samples of your work. Only inexperienced people do this. A supervisor has no idea if you or someone else generated the work samples.

You should be able to transcribe a minimum of eighty-two 65-character lines per hour of authentic physician dictation. If you are transcribing slower than that, the facility may not consider you a good investment. Remember, repetition and practice on authentic physician dictation during training will increase your speed and accuracy.

If you are prepared to work at minimum wage, or even as a trainee for no pay for a short period of time, you may be able to convince a supervisor to take you on for a probationary period. This demonstrates your commitment to learning and communicates your belief in yourself.

4. Be prepared to demonstrate reference use skills and familiarity with reference books used in medical transcription. Although a few supervisors may request that you test without reference books, the majority will want to see if you have good referencing skills. The ability to use reference materials has been identified as an important skill lacking in classroom-trained medical transcriptionists. If your medical transcription program did not include heavy reference book use, start using those books immediately. On the job you will be delving into books on a regular basis. Don't guess a word if you don't know it or can't find it. It's better to leave a blank rather than demonstrate sloppy work habits.

5. Be prepared to demonstrate good editing skills. If you are confident in your ability to recognize dictation errors, the supervisor will likely expect you to make appropriate editing changes, including correction or flagging of errors in dictation (e.g., wrong medication dosage), inconsistencies in dictation (the physician said 'left leg' and later 'right leg'), and skill in clarification without altering meaning or style (editing poor grammar, deleting a redundancy). It is advisable, however, to clarify the supervisor's expectations in this regard before you begin testing.

6. Know when to ask a question. Don't hesitate to ask for clarification if you don't understand the supervisor's instructions or have questions about the equipment. It is better to risk fleeting

Job Searching, Continued

embarrassment than to make a major error because of communication breakdown. As mentioned earlier, if you do not understand a word in the dictation after diligent searching in reference books, leave a blank.

7. Make it clear that you are able to work independently but are a team player. Basically, all medical transcriptionists work independently. However, it is important that everyone share the workload, especially when it comes to poor dictation. Indicate that you are willing to learn to transcribe the difficult dictation and that you will accept any dictation challenges that come your way.

By following the above steps, you will greatly increase your chances of getting a job as a medical transcriptionist. If you have the skills to do the job, don't give up! It's just a matter of time before you succeed.

Worksheet

Answer the following true or false questions by placing a T for true or F for false in the blank next to the question.

_____ 1. Surveys show that most newcomers to the MT profession are well-educated in referencing and editing skills.

_____ 2. Job applicants should inform themselves about an employer's business and its policies and goals prior to interviewing.

_____ 3. Instructions given to a job applicant prior to a transcription test are window-dressing.

_____ 4. Both keyboarding skills and medical knowledge are important to employers of medical transcriptionists.

_____ 5. English grammar and punctuation skills should be learned on the job.

_____ 6. Medical transcriptionist applicants should be prepared to work independently.

_____ 7. An interviewer will be impressed if you bring samples of your previous work.

_____ 8. Do not leave blanks on a transcription test.

_____ 9. Potential employers don't want to waste time reading thank-you letters from people they have interviewed.

_____ 10. Know when to ask a question.

_____ 11. On a transcription test, you should be able to transcribe a minimum of eighty-two 65-character lines per hour.

_____ 12. It is important to get past the human resource manager to the medical transcription supervisor when applying for a transcription job with little experience.

_____ 13. If you are asked to fill out a job application at a facility, attach your resumé and write "See resumé" on the application.

_____ 14. When searching for your first medical transcription job, consider only those job options that hold great appeal for you.

_____ 15. The majority of medical transcription supervisors will expect you to test without the use of reference books.

Productivity

Productivity, as the term is used in medical transcription, indicates the amount of transcription that can be produced within a given period of time—minute, hour, day, week, month—and is measured by a number of yardsticks—words, pages, keystrokes, minutes of dictation, lines, characters.

Why track productivity? In order to determine the amount of work any department or individual can handle in a defined period of time, productivity must be monitored. (See the gray box on this page.)

While transcription productivity can be based on any unit of time, the most common unit of time is the *hour* (i.e., so many words, pages, keystrokes, minutes, characters, or lines per *hour)*. Long-term measurements (day, week, month) can be extrapolated from the amount of transcription produced in one hour. Because transcription is usually produced on computers, the measurement capabilities of the computer must therefore be taken into consideration.

There are several other quantitative units that are applied to medical transcription:

Word. Most definitions of a *word* are based on the old typing rule that five characters equal one word. In order to count words, one would first have to count characters. While popular word-processing programs have word-counting functions, these are generally based on actual words. Thus, a four-syllable word would have the same value as the article *a*, resulting in an inaccurate measurement. (See *characters*, below.)

Page. Using the *page* as the basic unit of measurement leads to the obvious question: What is a page? Is it 54 lines on a sheet of 8½" x 11" paper? Is it the same sheet of paper with only a few words printed on it? Would one then have to determine what constitutes a quarter page, a half page, three quarters of a page? This is a totally inaccurate method of determining quantity in medical transcription, yet it is still used in the industry by some.

Keystrokes. A *keystroke* is defined as the pressing of a key on a keyboard to produce a character. In the past, the number of times the transcriptionist hit the keyboard equaled the number of characters on the printed page. Today, however, there are computer programs with macros (short keyboard commands that automate tasks) and abbreviation-expander software (allowing the user to type in "shorthand"), allowing the MT to produce much more work with fewer keystrokes.

Tracking Productivity

Productivity is measured for a number of reasons:

✓ To balance staffing needs with volume of dictation

✓ To aid in budgeting

✓ To assist in preparing requests for proposals or contracts

✓ To determine compensation for medical transcriptionists paid either by incentive or by straight productivity

✓ To include in performance reviews

✓ To provide a basis for employee promotions

✓ To set prices for transcription services

Productivity, Continued

Minutes of dictation. Since measurement of *minutes* of dictation actually measures access time to a dictation system, this is not a consistent measure when applied to different dictation systems, given the variety of dictators. Nevertheless, some facilities do measure production by minutes of dictation transcribed.

Lines. In the past, transcription was often measured by *gross line* (any line with print, no matter how many characters, constitutes a line) or *full line* (a line extending from margin to margin, no matter what size the print). While this is still acceptable in some transcription environments, it is not accurate and can be manipulated by a number of factors—margins, size of type, number of carriage returns. Given the capabilities of the computer, it is therefore logical to set a unit of measurement that cannot be manipulated by either the medical transcriptionist, the employer, or the client.

Characters. A character is described as any letter, number, symbol, or function key necessary for the final appearance and content of a document, including the space bar, carriage return, underscore, bold, and any character contained within a macro, header, or footer. Because fonts, margins, carriage returns, etc., do not affect character count, one need only total the number of characters in a day's work or a document to get an accurate measure of productivity. *The character is the preferred method of measuring productivity and has been supported by several national allied health organizations.*

It is important that employers, employees, clients, and managers all understand the method of measuring productivity actually used in a given situation and that all abide by the measurement mutually agreed upon.

Compensation

Medical transcriptionists should become familiar with the various methods of compensation used in medical transcription environments in order to make an informed decision when seeking employment or pricing transcription.

Hourly wage. Wage levels vary considerably by geographic location and may be based on experience at the time of hire. The hourly wage offers security and predictability of income, and it rewards not just production but all the characteristics and qualities that constitute a good employee. MTs are more likely to be enthusiastic to try new or difficult dictators when their compensation is not adversely affected.

Hourly wage plus incentive. The transcriptionist receives a base hourly wage, plus compensation for additional productivity above a certain level. (Example: An MT is paid $15 per hour for the first 1500 lines, $15.25 for 1501-1700 lines, $15.50 for 1700+ lines, etc. Some incentive plans do have ceilings.) This method compensates the speedy transcriptionist (hopefully without compromising quality) while guaranteeing a standard rate of pay for those who may be less productive.

Production only. Income is derived solely on the basis of work produced in a given period of time. (Example: 8 cents per line x 1500 lines in one day = $120.) Obviously, the more experienced and faster the MT, the more money that can be made on production. Inexperienced, methodical, or slower transcriptionists may not do well with this scenario, although by law minimum wages must be paid, no matter how little transcription is produced. Poor or difficult dictation may slow productivity, thus creating the temptation to avoid difficult dictation.

Production plus incentive. Pay is determined by quantity alone, with additional pay for productivity above a certain level. (Example: 8 cents per line for up to 800 lines per day, 10 cents per line for every line over 800.)

Some compensation plans require that the transcriptionist maintain a certain level of productivity in order to remain employed. A demonstrated level of quality may also be required, based on medical and English language usage. Unfortunately, some employers also see fit to dock the pay of an employee who falls below a certain level or leaves "too many" blanks. And, while a quality assurance program should be a teaching/learning experience, some employers choose to make it punitive by docking pay for errors.

In the past most hospitals compensated MTs using the hourly wage method; any monitoring of production was for statistical purposes only. More recently, due to escalating healthcare costs, transcription departments have had to account for every expenditure, and some have switched to production-based pay of one kind or another.

Compensation, Continued

Transcription services have traditionally paid on production. However, with the advent of capitation in the healthcare industry (paying a lump sum per year for a specified amount of work), transcription services may have to determine economical ways to provide transcription on a capitation contract basis, which may mean paying their transcriptionists in alternative ways.

When considering methods of compensation, the MT must take into consideration any fringe benefits that are offered. Hospitals have traditionally offered generous benefit packages (insurance benefits, disability coverage, paid vacation time, retirement plans). Many transcription services have become more competitive in recent years by offering similar packages. A benefit package is often worth 30 percent or more of one's salary, much of it nontaxable.

Compensation on the job includes both tangible and intangible rewards, even in a performance-based incentive pay environment.

Does Money Matter?

While the method of compensation preferred by medical transcriptionists varies, certainly money is a key factor in an employee's choice of employer. But as with other employees, medical transcriptionists are not apt to be long-term employees in a workplace that does not meet other personal needs.

An intangible compensation method not to be overlooked is the value of a technologically advanced, reference material rich, ergonomically correct, and esthetically pleasing transcription department. Additional direct benefits that do not translate into dollar earnings, but can go a long way in recruitment and retention, include a teamwork environment, flexible scheduling, work-at-home options, and responsible supervision.

Kathy Cameron, CMT, ART
Perspectives on the Medical Transcription Profession

Worksheet

Fill in the blanks below with the correct answers. Some answers may require more than one word.

1. List six measurements of productivity.

   a._____

   b._____

   c._____

   d._____

   e._____

   f._____

2. The most common unit of time on which productivity is based is the _____.

3. The suggested industry standard as the basic unit of measure in transcription is the

   _____.

4. Name the four most commonly used methods of compensation for transcription.

   a._____

   b._____

   c._____

   d._____

5. Paying a lump sum per year for a specified amount of work is known in the industry as

   _____ .

6. According to federal labor laws, at least _____ wage must be

   paid, no matter how little transcription is produced.

7. Compensation for additional productivity above a certain predetermined level is known as

   _____ pay.

Answer the following true or false questions by placing a T for true or F for false in the blank next to the question.

_____ 8. Wage levels for MTs are remarkably similar throughout the country.

_____ 9. Medical transcription companies traditionally pay their MTs on production or by the unit method of compensation (characters, lines, words).

_____ 10. When an MT is paid hourly wage plus production, pay is determined by quantity alone with additional pay for productivity above a certain level.

Avoiding Work-Related Injuries

Promoting Wellness by Elaine Aamodt

In recent years repetitive stress injury (RSI), also known as cumulative trauma disorder (CTD), has become one of the fastest growing occupational hazards in the U.S. In the mid-1980s the Department of Labor statistics showed RSI accounting for 20 percent of all occupational injuries, but since then that figure has increased to over half.

Such injuries have long been common among butchers, carpenters, and assembly line workers; however, with the advent of widespread computer use, RSI has now become the scourge of the white-collar world as well. A job such as medical transcription, which was only recently performed on a typewriter, is now done on computer, and unlike the typewriter of old, the computer allows its user to sit at the keyboard for entire shifts, striking keys four or five times per second without even the occasional break to change paper and ribbon or to hit the carriage return. Such a work environment can easily lead to repetitive stress injuries, and those involved in the transcription field must become aware of the possible risks as well as ways to avoid those risks.

Repetitive stress injuries arise precisely as their name indicates, from repetitive stress, and any job in which continuous repetitive motion is required is a potential offender. Among keyboard users, one of the most common cumulative trauma disorders is carpal tunnel syndrome (CTS). In fact, it was estimated in 1990 that 15 percent of all workers in high-risk industries (such as medical transcription) would develop carpal tunnel syndrome.

Carpal tunnel syndrome develops when the median nerve leading to the hand becomes pinched by swollen tendons or tissue in the carpal tunnel—the narrow tunnel in the wrist formed by the carpal bones. The results are numbness, tingling, pain, or burning sensations in the fingers and hand.

CTS injuries vary both in severity and longevity. In some cases, symptoms subside with such self-help treatments as rubbing or shaking the hand, running warm or cold water over the hand, ice packing, elevation, or rest. Symptoms may return when the stressful motions of the job are resumed. In other cases, symptoms are more severe, often becoming especially painful at night, and can make even the simplest daily task, such as buttoning a shirt, strenuous if not impossible. If further damage is not prevented, pain can also travel to the shoulders, neck, and upper back.

Symptoms of carpal tunnel syndrome usually appear gradually and, in the early stages, are often hard to distinguish from arthritis. However, it is extremely important that anyone suspecting CTS development take preventive steps and see a doctor as soon as possible because symptoms that go ignored for several months can lead to permanent disability.

Avoiding Work-Related Injuries, Continued

Not only is this a frightening prospect from a health perspective, it is also a potential financial disaster. The American Academy of Orthopaedic Surgeons in 1990 estimated the cost of CTD-related injuries in medical bills and lost workdays at approximately $27 billion. Estimates indicate that direct cost to employers in worker compensation claims, increasing insurance premiums, and medical expenses would average $20,000 per injured worker in just one year, and some cases would exceed $200,000.

These are the simple, easy-to-measure costs. More difficult to quantify is the suffering of the victims. I recently spoke with a transcriptionist in Texas who was plagued with CTS for over a year before doctors were able to diagnose her condition. During that year, because her pain was not diagnosed as resulting from a work-related injury, she was ineligible for worker compensation. (She had been told that pain without an actual diagnosis of injury was not an acceptable reason for missing work.) Unable to continue in her job, she was forced to go on unemployment until a diagnosis was finally made several months later. Since that time she has undergone surgery on both wrists, and while her condition has improved greatly, the damage done is permanent. Not only will she never be able to work at a keyboard again, she can no longer do simple household chores such as washing dishes or hanging clothes in the closet without experiencing excruciating pain. No price tag can be put on that kind of suffering.

Because carpal tunnel syndrome can be so debilitating and costly, in both human and financial terms, it is something that cannot be ignored in any high-risk field. And while treatments do exist, their results are not always guaranteed. As with most injuries, an ounce of prevention is worth a pound of cure.

Most preventive measures are fairly simple, but they must begin with education (both of management and employees) to be effective. There has to be an atmosphere in the workplace of understanding and an acknowledgment of CTS as a legitimate health concern. Too often employers do not take complaints about pain seriously, and employees are afraid to discuss or even admit discomfort for fear of losing their jobs. This kind of production-first, workers-last environment is not only dehumanizing, it greatly increases the risk for work-related injuries.

Fostering a positive environment, on the other hand, can lead to improved morale and higher productivity in the long run. The crucial element of education will help transcriptionists to recognize the signs and dangers of wrist pain while still in the early, reversible stages. Secondly, understanding and compassion will keep lines of communication open and allow supervisors and transcriptionists to work together to find ways of resolving a problem before it becomes a disaster.

Preventing injury. A good first step is evaluation of the work environment. The service owner or supervisor may want to have a physical therapist come into the workplace to counsel employees on the safest and most comfortable ways to perform their tasks.

A transcription service owner recently hired a physical therapist to counsel her employees in the office. With a biofeedback machine, the therapist was able to demonstrate for the transcriptionists

how tension is built or released depending on chair position, hand position, screen position, and so on. In this way the transcriptionists became aware of the possible flaws in their usual working positions and consequently learned how to minimize stressful positions and movements.

Often medical transcriptionists who have been working for years feel that they have no need to make any adjustments. To an extent that may be true; a transcriptionist who has been working for ten years or more and hasn't gotten CTS probably never will, according to the medical experts. However, all transcriptionists should be trained to minimize stress and to find the position with the lowest tension, reducing their risk for injury.

Sitting. The workplace must, of course, be completely adjustable. Chairs, for example, must be comfortable and fit their occupants. The jury is still out on what comprises the perfect chair; however, many ergonomists now say that a chair should be adaptable to the diversity of every human body type and seating preference that comes its way. The ergonomically correct chair, they say, should come with an operator's manual and have about 150 parts. Proper seating will not only help stave off CTS, it will also assist in prevention of lower back pain and other injuries.

Once seated, transcriptionists should have the computer screen at eye level so that they will not have to crane their necks this way or that. Wrists should be in a level position, and feet should be comfortably planted on an appropriate footrest. However, even this supposed cure-all position which was once touted as the only correct way to sit has its shortcomings.

According to Marvin Dainoff, Director of the Center for Ergonomic Research at Miami University in Ohio, "Static posture is the enemy." Quoted by Steve Lohr in an informative article in the *New York Times*, "Sit Down and Read This (No, Not in That Chair!)" (July 7, 1992), Dainoff explains that remaining perfectly still in any position for too long is not good for anyone. Small movements, called "micromovements" (wiggling and fidgeting), are important in that they help relieve stress on the back, shoulders, hands, and wrists. This will not only help avert CTS, but also will help reduce other injuries related to long periods of sitting.

In *Sitting on the Job* (Houghton Mifflin, 1989), author Scott Donkin also recognizes the problem: "People who sit a great deal tend to develop weak abdominal, buttock, and front and inner thigh muscles. Their neck, shoulder, and back muscles tend to be tense, and their spinal movements are usually restricted." Exercise and the freedom to move about and to take stretching breaks are crucial in combating repetitive stress injury.

Breaks. Not only are breaks a vital part of CTS avoidance, but the manner in which breaks are taken actually makes a difference as well. Statistically, it appears that people working in a mentally or emotionally stressful environment are more prone to developing CTS due to the general effects of stress on the body. Psychologically, and consequently physically, it is therefore crucial that supervisors and service owners not only allow, but actually encourage or mandate frequent breaks for employees. The feeling that breaks are encouraged helps employees feel that their well-being is a top priority (as well it should be), which improves morale and can actually contribute to the healing effect in and of itself.

The *Los Angeles Times* office, where nearly 40 percent of its editorial staff was suffering from CTS to varying degrees, has seen positive results from having messages programmed into the computer terminals that automatically remind employees to take a break every fifty minutes. The newspaper office also provides a break room where employees have access to exercise equipment and a refrigerator with ice packs to help them ease the pressure in their wrists.

Self-help. If symptoms of CTS do appear, there are some self-help efforts that can be very effective. However, if implemented incorrectly these same efforts can actually do more harm than good. For example, wearing a forearm splint works well for some, but if used improperly, this same splint can increase pressure on the wrist and increase damage. Similarly, some researchers have asserted that a vitamin B_6 deficiency is a leading cause of CTS. However, trying to treat your CTS by taking B_6 supplements on your own can be extremely dangerous since high B_6 intake can lead to permanent nerve damage. Exercise is also important in combating CTS, but the wrong kinds of exercise will also lead to further damage. For reasons such as these, it is wise to consult a physician or physical therapist and to do plenty of research on your own while planning your attack on carpal tunnel syndrome.

If your office cannot afford state-of-the-art ergonomic chairs, fully adjustable work stations, and all the other available gadgetry, there are still many simple steps that can be implemented quickly and easily that will reduce the chance of injury in your workplace.

A medical transcription service owner suffering from CTS found that a good wrist pad running along the lower edge of the keyboard was enough to get her back on the job. Such a pad helps prevent the wrists from flexing or bending in unhealthy ways and generally costs only about $30.

It is also important to give your hands frequent breaks from the keyboard in order to stretch. If possible, consult a physical therapist or physician to find out about specific exercises you can do both at home and at the keyboard to keep carpal tunnel syndrome at bay. You may also find such exercises in the popular literature. Scott Donkin's highly recommended book *Sitting on the Job* (Houghton Mifflin, 1989) contains detailed diagrams of exercises for back, neck, shoulder, and hands, as well

How to Avoid Carpal Tunnel Syndrome

- Don't bend or flex your wrists while at the keyboard. If needed, buy a wrist pad to help you maintain the right position.

- Take frequent breaks.

- Incorporate an exercise and stretching program into your daily routine.

- Evaluate your office. Be sure chairs and keyboards are adjusted properly for the individual user.

- Consult a physical therapist to learn the most healthful ways to carry out your work.

- Take carpal tunnel syndrome seriously and become educated!

as diagrams and descriptions of healthful sleeping positions, sitting positions, and even breathing exercises for relaxation.

While there are many new and innovative ergonomic products on the market, we must realize that, while these products can be very helpful, a major component in fighting carpal tunnel syndrome is attitude. Everyone involved must become educated about carpal tunnel syndrome and accept the fact that some fundamental changes will have to be made in the way we go about our work before this problem can be eliminated.

Worksheet

Answer the following true or false questions by placing a T for true or F for false in the blank next to the question.

_____ 1. Carpal tunnel syndrome develops when the ulnar nerve in the hand is pinched by swollen tendons or tissue in the wrist formed by the carpal bones.

_____ 2. Carpal tunnel syndrome symptoms that are ignored can lead to permanent nerve damage.

_____ 3. An ergonomic chair will help stave off lower back pain and other injuries.

_____ 4. It is important to keep the wrists flexed while keyboarding to avoid compression of nerves.

_____ 5. Small doses of B_6 can lead to permanent nerve damage.

_____ 6. People who sit a great deal tend to develop weak abdominal, buttock, and front and inner thigh muscles.

_____ 7. Repetitive stress injuries account for nearly 20% of all occupational injuries in today's workforce.

_____ 8. A physical therapist is a good choice to counsel employees on the safest and most comfortable ways to perform their tasks.

_____ 9. Trauma can occur with any job in which continuous repetitive motion is required.

_____ 10. There is a higher incidence of carpal tunnel syndrome among people working in nonstressful environments than in emotionally taxing environments.

_____ 11. It is crucial that supervisors and employers encourage frequent breaks for all employees.

_____ 12. Wiggling and fidgeting are important in that they help relieve stress on the back, shoulders, hands, and wrists.

_____ 13. The wrong kind of exercise can lead to increased damage for those suffering from carpal tunnel syndrome.

_____ 14. According to experts, a transcriptionist who has been working for ten years or more and hasn't gotten CTS probably never will.

Your Professional Image

There was once a large transcription company located in a lovely building with an open atrium in the center. Several people were seated on benches in the atrium, evidently enjoying a cigarette break. They were all dressed in jeans and T-shirts, many imprinted with beer company logos, and their conversation was loud, completely out of keeping with the lovely building and the professional appearance of most of the people who were walking through the atrium. When the break was over, the people in the atrium went in the door of the transcription service and to the transcription stations. The receptionist and the manager in the transcription office, neither of whom was paid as high as the lowest-paid transcriptionist, were neatly and professionally dressed.

What attitude is reflected in the scenario above? How does one's appearance reflect an attitude toward the importance of one's work? Surely the other occupants of that lovely building had formed an opinion of the medical transcription profession as they observed these individuals each day—perhaps not a very positive impression.

Medical transcriptionists have been involved for many years in a struggle for recognition as allied health professionals. Every step upward has been won only with great difficulty. Because their primary tool in the past has been the keyboard, MTs are often viewed by others as simply "typists." Indeed, many MTs have been heard to describe themselves as "just a transcriptionist." It is this attitude that has made the journey an uphill one.

While medical transcription environments are often informal, MTs can influence their own attitudes (and the attitudes of others) about their professionalism by remembering that dress and behavior play an important part in the way we feel about ourselves and our work. Good taste does not have to be expensive, and it takes very little effort to project a professional image. If there is no dress code in the hospital or office, we can establish our own by always wearing neatly tailored clothing and shoes that are in good repair and appropriate for our outfits.

What if we work from home, either for an employer or as a business owner? If we remain at home all day, we can certainly choose less formal clothing, but we will feel better about ourselves if we do dress for the day in outfits that reflect our attitudes toward our work, rather than remaining in pajamas and robes. If we must visit the offices of clients, we should avoid the jeans-and-T-shirt look, instead choosing apparel that will not cause us to look out of place if we chance to encounter either physician or patients. Often the impression made upon the physician's office staff by our appearance has a direct bearing on their attitude toward us as professionals. If they always see us dressed as if we are on the way to a soccer game, they will find it difficult to regard us as serious business owners.

Your Professional Image, Continued

Attitude should be reinforced by behavior, which would include speaking in quiet and professional tones, avoiding discussion of patients or their problems where our conversations might be overheard—in reception areas, elevators, lunchrooms, hallways, or other public places. No matter how professionally dressed we may be, we can destroy appearance by the use of vulgar language or raucous laughter.

We should exercise restraint in our dealings with others in the workplace, avoiding backbiting or argument. If there are policies and procedures in place, the professional abides by them, dealing with problems through the proper channels. Our interaction with employees in other departments and with physicians should be carried out on the same level, thus enhancing our image as allied health professionals.

What we think of ourselves often influences what others think of us and our profession. Create a professional image, and others will carry that image in their minds when they think of medical transcription.

Networking

A visit to *Merriam-Webster's Collegiate Dictionary* reveals *networking* defined two ways: "the exchange of information or services among individuals, groups, or institutions," and "the establishment or use of a computer network." In medical transcription, both definitions apply.

Networking has always been vital to students and practitioners of medical transcription, as it provides apprenticeship and mentoring opportunities for learning and growth. In the past, when medical transcription was learned almost exclusively in the hospital setting, access to human resources—fellow transcriptionists, physicians, nurses, medical record personnel—was taken for granted. Today, most medical transcription students are learning their craft outside of a hospital setting and simply do not have access to those resources as their predecessors did.

What alternatives, then, do today's students have? What networking opportunities are available? Whether you're learning independently, are enrolled in a medical transcription program at a school or other facility, or just starting out as a practitioner, the following information will help you sort through networking issues.

Fallacy: *You need to be on-line to network properly with other transcriptionists.*

Fact: There are opportunities for medical transcriptionists (MTs) to network on-line, but this should not be your only networking resource. Some of your best resources are probably right in your own town. Typically, in a city of 50,000 people, there may be 25 full-time MTs or more. Most of them would be willing to help a less experienced person as long as you don't take advantage of them. Joining a local medical transcription association is another good way to meet people, make friends, find out who's hiring, and take advantage of continuing education opportunities.

Fallacy: *The on-line medical transcription community speaks for the majority of MTs.*

Fact: If you are new to the industry, or if your only communication with other medical transcriptionists is limited to on-line, this might appear to be the case. However, the on-line community is only one network of many in the MT industry. MTs have been networking via "human interface" since the profession began, and professional associations for medical transcriptionists have been in existence over 20 years, serving the interests of thousands of medical transcriptionists. All of the MT networks are valid and vital. They should work in conjunction with, and not exclusive of, each other.

Fallacy: *The most professional MTs who have been involved in the MT industry for years are on-line and willing to help.*

Fact: There are some professional, experienced MTs on-line, and some even offer free services for MTs. There are also those who claim to be professional but may actually be doing a

Networking, Continued

great disservice to the medical transcription industry. If you want to affiliate with MTs on-line or use any services they have to offer, make sure they truly are professional. Some good rules of thumb:

- Check out what kinds of issues are being discussed. Those who use medical transcription as a platform for other causes do not have your best interests at heart.

- Avoid aligning yourself with those who use off-color language or perpetuate humor of questionable taste. This is just not professional.

- Be wary of those who are quick to criticize tried-and-true MT traditions. There really are no simple solutions to complex issues.

Fallacy: *The best way to get a medical transcription question answered is to go on-line and ask.*

Fact: Sometimes this works, sometimes it doesn't. Unquestionably, there is some very good information to be found on-line, but there are also inexperienced MTs perpetuating misinformation on a variety of subjects. Most experienced medical transcriptionists are far too busy working to be on-line on a regular basis; however, many of them do check in from time to time and can be of great assistance when they do. In any case, you will probably have to wait several hours to a day or more to get your answer, assuming it's the correct one.

Your best bet is to use your on-line connections as a backup resource. Your first line of defense should be your own reference library. It's really worth your time and money to invest in the basics—medical dictionaries appropriate for the MT industry, current drug references, specialty word books, spellers, and glossaries. Next, make use of any local MT contacts you've made. As mentioned, most of them are willing to help as long as you do some basic groundwork first. When you can't find a word in question or you have a question about the field in general, tell your MT mentor what resources you've already tried. That way they'll know you are sincere in your efforts to learn and can suggest other resources you may not know about.

Going on-line can certainly enhance your medical transcription resources. And there are some very generous individuals who maintain Web sites for the sole purpose of helping educate you. As you expand into MT cyberspace, choose wisely!

Worksheet

Answer the following true or false questions by placing a T for true or F for false in the blank next to the question.

_____ 1. Your appearance often reflects your attitude toward your work.

_____ 2. Medical transcriptionists are just typists.

_____ 3. Medical transcriptionists can't afford to dress appropriately for the workplace.

_____ 4. An independent contractor should dress appropriately when delivering finished work to a client's office.

_____ 5. Contractors should be sure to laugh and joke about patients in order to establish a good rapport with a physician's office staff.

_____ 6. What we think of ourselves can affect what others think of us.

_____ 7. Communication with other MTs on the Internet should be the primary resource for the independent working from home.

_____ 8. It is considered acceptable to become involved in networking that involves off-color language and humor.

_____ 9. You must be on-line to network properly with other medical transcriptionists.

_____ 10. Be wary of those who are quick to criticize long-standing MT traditions.

Fill in the blanks below with the correct answers. Some answers may require more than one word.

11. "Networking" can be defined as the exchange of _____ or _____ among individuals, groups, or institutions.

12. Some of an MT's best resources can be found in his/her _____.

13. A valuable networking tool is membership in _____.

14. Always do your own _____ before asking for assistance from others in your local or on-line groups.

15. Today's medical transcriptionists are learning their craft outside the _____ setting.

Section 2.
Style & Usage

Spelling Rules

Misspelled words can spell disaster when applying for a job. Even one misspelled word can cause an employer to reject an application. Poor spelling may brand you as unintelligent, uneducated, or careless.

Do not depend on the spellchecker in your word processor to proof your work. Many errors may consist of correctly spelled but **wrong** words. Leaving the "d" off *and*, for example, results in a correctly spelled word. The typographical error *tot he* (to the) will go through most spellcheckers. Furthermore, a good many proper nouns as well as plurals and the present tense, second person verbs (the ones that end in *s*) are not found in spellcheckers.

Spelling is a skill that can be learned. Having a good phonics background seems to help, but even if you have not learned to read by the phonics method, you can learn to spell well. Reading extensively helps. There are books and computer programs that can help you master basic spelling.

Here are some rules that will help. Most of these are easy to memorize, but you can also keep the rules in a notebook.

1. a. Write *ie* when the sound is a long *e*, except after *c*. Remember this rhyme: *i* before *e* except after *c* or when sounded as *a* as in *neighbor* and *weigh*.

    chief, believe, relief, hygiene

    Exceptions: either, neither, leisure, seize, weird

    b. Write *ei* when it comes after *c*, when the sound is not long, and specifically when it sounds like a long *a*.

    receive, conceive, weigh, neighbor, vein

2. *-cede, -ceed* and *-sede*

    a. Only one English word ends in *-sede: supersede.*

    b. Only three English words end in *-ceed:* exceed, proceed, and succeed.

    c. All other words of similar sound end in *-cede:* precede, recede.

3. a. Only two frequently used words end in *ery:* cemetery and stationery.

    b. More than 300 end in *ary* including *missionary* and *stationary* (not moving).
    Hint: To remember *stationery,* remember that **letter**s (spelled with *e)* you write are on pa**per**.
    To remember *stationary,* one is **sta**nding (with an *a*) still.

Spelling Rules, Continued

4. Only a few nonmedical words end in *ar* and should be memorized:

    beggar, calendar, collar,
    dollar, regular, singular

5. When a prefix is added to a word, the spelling of the word itself remains the same.

    misspell, dissatisfied

6. When the suffixes *-ness* and *-ly* are added to a word, the spelling of the word itself is not changed.

    casually, sterilely, plainness

7. Drop the final *e* before suffixes beginning with a vowel.

    movable, bony

    a. To prevent change in pronunciation in a word ending in a soft *c* or *g*, retain *e* before suffixes beginning with *a* or *o* (changeable, manageable, noticeable).

    b. In words ending in *-ie*, change this combination to *-y* before adding *-ing*.

        tie, tying   die, dying   lie, lying

8. Keep the final *e* before a suffix beginning with a consonant:

    lovely, hopeful

9. With words ending in *y* preceded by a consonant, change the *y* to an *i* before adding any suffix not beginning with *i*.

    satisfies, modifying

10. Double the final consonant before a suffix that begins with a vowel:

    a. If the word has only one syllable or is accented on the last syllable.

    b. If the word ends in a single consonant preceded by a single vowel.

        occurred, referred, swimming; **but** *referable* and *benefited* (stressed on first syllable)

Spelling Rules, Continued

11. The plural of compound nouns written as one word is formed by adding -s or -es.

    spoonfuls, cupfuls, fingerbreadths

12. The plurals of compound nouns consisting of a noun and a modifier are formed by making the modified word plural.

    mothers-in-law, runners-up, idiots savant

Here are some selected mnemonic devices for easily confused words.

- **Irresistible.** Many people confuse their -*ibles* and -*ables*. To remember the -*ible* on this one, think: "*I* am irresist*ible*."

- **Discrete** vs. **discreet.** Dis*crete* (separate) is the opposite of con*crete* (solid). Also, the *e*'s are separated by a *t*. Dis*creet* refers to good judgment in behavior, especially in keeping a prudent silence. Not a word you'll hear used to describe a tumor! To be dis*creet*, you need to *keep* your lips together, just like the *e*'s.

- **Principal** vs. **principle.** *Principal* means *main* (principal diagnosis), a *person* (school principal), or *capital sum* (principal and interest). *Principal* can be a noun and adjective. *Principle* means *rule* or *law* (a woman of principle, the principles of thermodynamics). *Principle* is a noun only.

Worksheet

Circle the correct term in the following sentences.

1. The patient had a (discrete, discreet) mass in her left breast.

2. He was always (discrete, discreet) with regard to patient information.

3. She was unwilling to sign the contract as a matter of (principle, principal).

4. The (principle, principal) reason for her visit was to consult with me regarding her chest pain.

5. We encouraged the patient to make regular use of his (stationery, stationary) bicycle.

Write the correct plural form of each of the following words.

6. fingerbreadth   _____

7. brother-in-law   _____

8. ovary   _____

9. lady-in-waiting   _____

10. teaspoonful   _____

11. allergy   _____

In the following exercise, circle words that are spelled incorrectly and correct them.

12. Pharmacology is the study of drugs and there interaction with liveing organisms.

13. The following dictations are breif examples of dictated labortory test results.

14. The labia minora is erythematous, without discreet lesion.

15. He has had recurence of the catching feeling when he trys to breath, usualy at night.

16. It was elected to admit the pateint for I.V. hydration and parental antibiotic therapy.

17. The patient was advised that she may get some acumulation of fluid in the middle ear.

18. She returned for revaluation of her complaints of dizziness.

19. A seperate consult was requested in order to assist with discharge planing issues.

20. The distribution of pain does seem to follow the course of the radial nerve in the humorous.

21. His speech is slured, and he has some tingleing and weakness in the right arm.

22. He has moderate weakness of the extremities both distaly and symetricaly.

Parts of Speech

Grammar may be defined as a set of rules that reflect how the language is used in spoken and written form. *Words* are traditionally classified according to their function into eight parts of speech. There have been other, more complex systems of grammar proposed which have made distinctions among the many functions a word can take, but the system most used today is the traditional one that you, your parents, your grandparents, and probably several more generations have learned.

The eight parts of speech are *verbs, nouns, pronouns, adjectives, adverbs, prepositions, conjunctions,* and *interjections.* The latter three do not change their form.

1. **Interjections** are exclamations and may be followed by an exclamation point or a comma. Interjections are rarely used in medical reports.

   Wow! Oh, what a surprise!
   Ah, that's my idea of a good response.

2. **Prepositions** and **conjunctions** are function or structure words and serve to connect and relate other parts of speech. A preposition always has an object, a noun, pronoun, or perhaps a verbal (gerund, infinitive, participial) functioning as a noun. Sometimes the object of a preposition can be an entire phrase. A prepositional phrase consists of the preposition, its object, and any modifiers. Prepositions establish a relationship, such as time, cause, manner, or accompaniment between their objects and another word in the sentence. See the list of prepositions (page 135).

3. **Conjunctions** are connectors. Coordinating conjunctions and correlative conjunctions connect words, phrases, or clauses of equal grammatical rank. Subordinating conjunctions connect clauses that are not equal in grammatical rank with main clauses. Adverbial conjunctions or conjunctive adverbs serve to connect two somewhat contrasting main clauses. See lists of subordinating conjunctions, coordinating and correlative conjunctions, adverbial conjunctions or conjunctive adverbs (pages 133-135).

   Many words can function as more than one part of speech. How they are classified depends upon their use (function) in a given sentence. For example, *living* can be a verb (*All the patient's siblings are living.*), an adjective (*The patient has no living relatives.*), or a noun (*He makes a living as a carpenter.*) See how the word *up* is used in the following sentences.

   Dr. Solomon will *follow up* this patient in two weeks. (part of phrasal verb)

   They carried the patient *up* to the third floor on a gurney. (adverb, *up* modifies *carried*)

   The patient was stepping off the *up escalator* when her shoelace caught in the mechanism and she fell. (adjective)

   The patient complained that the pharmacy *upped* the cost of her prescriptions. (verb)

   The patient is concerned about the *ups* and downs in her health. (noun)

Parts of Speech, Continued

4. **Verbs** function as the predicate of a sentence or clause. They may show action, occurrence, or existence. Verbs take different forms depending on tense, person, number, and mood. A verb may be transitive (takes an object to complete the meaning). A transitive verb may be active (subject performs the action) or passive (subject receives the action). A verb that does not take an object is said to be intransitive. Some verbs may be transitive in one sentence (*The patient sees spots before her eyes.*) and intransitive in another (*The patient sees well.*). In medicine, as in English, verbs are often coined by adding the suffixes *-ize* or *-ify* to nouns (e.g., heparinize).

   The present participle (the *-ing* form) and past participle (usually the *-ed* form) are considered verbs only when used with a helping (auxiliary) verb and when they function as the predicate of a sentence or clause. When used alone, they are considered *verbals* (words made from verbs) and assume the part of speech based on their function. In this context, the present participle is called a *gerund* (ends in *-ing*) and the past participle is called a *participle* (*-ed* form in regularly conjugated verbs).

5. **Nouns** name persons, places, animals, or things. They may also name ideas or concepts. Nouns are often preceded by the articles *a, an,* or *the,* although sometimes one or more adjectives may separate the noun from the article (the patient, a test, an x-ray, an elderly woman). A noun may function as the subject of a sentence or clause; the object of a verb, preposition, or verbal; as a subject complement (coming after the verb); as an appositive (coming after the noun to which it refers); as modifiers; and in absolute constructions (noun plus participle acting as a modifier). Each of these uses is discussed in more detail later.

   Regular nouns form the plural by adding *-s* or *-es,* the possessive by adding *'s* or *s'.* Suffixes frequently used to coin nouns from other words include *-ance, -ation, -ence, -er, -ism, -ity, -ment, -ness, -or, -ship, –tion, -um, -us.*

6. **Pronouns** (*he, she, it, who, what*) substitute for nouns; they change form according to their function. Since pronouns substitute for nouns, they may assume all the functions of a noun.

7. **Adjectives** describe (modify) or qualify nouns or pronouns. They are generally placed near the word they modify, although they may come before (the usual position) or after (as often happens in medical dictation). The articles *a, an,* and *the* are sometimes classified as adjectives, determiners, or (like conjunctions and prepositions), as function words. Sometimes an adjective that modifies the subject may come after a linking verb (the various forms of the verb *to be* and *seem, become, feel, look, smell,* and others); then it is called a subject complement. Adjectives can often be identified by their suffixes, such as *–al, -able, -ant, -ative, -ic or -ical, -ish, -less, -oid, -ous,* and *-y.* These suffixes are added to nouns or verbs to make adjectives.

8. **Adverbs** modify verbs, adjectives, and other adverbs. An adverb may also modify a phrase, a clause, or even the rest of the sentence in which it appears. The suffix *-ly* almost always converts adjectives to adverbs, but there are a few adjectives that end in *-ly.*

Subjects and Predicates

Your English teachers undoubtedly warned you repeatedly against writing incomplete sentences, or sentence fragments. Your teachers were correct in warning you against such constructions, for the sentence is the basis of all writing.

A sentence fragment is a group of words, a clause, or a phrase that, while it may have meaning, does not contain both a subject and a verb or have the ability to stand alone. In medical reports, however, there are many times when some sentence fragments, which we call **clipped sentences**, are entirely acceptable. Clipped sentences are most frequently found in the context of the physical examination report, report of laboratory data, and in chart notes (the short reports a doctor dictates on a patient's follow-up visits).

Often a clipped sentence is missing a word or words, a subject or a passive verb, which is actually understood though unspoken. Here are some examples of acceptable clipped sentences.

CHEST: Clear to percussion and auscultation. Heart rate and rhythm regular.
ABDOMEN: Normal bowel sounds. No pain, guarding, or tenderness.
(*Meaning*: Chest is clear to percussion and auscultation. Heart rate and rhythm are regular. Abdomen has normal bowel sounds. There is no pain, guarding, or tenderness.)

LABORATORY DATA: CBC: Hemoglobin 12, hematocrit 36, WBC 10,000, with 62 polys, 30 lymphs, 1 eosinophil, and 7 monos.

CHART NOTE: (after identifying patient and stating date of visit)
Returns to office for follow-up of abdominal pain and cramping. No further complaints. Pain and cramping resolved. Return visit only if needed.

You can see that in the above examples of clipped sentences, the meaning is still clear. Many physicians and supervisors would not appreciate a transcriptionist editing the above dictation to include missing words. In general, you should not edit this type of dictation unless instructed to do so by your supervisor or the dictator.

Certain sentence fragments are *not* acceptable, even in medical reports. In the examples below, the meaning is unclear, or incorrect punctuation or a physician's slip of the tongue has separated the fragment from the sentence or phrase to which it should be attached.

Example: The patient was told to return in one week. During which time she improved.
Correctly punctuated: The patient was told to return in one week, during which time she improved.

Example: The CBC revealed a hemoglobin of 8 and a hematocrit of 24. Both of which are below normal.
Correctly punctuated: The CBC revealed a hemoglobin of 8 and a hematocrit of 24, both of which are below normal.

Subjects and Predicates, Continued

Most sentences, however, require two basic elements—a subject and a predicate. The **predicate** is the part of the sentence that consists of what is said about the subject. The essential part of the predicate is the verb. Often, in the discussion that follows, predicate and verb will be used interchangeably. If the phrase *predicate of the sentence* is used, it will be talking only about the verb that goes with the subject of the sentence. If *complete predicate* is used, it will refer to the main verb plus the accompanying modifiers.

Verbs can be recognized by observing their meaning and form. They may express action, occurrence, or existence. They may be used to make a statement, ask a question, or to give a command or direction.

The simple predicate is the verb, including "helping" verbs (*was, has, will* are just three examples). The complete predicate includes the simple predicate plus any modifiers and complements that may follow it (more about the latter two later).

NOTE: There may be several verbs in a sentence, each of which may have a separate subject or they may share the same subject. When thinking about verbs, don't just think of the main verb in the sentence but look for verbs that may be part of other clauses as well.

> Though vaccinated for rabies, the dog that bit the boy was quarantined for six weeks anyway.

Was quarantined is the simple predicate, and *for six weeks anyway* completes the predicate.

The subject of a verb has several characteristics:

1. It is the part of the sentence or clause that performs or receives the action indicated by the predicate (verb) or about which something is said or asked in the predicate.

> Who treated this patient? Dr. Smith treated this patient.

In the first sentence *who* is the subject; in the second sentence *Dr. Smith* is the subject.)

2. It usually, but not always, precedes the predicate (verb).

3. Sometimes, especially in imperative (command) sentences or in answers to questions, the subject is not stated, but implicitly understood. (*Order the chest x-ray for tomorrow morning. You* is the understood subject of this sentence. See essay on clipped sentences on page 127.)

4. The subject of a sentence or clause can be a single word (noun or pronoun), a group of words (compound nouns or noun phrases), and even verbs used as nouns (called gerunds or infinitives).

> The depth of the laceration was almost an inch.

Subjects and Predicates, Continued

The drainage from the wound finally stopped.

Note the adjective (article) *the* in front of *depth* and *drainage*. Also, ask the questions, "What was almost an inch?" and "What finally stopped?"

Subjects can be nouns or pronouns. A **noun** is a word that names things. It can name *living things* (people, animals, plants), *nonliving things* (objects such as chairs, cars, stars, atoms), and *concepts* or *ideas* (such as titles of books, movies, stories, or poems; traits or characteristics, such as softness, ambition; or philosophy).

A **pronoun** is a word that can take the place of a noun (see discussion of pronouns beginning on page 133).

Worksheet

In the following sentences, use a single underline for the simple subject and a double underline for the predicate.

1. Febrile <u>agglutinins</u> <u>were drawn</u>.

2. Neurologic examination reveals normal deep tendon reflexes.

3. Vocal cords were fibrotic in appearance.

4. This is the first ENT evaluation for this 39-year-old professional singer.

5. The patient complains of pain and swelling of the left knee.

6. No nodules are palpated in the axillae.

7. There have been no recent infections.

8. The patient denies foreign travel.

9. A complete subject consists of the simple subject and the words that accompany it.

10. The dog that bit the boy had been vaccinated for rabies.

    (Hint: *Dog* is the simple subject, *the* and *that bit the boy* complete the subject.)

11. Dr. Johnson saw this patient in consultation.

12. The patient was admitted in extremis.

13. No amount of persuasion would convince the patient to have surgery.

14. Surgery was performed uneventfully on September 7.

15. Admission and discharge dates were January 5 and January 10, respectively.

16. Who will be the patient's primary caretaker after discharge?

17. The purulent, sanguineous drainage from the right leg wound was sent for culture and sensitivity studies.

18. There were no contusions or abrasions on examination.

19. Examination of the heart, lungs, and abdomen was normal.

20. There was 600 cc of blood loss during the procedure.

21. The patient denies abuse of cigarettes or alcohol.

22. This patient, a resident of a nursing home, drinks a glass of wine with lunch and dinner.

23. No history of nausea, vomiting, or diarrhea was given.

24. There was no evidence of abrasions, contusions, or lacerations.

25. The patient's mother had valvular heart disease, colitis, and gallstones.

26. The patient complains of a six-month history of insomnia.

Worksheet, Continued

27. On chest examination, the lungs were clear to auscultation and percussion.

28. There were no signs of weakness, lethargy, or confusion.

29. Carotid arterial pulsations are equal and full.

30. No third or fourth heart sound was present.

31. The patient also had a rather loud heart murmur, which may be functional.

32. The patient has a history which is consistent with angina pectoris.

33. There is no cyanosis, clubbing, or edema of the extremities.

34. No abnormalities of rate or rhythm were noted during the stress EKG.

35. I find no frank evidence of cardiac problems in this gentleman.

36. The patient's present episodes of chest pain are probably on a musculoskeletal basis.

37. There is no diabetes or history of rheumatic fever in the past.

38. This 19-year-old male of Italian descent presented to the office with acute onset of dizziness and confusion.

39. There is a soft bruit over the entire right carotid artery.

40. This 68-year-old male with a history of diabetes and arteriosclerotic heart disease was apparently in good health otherwise.

41. On neither occasion were the stones preserved for analysis.

42. Impression is possible hypertension in an otherwise healthy-appearing woman.

Types of Sentences

Sentences are classified as simple, compound, complex, or compound-complex based on their structure. A **simple sentence** has one subject and one predicate, either or both of which may be compound.

The child was operated on for strabismus at age 2.

The other nails, toe webs, and soles are clear.

A **compound sentence** has at least two main clauses.

The chest pains were not triggered by exertion or eating, nor were they associated with dyspnea or diaphoresis.

He is on no oral medicine, and he is in good health.

The scar is well healed, and there is no evidence of local or deep recurrence.

A **complex sentence** has one main clause and at least one subordinate clause.

The patient returned today with a spreading rash on her shoulders, upper chest, and back, which has been present for the last couple of months.

This 23-year-old gentleman was in good health until 4 days ago, when he developed acute onset of high fever, abdominal cramping, nausea, and profuse watery diarrhea.

If the cyst recurs, it will be excised.

A **compound-complex sentence** has at least two main clauses and at least one subordinate clause.

I have advised her that I do not feel this eruption is related to her previous breast carcinoma, and I definitely do not feel that there is any relationship to her tamoxifen therapy.

I tried to convince his mother that he should be there, and his mother was even more adamant that the patient should return home.

Subordinating conjunctions (page 133) are used to introduce a dependent clause (one that is not a complete sentence) or to join a dependent clause to an independent clause. When a clause beginning with a subordinating conjunction is used at the beginning of a sentence, it is usually followed by a comma. Subordinate clauses may appear in the middle of a sentence or at the end.

If the clause is considered essential (restrictive) to the meaning of the sentence and cannot be removed without affecting meaning, no commas are needed. If the subordinate clause is not essential or is parenthetical (nonrestrictive) and can be removed without significantly affecting the

Types of Sentences, Continued

sentence, it is set off by commas (if within the sentence) or preceded by a comma (if at the end of the sentence).

Relative pronouns may also introduce subordinate clauses. They include *that, what, which, who, whoever, whom, whomever, whose.*

> Excessive alcohol consumption is denied by Mr. Thompson, whose wife stands behind him shaking her head in contradiction.

> The patient will be sent for a complete chemistry and radiological workup before the surgery is performed.

Relative Pronouns

that	whoever
what	whom
which	whomever
who	whose

Subcoordinating Conjunctions

after	now that
although	once
as	provided that
as far as	since
as soon as	so that
as if	supposing that
as though	than
because	that
before	though
even if	till
even though	unless
how	until
if	when
inasmuch as	whenever
in case	where
in order that	wherever
insofar as	whether
in that	while
lest	why
no matter how	

> After the patient returned to his room, he developed a large hematoma in the groin area at the catheterization site of the femoral vein.

> Inasmuch as this poorly controlled diabetic patient has already had a triple bypass, I think his chances of benefiting from an additional bypass operation are minimal.

> The patient is scheduled for elective hip replacement surgery at 7:00 a.m. Monday, provided that his preadmission preoperative lab studies are acceptable.

That, which, and *who* are probably the most confusing pronouns in the English language. You say, "I'll simply never use them, and that way I don't have to learn *when* to use them." Unfortunately, we cannot remove them from our vocabulary, so we need to learn a few rules regarding their use. The following explanation should stand you in good stead 95% of the time.

Which used as a relative pronoun refers to animals and things, and *who* (or *whom*) to people (and sometimes animals). *That* can refer to animals, things, or people, the latter usually when the people being referred to represent a group or an unspecified person.

That is used almost exclusively to introduce restrictive clauses (clauses that are essential for the understanding of the sentence and that don't require a comma or commas to set them off).

> The medicine that he took is unknown to me.

Types of Sentences, Continued

A test of a restrictive clause that works most of the time is to leave out the relative pronoun (*the medicine he took . . .*) and see if the sentence still makes sense.

Which is more often used in nonessential clauses, which are set off by commas if in the middle of a sentence, followed by a comma if at the beginning of a sentence, and preceded by a comma if at the end of a sentence. Another word for *nonessential* is *nonrestrictive*. Nonrestrictive clauses can be removed from the sentence without significantly affecting the understanding of the sentence.

The medicine that he took, which he left at home in Virginia, was Dyazide.

Which he left at home in Virginia is a nonessential or nonrestrictive clause. Notice also that *which* is separated from the noun it modifies by several words—another clue to the need for commas. There is a growing tendency to use *which* and *that* interchangeably.

Who and *whom* can be used in essential or nonessential clauses. If the clause being introduced by *who* or *whom* is essential, no comma is required; if it is not essential, the same punctuation is required as for *which* described above.

I have asked Dr. Jablonski to see this patient who was admitted with acute urinary retention.

Mr. Goodweather, whom you asked me to see in consultation, is cleared medically for orthopedic surgery.

The patient whom you sent over to my office on Wednesday never showed up.

Here is a rhyme to help you remember the above guidelines:

> *Who* is used for persons,
> *Which* is used for things,
> *That* is used for either,
> What peace this knowledge brings.

Coordinating and **correlative conjunctions** (see list on page 134) connect sentence elements (words, phrases, or clauses) of equal rank. In sentences with independent clauses (that can stand alone as a sentence), a comma precedes the coordinating conjunction.

The patient complains of difficulty finding the right word, but he denies any extremity weakness.

Not only is cardiac catheterization advisable for this patient with repeated angina pectoris, but also a PTCA will most likely be required.

Coordinating Conjunctions

and	or
but	so
for	yet
nor	

Correlative Conjunctions

both . . . and
either . . . or
neither . . . nor
not only . . . but also
whether . . . or

Types of Sentences, Continued

Conjunctive adverbs and **transitional phrases** are used to join two independent clauses of equal value. They are different from coordinating conjunctions, however, in that when placed at the beginning of the second independent clause, conjunctive adverbs and transitional phrases are preceded by a semicolon, rather than a comma.

Conjunctive Adverbs

also	meanwhile
anyway	moreover
besides	nevertheless
consequently	next
finally	nonetheless
furthermore	otherwise
hence	still
however	subsequently
incidentally	then
indeed	therefore
instead	thus
likewise	

The patient's condition was improved; he was *therefore* transferred to a regular bed. (Commas before and after *therefore* are optional in this sentence.)

The patient's chest x-ray revealed only atelectasis and no evidence of pneumonia; *however*, we should continue to watch for progression of disease.

The patient's chest x-ray revealed only atelectasis and no evidence of pneumonia; we should, *however*, continue to watch for progression of disease.

The patient's cardiac catheterization revealed only moderate stenosis of the left circumflex and no other serious stenoses; *thus*, we will treat him conservatively.

Prepositions and Phrasal Prepositions

about	because of	except	near	throughout
above	before	except for	of	till
according to	behind	excepting	off	to
across	below	for	on	toward
after	beneath	from	on account of	under
against	beside	in	onto	underneath
along	besides	in addition to	out	until
along with	between	in case of	out of	up
amid	beyond	in front of	outside	upon
among	by	in lieu of	over	up to
apart from	by means of	in place of	past	with
around	by reason of	in regard to	pending	within
as for	concerning	inside	regarding	without
aside from	despite	in spite of	respecting	with reference to
as regards	down	instead of	round	with regard to
as to	due to	into	since	with respect to
at	during	like	through	with the exception of

The patient's cardiac catheterization revealed only moderate stenosis of the left circumflex and no other serious stenoses; we will thus treat him conservatively.

> *but:*

The patient's cardiac catheterization revealed only moderate stenosis of the left circumflex, and we will treat him conservatively.

Prepositions and **phrasal prepositions** (see box examples on page 135). Nouns that follow prepositions or phrasal prepositions are called objects of the preposition and cannot function as the subject of a sentence. A prepositional phrase is different from a phrasal preposition.

A phrasal preposition is a group of words that begins and ends with a preposition (*by means of, with the exception of*) or a two-word combination that ends with a preposition (*apart from, because of, except for*). A prepositional phrase is the preposition or phrasal preposition plus the object and any modifiers of the object (*with regard to his sexual contact*). Prepositional phrases often function as adjectival or adverbial phrases.

137

Worksheet

In the following exercise, classify the type of each sentence (simple, compound, complex, or compound-complex) and identify the part of speech for each underlined word or phrase.

    prep   adj   n
1. For the medical transcriptionist, medical words—their origins, their meanings, and

                     v   adj
   their spellings—are of paramount importance. (simple sentence)

2. The study of microscopic anatomy, however, could not begin until the invention of the

   microscope. (_____ sentence)

3. One sister is deceased with brain cancer at the age of 50 years, and another sister is alive at

   the age of 63 years with a history of rheumatic fever. (_____ sentence)

4. Nephrology consultation was obtained, and arrangements were made for transfer of the

   patient for dialysis. (_____ sentence)

5. Physical examination was remarkable for abdominal tenderness; otherwise, the examination

   was within normal limits. (_____ sentence)

6. Paternal grandparents are diabetic, but neither the father nor his siblings have diabetes.

   (_____ sentence)

7. Hey! What do you think you're doing? (_____ sentence)

8. With regard to his sexual contact, I discussed with him the risk of lues and CMV infection

   and feel the screening is appropriate. (_____ sentence)

9. This 68-year-old male with a history of hypertension and congestive heart failure was

   apparently in good health, although he had failed to show up for his office appointments

   and ran out of refills on his Lasix one week ago. (_____ sentence)

Worksheet Continues

Worksheet, Continued

10. <u>With the patient</u> in the <u>supine</u> position after placement <u>of</u> an adequate <u>subarachnoid</u> block anesthetic catheter, a <u>bolster</u> was placed beneath the left thigh, a tourniquet was placed <u>high</u> on the left thigh, <u>well padded</u>, and the left lower extremity <u>was prepped</u> and draped in a <u>sterile</u> fashion. (_____ sentence)

Verb Tense in Medical Reports

Verb tense is often confusing to medical transcription students because multiple tenses may be correctly used in the same report, even in the same paragraph. Also, verb tense does not necessarily indicate a rigid division of time.

For example, the present tense may be used to indicate something that is happening now, at the present time. That's the most common assumption of the present tense. It may also, however, indicate habitual action (*The patient uses sleeping pills nightly.*); habitual action with passive verb (*Prescription mistakes are not often made.*); universal or timeless truth (*Heart disease is the leading cause of death in the U.S.*); or the historical present (*The patient comes to my office complaining of chest pain of uncertain duration.*). The present tense may also be used to indicate a literary present, used with an adverb to indicate future time, and as a progressive form denoting past, present, and probably future.

The past tense may be used to indicate a definite time before now (*The patient abused alcohol in the past but no longer drinks.*); continuing action in the past (*The patient was enjoying a cup of hot tea when the pain hit.*); or passive voice (*The patient was given a nitroglycerin spray under the tongue.*). Physicians also use the future tense and all the perfect tenses in dictation.

Frequently, a particular tense may dominate a particular type of report. For example, the Chief Complaint and History of Present Illness may be written predominantly in the present tense, as might the Physical Examination. The Past Medical History and Review of Systems are usually past tense. Surgeons sometimes dictate the Findings and Procedure as though they are still in the operating room performing surgery, so operative reports may be dictated in the present tense.

Pathologists often dictate in the present tense because they usually are examining the body or tissue as they dictate. (You may even hear the metal utensils and basins clanging, saws whirring, or fluids sloshing in the background.)

In a Discharge Summary, physicians typically use the past tense throughout (except for the most current lab reports, the prognosis, and the disposition), but if reading from another report, such as the History and Physical dictated on admission, they may use the tenses given in that report. In that case, transcriptionists may edit to the past tense certain portions of the report.

Verb tenses and verb tense consistency are seldom the problem in dictation that students first think. What sounds strange to a student's ears now will one day be very comfortable and ordinary. Students who have a question about tense in a report that they are transcribing should ask for their instructor's advice.

The following example from dictation illustrates varied tenses used in one paragraph:

> The patient *is being discharged* home and *will be followed up* in the office, both by me and Dr. Blank. I *spoke* with Dr. White on 15 April, and she *suggested* that we *transfer* the patient to Springfield on the evening of the 15th for cardiac catheterization the following day. I *discussed* this at some length with the patient, and he *was* unwilling to proceed with this.

Verb Tense in Medical Reports, Continued

In spite of the known risks of myocardial infarction which I *have explained* at some length to the patient, he *wishes* to go home at this time and *states* that he *will call* Dr. White tomorrow and *make* arrangements for cardiac catheterization during the latter part of this week or next week. He *tolerates* nitroglycerin poorly due to hypotension and diaphoresis, and I *will* not *treat* him with nitrates after discharge. Once the patient *was hospitalized*, his pain *subsided*, and through the night he *was* essentially without symptoms, requiring none of the patient-controlled analgesia.

Subject-Verb Agreement

Agreement in number. In the preceding sections we have discussed how to identify subjects and predicates (verbs) of sentences. Remember that the subject may be a single noun or pronoun, or a group of words (phrase or clause) that act as a noun. Nouns and pronouns are said to have number; that is, they can be singular (one) or plural (more than one). A singular subject takes a singular verb. A plural subject takes a plural verb.

Agreement in person. Subjects and verbs must also agree in person. Pronouns and verbs may be distinguished by person (first, second, and third). Person depends on who is speaking. First person pronouns are *I* and *we*; the second person pronoun is *you*. *He, she, they, it,* and *who* are third-person pronouns. Nouns use the same form of a verb as third-person pronouns. The subject of a sentence must agree with its verb in both number and person.

> The patient is reluctant to quit smoking.
> Patients who smoke are often poor surgical risks.
> Mr. Balboa says he has no history of heart disease.
> Mrs. Adams sees her family physician about once a month.
> We were waiting for the clotting times when this patient threw a clot to the lung.
> Dr. Andrews and Dr. Carter are on call tonight.

Most problems with subject-verb agreement occur with the verbs *be* and *have*, which change forms in the various tenses (is, was, will be; have, has, had), and with other verbs only in the present tense. (Verbs other than *be* and *have* do not change form in present and past tense.)

> Dr. Smith agrees with Dr. Jacobson that a radical thyroidectomy is required for this patient.
> He agrees that a radical thyroidectomy is required.

Agrees is in the third-person present tense. Remember that nouns require the same form of the verb that the third-person pronouns require. *Dr. Smith*, the subject of the first sentence, and *he*, the subject of the second sentence, are both singular and both require the third-person singular verb *agrees*. The following sentences illustrate the verbs *be* and *have* as they are used in the third-person singular and plural form.

> Mrs. Johnson is admitted for a complete GI workup.
> She is admitted for a complete GI workup.
> John Thompson and Ray Acabado are both scheduled for surgery at 7 a.m.
> They are scheduled for surgery at 7 a.m.
> The patient has to be kept n.p.o. for at least 24 hours.
> He has to be kept n.p.o. for at least 24 hours.
> Mr. Thompson and Mr. Acabado have to be kept n.p.o. for at least 24 hours.
> They have to be kept n.p.o. for at least 24 hours.

Subject-Verb Agreement, Continued

Do not be confused by nouns, pronouns, or phrases that appear between the subject and the verb.

The incision from the shoulder cuff to the anterior humeral ligament and the subscapularis muscle was reapproximated with 3-0 Vicryl.
(*Incision* is the subject; *was reapproximated* is the verb.)

History and physical examination of the patient, who was sent over from the county jail with a 3-inch forearm laceration, were otherwise normal.
(*History* and *physical examination* are the subjects; *were* is the verb.)

Evidence of recent cardiac surgery with placement of four bypasses and a temporary pacemaker wire was seen on the AP chest x-ray.
(*Evidence* is the subject; *was seen* is the verb.)

Subjects joined by *and* are usually plural.

Lab results and chest x-ray were both normal.
Febrile agglutinins and white blood count were elevated.
A KUB and intravenous pyelogram were performed to rule out ureteral stone.

but:
Dilatation and curettage was performed on October 15, 1995.
"But bacon and eggs is my favorite breakfast," said the patient after I warned him to cut fat.

Every or *each* preceding singular subjects joined by *and* calls for a singular verb. Placed after a plural subject, however, the word *each* does not affect the verb form.

Every physician and nurse has an ethical responsibility to keep patient information confidential.

Each lab tech, x-ray tech, and nurse is required to attend the OSHA workshop.

Every x-ray, blood test, and EKG done on this patient shows absolutely no abnormalities.

but:
The x-ray, blood test, and EKG each show absolutely no abnormalities.

Singular subjects joined by *or, either . . . or,* or *neither . . . nor* usually take a singular verb.

Dr. Silverado or Dr. Angulo has seen this patient before, but I don't know which.
Either Dr. Sainz or Dr. Garrett has been scheduled to performed the cardiac catheterization.
Neither the patient nor anyone else in the family smokes.

Subject-Verb Agreement, Continued

In subjects joined by *or, either . . . or,* or *neither . . . nor*, if one is singular and the other plural, the verb is singular or plural as determined by the subject nearest the verb.

>   Neither the patient nor his brothers remember the name of the medication he was on.
>   Neither his brothers nor the patient remembers the name of the medication he was on.
>   Either the floor nurses or the physician on call records the time of death.
>   Either the physician on call or the floor nurses record the time of death.
>   No liquids or food is allowed until the doctor examines this patient.

When *each, either, neither, one, this, that, who, everybody, everyone,* and *anyone* (called indefinite pronouns) are used alone as subjects, rather than to modify the subject, they regularly take singular verbs.

>   Everybody on the floor was attending to other patients when Mr. Samson went into cardiac arrest.
>   Anyone with any knowledge of risk to patient health is obligated to report it.

When *all, any, half, most, none,* and *some* are used alone as subjects, they may use either singular or plural verbs. The context (the noun being referred to) usually determines the number of the verb.

>   All of the reports were negative.
>   All of the patient's lunch was eaten.
>   Most nurses take their responsibility for patient care seriously.
>   Most of the barium was evacuated within 24 hours after the completion of the upper GI series.

Nouns and phrases that are used collectively take a singular verb when referring to the group as a unit and a plural verb when referring to individuals or parts of the group. Units of measure, however, always take a singular verb.

>   The patient was admitted in severe respiratory distress, and 2 L of oxygen was begun.
>   Two thousand milligrams of niacin a day was prescribed for hypercholesterolemia.
>   A number of adhesions were dissected before we reached the uterus.
>   A minimal amount of bleeding was observed prior to closure of the wound.
>   The number of patients who develop a staphylococcus infection following surgery is sizable.
>   Dr. Rodriguez, Dr. Garcia, and Dr. de Carlos are to follow this patient for congestive heart failure.

Who, which, and *that* (called relative pronouns) require a singular or plural verb depending on the number of the antecedent. The antecedent is the noun or pronoun to which the relative pronoun refers. In the following examples the antecedent and the relative pronoun are italicized; the verb for the pronoun is in bold.

>   Laparoscopic *cholecystectomy, which* **is** an elective procedure, is one of the most frequently performed operations in the U.S.

Subject-Verb Agreement, Continued

Cesarean *sections, which* **have been** getting a lot of bad press, are on the decline, even in patients who have already had a cesarean section.

Dr. Sprinkle is *one* of those doctors *who* **are** always prompt with their dictation.
Dr. Calvert is among those *doctors who* **are** always late with their dictation.

Notice the difference between the last two sentences above. In the former, you might think that *doctors* (a plural noun) is the antecedent for *who*, but it is actually the pronoun *one* that is the antecedent of *who*. In the latter sentence, *doctors* is the antecedent for *who*.

When a sentence has a subject and a subject complement, the verb agrees with the subject, not the complement. The complement is a noun, or sometimes a pronoun, that restates, renames, or is equal to the subject. These types of sentences usually contain a form of the verb *to be*.

The patient's admitting complaint is frequent headaches.
  but:
Frequent headaches are the patient's admitting complaint.

Note: When used as the subject of a verb, the pronoun *what* has the same number as the word to which it refers. That is, if its antecedent is singular, *what* is singular; if its antecedent is plural, *what* is plural.

More frequent follow-up is what is needed to keep this patient from experiencing erratic blood sugar levels.

"What are the risks of this surgical procedure?" the patient asked.

AP, lateral, and oblique x-rays of the right hand reveal what *appear* to be *residuals* of a well-healed fracture with a large ball of mature callus.

AP, lateral, and oblique x-rays of the right hand reveal what *appears* to be a *residual* of a well-healed fracture with a large ball of mature callus.

Some nouns frequently used in medical dictation sound singular but are actually plural. These include *adnexa, feces, genitalia, menses, scissors, tongs,* and *tweezers;* they are plural in meaning, have no singular form, and always take a plural verb.

The adnexa were unremarkable.
Menses were regular until she began college.
Metzenbaum scissors were used for sharp and blunt dissection.
The genitalia were examined and are normal.

Subject-Verb Agreement, Continued

Data, however, may be used as a singular or plural noun. (The singular form, *datum*, is rarely used.) *Data* is used as a plural noun (like *earnings*), taking a plural verb, plural modifiers (such as *these, many, a few*), and plural pronouns (*they, them*). It is also used as an abstract mass noun (like *information*), taking a singular verb, singular modifiers (such as *this, much, little*), and singular pronoun (*it*).

The pronoun *none* may also be singular or plural. It can mean "not one" and take a singular verb, or "not any" and take a plural verb.

Some nouns that appear to be plural are actually singular and take a singular verb. These include *agenda, ascites, herpes, facies, lues, measles,* and *mumps*. Some words may be either singular or plural, depending on their use, including such words as *biceps, data, forceps,* and *series*.

> Up- and down-biting forceps were used to remove the lesion piecemeal.
> Moon facies was evident on initial examination.
> Mumps in childhood was denied as was measles.
> A series of EKGs was performed and revealed improvement in ST-T waves.

Singular verbs are usually required for words used as subjects, nouns plural in form but singular in meaning, and titles of books, movies, and other types of works.

> *Cases* is an impersonal and demeaning way to refer to patients.

> *Doctors and the Gods They Think They Are* is a book I always thought I should write.

> "Kids" is how Dr. Brownstone, the pediatric endocrinologist, refers to his patients.

Hint: Do not be confused by sentences that begin with *there* and a verb followed by the subject. Sometimes inverting the sentence (rewording it so that the subject comes first) can help you be sure you have chosen the correct verb form.

> There are multiple side effects to this treatment. (Multiple side effects . . . are there.)
> There were no complications to the operation. (No complications . . . were there.)
> There was 600 cc of blood loss during the procedure.
> There was no evidence of abrasions, contusions, or lacerations.
> There is no cyanosis, clubbing, or edema of the extremities.
> On EEG, there is low to moderate voltage spike and wave activity.
> There appear to be no frank pus pockets evident.

Worksheet

In the sentences below, make sure that the verb agrees with the subject in person and number. If it does not, change it so that it does agree.

1. There were no evidence on chest x-ray of any atelectasis, pneumonia, or tumor.

2. Findings on chest x-ray was consistent with bilateral lower lobe pneumonia.

3. There was no findings of a stone or other obvious abnormality on KUB.

4. Findings at cardiac catheterization includes left ventricular end-diastolic pressure of 4.8 mm.

5. There has been no travel outside of the country.

6. On examination of the neck, no bruit or venous hum are noted.

7. No bruits or venous hum are noted on examination of the neck.

8. On examination, no venous hum or bruits are noted.

9. No masses or discharge are present.

10. There is normal deep tendon reflexes present on neurologic examination.

11. No facial or palatal weakness were observed.

12. Review of multiple x-rays of the face and sinuses reveal no fractures.

13. The remainder of the history and physical were unremarkable.

14. There were no organomegaly or masses.

15. There was no masses or organomegaly.

16. Shortness of breath, dyspnea on exertion, orthopnea, and paroxysmal nocturnal dyspnea is denied by the patient.

17. The patient's insight and judgment appears to be poor.

18. Then, 6000 cc of sterile saline with Bacitracin were irrigated through the knee joint with outflow through the anterior wound.

19. At surgery, however, there was no purulent exudates, although she did have chronic synovitis.

20. Abdomen: No tenderness or organomegaly were present. Bowel sounds was normoactive.

Worksheet Continues

Worksheet, Continued

21. The patient had serial EKGs and enzymes, all of which was unremarkable for evidence of ischemic heart disease.

22. The patient was admitted with complaints of fever, chills, dysuria, coughing, and wheezing which has gradually gotten worse over a one-month period.

23. Five days of intravenous Claforan was given, and the patient was discharged home on oral antibiotics.

24. On auscultation, there were no murmur, gallop, or rubs heard.

25. Doppler studies of the right leg was obtained and was suggestive of some deep venous thrombosis.

26. Bed rest, leg elevation, and warm heat to the affected leg was ordered for at least seven days.

27. The chest x-ray, which was read by Dr. Hines, reveal that the heart size, pulmonary vasculature, and hila was normal.

28. HEENT was within normal limits.

29. Lung fields were clear, and cardiac exam was normal.

30. A prothrombin time of 26 seconds on 5 mg of Coumadin was obtained.

31. Approximately six sutures of 10-0 Vicryl was placed in the epineurium of the nerve to effect an end-to-end anastomosis.

32. Necrotic ischemia from repeated thrombosis of his distal vessels was the unfortunate result following his arteriovenous injury.

33. Several centimeters of tumor-free colon were measured and a site identified for proximal transection.

34. All the risks and complications was explained to the patient, who seemed to understand.

35. After that point, the atrial lead was placed in seven different positions, six of which was unsatisfactory.

Worksheet Continues

Worksheet, Continued

36. Five liters of carbon dioxide gas were insufflated to a pressure of 14 mm Hg to create a pneumoperitoneum.

37. Much of the history that the patient gave were considered questionable.

38. There is no bruits over the subclavian artery.

39. There is no diastolic murmurs.

40. Laboratory data was reviewed and was completely normal.

41. Head, eyes, ears, nose, and throat was within normal limits.

42. Dry rales in both bases without wheezing or rub was present.

43. No murmur, gallop, or rubs was heard on auscultation.

44. Adnexa was without abnormalities on both sides.

45. Medications includes Tenex 1 mg p.o. q. h.s. and Lasix 20 mg p.o. q. day, as well as Clinoril 200 mg p.o. b.i.d.

46. Sensory and vascular status and motor status was within normal limits.

47. Two-thirds of the length of the small bowel were involved with ulcerative colitis.

48. After preop evaluation, the patient was brought to surgery, where an ileal conduit and left inguinal hernia repair was performed.

49. There are no history of hematuria or renal calculi.

50. One-half of the clips is removed at this time; the remainder will be removed at her first office visit.

Common Errors

Affect vs. **effect.** The word *affect* is most often used as a verb and, as such, is pronounced as though it begins with a short *ah* sound. The accent is on the second syllable (ah fekt'). *Affect* means "to change" or "to influence."

> The combination of narcotics affected (influenced) the patient's sensorium.
> The use of some drugs affects (changes) the effectiveness of others.

The verb *affect* is often accompanied by helping verbs, i.e., *was, is, shall, will, has, have*. The verb endings *-ed* and *-ing* may also be added.

> It is uncertain how the news of his terminal state will affect (influence) the patient.

The word *effect* is most often used as a noun. When used as a noun, it is preceded by the words *an, the, this, these,* as well as other adjectives such as *positive, good, poor*. It means "the outcome, result, product, sequel," or "end of an action."

> It is uncertain what effect (outcome) the news of his terminal illness will have on the patient.

> There appears to be a several millimeter right-to-left shift of the anterior cerebral artery, consistent with mass effect in the right cerebral hemisphere.

The noun *effect* is often the object of a verb. In one example below, it is not only the object of the verb *produced* but is preceded by an article and an adjective.

> The combination of drugs produced an adverse effect.
> The surgical procedure produced a good cosmetic effect.

Often, *effect* is used in the context of a drug's action or with names.

> digitalis effect   Doppler effect
> placebo effect   Tyndall effect

When used as a verb, *effect* is pronounced by some doctors as though it begins with a long *e* sound so that the transcriptionist will spell it correctly. As a verb, *effect* means "to accomplish, to cause, to create, to do," or "to execute" in such a manner as "to bring about a desired result."

> This therapy should effect a cure.
> Closure was effected (brought about) by interrupted sutures.
> This regimen effected (brought about) a reversal of the patient's symptoms.

In summary, *affect* is most often used as a verb; therefore, it will have verb endings (*-ed, -ing*), will be used with helping verbs (*has, is, was*), and will mean "to change" or "influence."

Common Errors, Continued

Effect is most often used as a noun and means "the result" or "outcome" of some action. It may be preceded by articles (*an, the*) and other adjectives (*this, these, good, placebo, ill, side, negative*).

In psychiatry, the word *affect* is commonly used as a noun, meaning "an outward appearance of an inner emotion." It is pronounced with the accent on the first syllable (af' fect.)

> The patient demonstrated a flat affect.

> This patient's *affect* has *affected* her ability to *effect* a normal relationship with others and work *effectively*, but has had no *effect* on her ability to care for herself.
> (This patient's *emotional state* has *changed* her ability to *achieve* or *accomplish* a normal relationship with others and work *with good results*, but has had no *influence* on her ability to care for herself.)

> The *effects* of transcribing difficult reports *affect* our *affect* to such an extent that we cannot *effect* transcription *effectively*.
> (The *results* of transcribing difficult reports *influence* our *emotional state* to such an extent that we cannot *accomplish* transcription *with good results*.)

Than vs. **then.** *Than* may be used as a conjunction or a preposition. As a **conjunction**, *than* is used as a function word in a comparison expressive of inequality, used with comparative adjectives and comparative adverbs.

> When I asked the patient her age, she stated she was older than Moses.
> Treating this disease process will be easier said than done.

Also, it is used as a function word to indicate difference of kind, manner, or identity, especially with some adjectives and adverbs that express diversity.

> This very pleasant gentleman stated that he would rather be anywhere than in the hospital.

As a **preposition**, *than* is used in comparisons.

> The patient stated she was younger than her twin by three minutes.

Then is an **adverb** meaning "soon after that," "next in order of time," "following next after in order of position," "being next in a series," and "in addition."

> The floor of the inguinal canal and internal ring weakness was then repaired by suturing the conjoined tendon to the shelving border of Poupart's ligament with interrupted 2-0 silk suture.

Common Errors, Continued

Lay (lays, laying, laid) vs. **lie (lies, lying).** To *lay* something down is to place it or put it somewhere. To *lie* is to rest in a horizontal position.

I asked the patient to *lay* her purse on the counter so that I could carry out the physical examination, but she refused to let go of it and would not *lie* back on the table.

The patient is worried that she may have Alzheimer's because she *lays* her keys in places where she can't find them.

She was advised to *lie* in a recumbent position with the head of the bed elevated to avoid gastroesophageal reflux.

I told the patient to get up slowly after *lying* down to avoid another postural hypotension episode.

Sit vs. **set.** To *set* something down is to place it somewhere. It is analogous to *lay.* To *sit* is to be seated.

The nurse *set* the surgical pack too close to the edge of the counter, and the contents spilled onto the floor.

I asked the patient to *sit* back in the chair as far as possible and look up at the ceiling.

This child would not *sit* still long enough for me to get a look at his fundi.

Worksheet

Circle the correct word in parentheses.

1. If the trauma (affects, effects) the emotions, then the reactions, the attitude, and the patient's performance will suffer.

2. During the hospitalization, the patient's (affect, effect) became more appropriate, although he still had some loose associations noted on mental status examination shortly preceding discharge.

3. To (affect, effect) a cure requires compliance from the patient.

4. There are multiple side (affects, effects) to this treatment.

5. There were no unexpected side (affects, effects) or complications of the therapy.

6. Approximately six sutures of 10-0 Vicryl were placed in the epineurium of the nerve to (affect, effect) an end-to-end anastomosis.

7. There has been a resurgence of measles, one of the childhood diseases easily prevented by vaccination, due to ignorance and the fear of side (affects, effects) of vaccination.

8. The medication as delivered by the Pulmo-Aide is much more (affective, effective) than the metered-dose inhalers.

9. Bed rest, leg elevation, and warm heat to the (affected, effected) leg was ordered for at least 7 days.

10. Triamcinolone cream 0.1% to be applied t.i.d. as needed to all (affected, effected) areas to control itch was prescribed.

11. The patient experienced a dizzy feeling and was asked to (lie, lay) down on the examining room table.

12. He was asked to give a clean urine specimen and (set, sit) it on the counter for the technician.

13. The patient was asked to (lie, lay) back and (set, sit) the pillow under his knees.

14. On proverb testing, the patient had an inappropriate response to "let sleeping dogs (lie, lay)".

15. I (then, than) measured the leg lengths, and it was apparent that the right leg was about an inch shorter (then, than) the left.

Commas

The appropriate use of commas has caused more ongoing debate and frustration than any other single issue in medical transcription. This is because there are only a few inflexible rules that govern comma use—in other words, there are many exceptions. Complicating the issue is that commas can be added for clarity in almost any instance, and in addition, comma rules can change over the years. It's no wonder that students especially seem to be plagued by indecision when it comes to comma choices!

The most important thing to remember is that commas take the place of pauses and variations in pitch in spoken English. They help to clarify meaning of written English. A comma signals a small interruption in the flow of the sentence comparable to the slight drop in pitch that occurs when a sentence is spoken or read aloud. Sometimes it helps to speak the written sentence to see where natural inflections of the voice occur; this can help determine where a comma should be placed in the written sentence.

Following are some basic comma rules, but note that there are often alternatives, exceptions, or rationales given.

1. Use a comma to separate two independent clauses (complete sentences) joined by a coordinating conjunction (*and, but, for, nor, or, so, yet*).

    The patient complains of difficulty finding the right word, but he denies any extremity weakness.

    Either the chemistry panel results are erroneous, or this patient's electrolytes are completely off the scale.

2. Use a comma to separate nouns in a series.

    The pancreas is of the usual size, shape, and consistency.
    or:
    The pancreas is of the usual size, shape and consistency.

    LABORATORY DATA: CBC: Hemoglobin 12, hematocrit 36, WBC 10,000, with 62 polys, 30 lymphs, 1 eosinophil, and 7 monos.

3. Use a comma to separate coordinate adjectives in a series, even when the adjectives follow the noun they are modifying.

    The tracheobronchial tree is partly filled with turbid, gray mucoid material.

    This loquacious, vivacious, well-dressed female had no specific complaints.

    Mr. Peters called his wife an interfering, domineering, hen-pecking heart-attack producer.

Commas, Continued

The hypertrophic scar at the present time is relatively quiescent, uninflamed, and non-symptomatic.

On her right mid lower back, she has a medium-brown, clinically benign, sharply marginated, evenly colored nevus, dermal in character, with normal skin lines.

Final diagnosis: Fracture of humerus, comminuted, right.

But, commas are *not* needed in the following adjective series:

Minor old healed granulomatous disease residuals appear stable.

There is *a moderate-sized direct sliding-type diaphragmatic* hernia with a prominent Schatzki's ring and moderate gastric reflux, with some lower esophageal segment spasm suggesting recent reflux esophagitis.

4. Use a comma to separate phrases in a series.

   She has had no urinary frequency, no blood in the urine, no flank pain, chills, or nausea, but she has been anorexic.

   This is a 49-year-old white male with a 2-year history of episodes of lightheadedness, an 18-month history of extreme fatigue, a 1-year history of a funny feeling in his right arm and numbness in his face, and a 2- to 3-month history of labile emotions and episodes of crying.

   Past traumas include a sprained wrist, a torn knee cartilage on the left, and an injury to her left eye during a shoe fight at school.

5. Use a comma to separate clauses in a series.

   She cries a lot, she gets angry over little things, and she throws things.

   Her underwear is of a heavy stretch type, they contain 12% spandex, and portions of her brassiere panels contain 16% spandex.

   The patient had a total protein of 5.4, albumin level was 3.2, chloride was 106, and total bilirubin was 1.2.

6. Use a comma after introductory adverb clauses.

   Unless the scar begins to enlarge, I would leave it alone.

   If the stone cannot be mobilized downward, push-back and extracorporeal shock wave lithotripsy might be considered.

Commas, Continued

7. Use a comma after introductory prepositional or participial phrases to prevent misreading. Commas are often omitted after introductory prepositional phrases if no misreading will result.

    On abdominal examination the patient has a healthy-appearing colostomy.
    or
    On abdominal examination, the patient has a healthy-appearing colostomy.

    Because of its increasing size, the possibility of malignancy of the thyroid had to be considered.

    Viewing the chest wall, I noted the patient to have subcostal-intercostal retractions.

    Even with ambulation in the halls, he had no significant chest pain, dizziness, or shortness of breath.

8. Commas have traditionally been used after introductory transitional expressions and conjunctive adverbs (*consequently, therefore*). Note, however, that there is a trend toward eliminating the comma if the introductory word can be moved to another part of the sentence with no comma.

    Apparently this man had two previous episodes of left-sided ureteral colic followed by spontaneous passage of stones.
    (This man apparently had two previous episodes of left-sided ureteral colic followed by spontaneous passage of stones. Note that the word apparently can be moved without the need for a comma.)
    or
    Apparently, this man had two previous episodes of left-sided ureteral colic followed by spontaneous passage of stones.

    Subsequently a CBC on April 2 showed her white count had increased to 20,100; hemoglobin and hematocrit remained stable, as did platelet count.
    (A CBC on April 2 subsequently showed her white count had increased to 20,100; hemoglobin and hematocrit remained stable, as did platelet count. A comma is not needed when the word is moved.)
    or
    Subsequently, a CBC on April 2 showed her white count had increased to 20,100; hemoglobin and hematocrit remained stable, as did platelet count.

    Distally, we allowed a several-centimeter margin of tumor-free colon and identified a site proximal to the peritoneal reflection within the rectum for distal transection.
    (To move the word distally could result in a change in medical meaning; therefore, the comma is retained.)

Commas, Continued

Approximately a year and a half ago, immediately concomitant with her radiation therapy, she developed a persistent and intensely pruritic dermatitis at the radiation port on the midchest.
(The comma after *ago* is retained to separate the two transitional expressions.)

9. Use a comma after an introductory *yes* or *no*.

   To reiterate, yes, I do believe that the patient is experiencing abdominal angina.
   No, the patient will not be admitted at this time.

10. Use a comma before and after nonessential (nonrestrictive) words, phrases, or parenthetical expressions or before a nonessential phrase or parenthetical expression that comes at the end of a sentence.

   There has been a resurgence of measles, which is one of the childhood diseases that are easily prevented by vaccination, due to fear of side effects of vaccination and ignorance.

   I have advised her that these reactions are quite rare, about one in 15,000 patients.

   The patient is scheduled for elective hip replacement surgery at 7:00 a.m. Monday, provided that his preadmission preoperative lab studies are acceptable.

   Essential elements are *not* set off by commas.

   Richard Jones is one of those patients whom we classify as drug-dependent and who are always seeking Demerol in the E.R.

   The patient whom you sent over to my office on Wednesday never showed up.

   Note: Expressions such as *also, too, of course, perhaps, at least, therefore,* and *likewise* are not set off by commas if they cause little or no pause in reading.

   The patient was therefore transferred to a regular bed.
   Epstein-Barr nuclear antigen was also positive at 1:40.

11. Use a comma before and after a nonessential clause within a sentence.

   Intravenous pyelography is requested in this 28-year-old female, who is recently status post cholecystectomy, because of a history of Bright's disease at age 10.

   Mr. Goodweather, whom you asked me to see in consultation, is cleared medically for orthopedic surgery.

Commas, Continued

In very rare cases these tumors have, when uncontrolled, resulted in a patient's death.

The stomach and duodenum, which usually lie in the left abdomen and epigastrium, are rarely felt unless they are involved with large tumors.

12. Use a comma to set off an absolute phrase if within a sentence, after an absolute phrase if at the beginning of a sentence, or before an absolute phrase if at the end of a sentence. An absolute phrase consists of a noun or pronoun followed by a participle and all the words associated with it. It is a grammatically unconnected part of a sentence that may function much like an adverb clause, but does not have the structure of an adverb clause.

The patient will be discharged Saturday morning, condition permitting.

Condition permitting, the patient will be discharged Saturday morning.

The patient was examined twice, by Dr. James in the morning and Dr. Oliver at night.

13. Use a comma before and after a nonessential appositive word or phrase. An appositive restates a noun. It may be nonessential or nonrestrictive if it adds additional but nonessential details about the noun. If it limits the noun by identifying which one or ones, it is essential; use no punctuation before or after it.

Dr. Alexander, an allergist, is board-certified.

She returns now, 20 days later, approximately one month postop, and demonstrates a healed wound and an excellent range of motion.

We outlined the surgery and the hopeful gains thereof, and she opted for surgery, namely, lateral retinacular release and VMO advancement.

14. Use a comma before and after contrasted elements within a sentence or before a contrasted element at the end of a sentence.

Fungal cultures grew yeast, not thought to be *Candida albicans*.

I have reviewed some, but not all, of his medical records from the factory and have examined documents shown to me by him.

The mother has been informed of possible complications including, but not limited to, death.

The bladder was left intact, not removed.

Commas, Continued

15. Use a comma before and after states when preceded by a city name, and countries when preceded by a state or city name.

    The patient underwent a battery of diagnostic tests at the Mayo Clinic in Rochester, Minnesota, before moving to California.

    When vacationing in Athens, Greece, the patient suffered from severe angina.

16. Use a comma before and after the year in a date when preceded by month and day. Do not use a comma with the year preceded only by the month or when used alone.

    This 24-year-old woman was seen in consultation on June 12, 1996, for repeated bouts of angina.

    The patient was seen twice in June 1996 for repeated bouts of angina.

17. Use a comma in addresses to separate street address from city, and city from state when used in a sentence. No punctuation is used between state and zip code, however.

    The patient has an appointment at the eye clinic at 125 South Main Street, Oakville, CA 95391, on Wednesday, June 18, 1996, at 2:00 p.m.

18. Use a comma in direct address. This use is rare in general medical dictation, but is used frequently in consultation or referral letters from one physician to another.

    Thank you, Dr. Taylor, for asking me to see this patient.

19. Occasionally, a comma may be required for emphasis or to prevent misreading, even though it is not required by any of the principles discussed above.

    IMPRESSION: Velopharyngeal closure is inadequate, with a residual small ovoid opening.

    A 5 French Mani catheter was used, and selective injections of right and left common carotid arteries were performed, with film of the head and neck.

    IMPRESSION: No significant interval change since previous study, with persistent cardiomegaly and subsegmental bibasilar atelectasis.

    They are all hemorrhagic, pinkish tissues with no consistent shape or size, of a firm texture.

    DIAGNOSIS: Hydatid of Morgagni, right.

Commas, Continued

The previous scan also revealed a very small *nodule* in the posterior segment of the right upper lobe, *which* also appears to be small in size on the present study.

(The nonrestrictive clauses above, *which is calcified* and *which also appears . . .* , are set off by commas because the antecedent of the relative pronoun *which* is *nodule*, not *lobe*.)

Unnecessary commas. Many people use unnecessary commas. Although a comma ordinarily signals a pause, not every pause needs a comma. If you use too many commas, check to make sure one of the principles noted above applies before inserting a comma.

The misplacement (or misuse) of commas is frequently due to one of the errors discussed below.

1. Do not separate the subject from its verb or a verb from its object with a comma.

    Incorrect: The dog that bit the <u>boy</u>, was quarantined for six weeks anyway.
    Correct: The dog that bit the boy was quarantined for six weeks anyway.

2. Do not use a comma before a coordinating conjunction joining any words or phrases other than independent clauses. It is, however, correct to use a comma before a coordinating conjunction and the last item in a series. This comma is usually optional unless it is needed to avoid misreading. Do not use a comma after a coordinating conjunction.

    Correct: The patient complains of difficulty finding the right word, yet he denies any extremity weakness.

3. Do not use a comma to set off necessary (restrictive) clauses, phrases, appositive, or short words and phrases that are not clearly parenthetical.

    Incorrect: <u>Perhaps</u>, mammography screening should be done every two years instead of every year.
    Correct: Perhaps mammography screening should be done every two years instead of every year.

4. Do not use a comma before the first item in a series or after the last item in a series.

    Correct: Examination of the submental, anterior, and posterior lymph nodes was negative.

5. Do not use a comma to join two independent clauses (without a coordinating conjunction). This is called a comma splice. A semicolon is used to join two independent clauses without a conjunction.

    Incorrect: He is on no oral medicine, he is in good health.
    Correct: He is on no oral medicine; he is in good health.

160

Worksheet

Insert commas where appropriate in the following sentences, and circle the commas.

1. He had 95 units of insulin the day prior to admission and I believe 80 units of combined NPH and regular insulin the day of admission.

2. He is showing more comedo formation and a higher proportion of pustular lesions than before and he now has a scattering of cysts over his upper back.

3. He has been on Pernox and Komed for about 2 months with no improvement; in fact he is showing more comedo formation and a higher proportion of pustular lesions than before.

4. He is on no oral medicine and he is in good health.

5. Approximately 20% of the lesions show some inflammatory reaction and some deep cysts are now palpable on the forehead and over the scapulae.

6. He was given his first allergy injection and he was made fully aware of all the problems related to injections.

7. Bacterial cultures grew mixed flora including *Pseudomonas lactobacillus* and group D streptococci.

8. Fungal cultures grew yeast not thought to be *Candida albicans*.

9. He was started on treatment with ephedrine Periactin and Sinequan and his hives are almost but not completely gone.

10. His urticaria has not been present for longer than 3 months; therefore I have elected to treat him only with drug therapy.

11. His hives seem to have almost cleared and I think that we should continue his drug therapy for a period of time before pursuing any further evaluation.

12. She was treated with both penicillin and prednisone and I have now followed her for a period of 2 months.

13. Her symptoms have completely cleared and there has been no recurrence; this is an alteration of the previous pattern in which she had episodes about every 2 to 3 weeks.

Worksheet Continues

Worksheet, Continued

14. This patient returned today with a spreading rash on her shoulders upper chest and back which has been present for over the last couple of months.

15. The patient is not a good historian and states only that the eruption started about 3 months ago and it is occasionally pruritic.

16. There is no nodule irregularity or active lesion and the recent biopsy site is well healed.

17. Examination of the submental anterior and posterior lymph nodes was negative.

18. These metastases have been treated with a combination of radiation plus tamoxifen and she has done really quite well.

19. Approximately a year and a half ago immediately concomitant with her radiation therapy she developed a persistent and intensely pruritic dermatitis at the radiation port on the mid-chest.

20. The scar is well healed and there is no evidence of local or deep recurrence.

21. I have advised her that I do not feel this eruption is related to her previous breast carcinoma and I definitely do not feel that there is any relationship to her tamoxifen therapy.

22. Under local anesthesia it was aspirated of the typical clear gelatinous material and a small amount of Kenalog was injected into the cyst.

23. It is suspected that the cyst will recur and if it does the cyst will be excised.

24. Patient agrees to surgery and we will make the necessary arrangements for his admission later next week.

25. Delay in having this done can result in a less satisfactory cosmetic result and greater expense and if it is delayed long enough could result in a tumor which becomes unresectable and could lead to severe disfigurement.

26. In very rare cases these tumors have when uncontrolled resulted in a patient's death.

27. The patient had a total protein of 5.4 albumin level was 3.2 chloride was 106 and a total bilirubin was 1.2.

Worksheet Continues

Worksheet, Continued

28. The patient was sent to whirlpool daily and patient tolerated this procedure very well.

29. This patient is instructed to return home and I wrote an order for Home Health to consult and help in the care of this decubitus ulcer.

30. I tried to convince his mother that he should be there and his mother was even more adamant that the patient should return home.

31. I instructed both the patient and the mother that there could be severe sequelae to having a large open sore of this type and after a great deal of discussion it was clear that this patient refused to follow my suggestions.

32. There is no history of lymphadenopathy and judging from the chart she has been afebrile.

33. Exam today shows a temperature of 37°C a blood pressure of 130/70 a respiratory rate of 20 and a pulse rate of 60.

34. After sterile preparation the two blisters were aspirated 0.2 cc of fluid was taken out and this was sent for Gram stain and culture.

35. The patient had a Gram stain done yesterday and it does show gram-positive cocci.

36. He is to take prednisone 40 mg q.a.m. for 3 days 20 mg x 3 days 10 mg x 3 days 5 mg x 3 days 2.5 mg x 4 days and then off.

37. The hypertrophic scar is at the present time relatively quiescent uninflamed and nonsymptomatic.

38. Examination reveals eczematous dermatitis that shows a fairly definite pattern over her buttock area low midback and shoulders.

39. I told the patient to switch to cotton underwear with as little elastic as possible do not bleach them and be sure that they do not contain spandex.

40. She was treated with multiple topical agents including miconazole Nizoral and Loprox.

41. It is noted however that the patient only used Loprox for about 3 months and no debridement was done.

Worksheet, Continued

42. The other nails toe webs and soles are clear.

43. I have advised her that these reactions are quite rare about one in 15,000 patients and this would be at present our only available medication.

44. A chemistry panel is to be done prior to onset of therapy 3 weeks from now and she is to return for follow-up in 6 weeks.

45. Medications on admission were Procardia Mellaril Aldactone Glucotrol and hydrochloro-thiazide.

46. The CBC was normal and she will see her private dentist on discharge.

47. This 27-year-old woman has complaints of being overweight recurrent kidney and bladder infections and intermittent fungal infections in body crevices.

48. Urological evaluation revealed a blockage in the right ureter and this was "cleaned out" cystoscopically at which time scar tissue was found.

49. Her right ureter is apparently open now and the pain has disappeared.

50. Her recent health is good and she denies recent upper respiratory infection.

Semicolons

Semicolons are stronger marks of punctuation than commas, but not as strong as periods. They signal a more significant pause in speech than commas. Often, it may appear that periods could be used in place of semicolons to separate two main clauses, but too many simple sentences in a row create a choppy, artificial rhythm that can be jarring whether read silently or spoken aloud.

In order to use semicolons properly, you need to be able to distinguish between main (independent) and subordinate clauses and between phrases and clauses. Review the sections on clauses and phrases if you are uncertain about them. The semicolon is used only between closely related coordinate elements. If two main clauses are not closely related and are not joined by a conjunction, a period would be more appropriate than a semicolon.

Errors in semicolon use usually involve the linking of sentence parts of unequal grammatical rank. Do not use a semicolon between a clause and a phrase or between a main (independent) clause and a subordinate clause.

1. Use a semicolon to join two closely related independent clauses not linked by a coordinating conjunction.

   Left ureteral stricture was dilated; there were no stones apparent.

   Neutrogena T/Gel shampoo is to be used on a daily basis with Diprolene lotion to be applied b.i.d. until clear; 2 ounces was dispensed plus 3 refills.

   We have already gone through her laundry products; these have been either eliminated or changed.

   This 60-year-old male states he has had a problem retracting the foreskin for some time; it is getting much worse.

   Does not smoke; quit about 12 years ago.
   (The subjects [the patient] of these two independent clauses are understood.)

   Note: Failure to punctuate at all between two independent clauses is called a fused or run-on sentence. This is a serious error.

2. Use a semicolon to join two independent clauses linked by a conjunctive adverb or a transitional phrase.

   His physical examination revealed that his liver extended 3 to 4 fingerbreadths below the right costal margin and was firm; however, no other signs of liver disease, namely, spider angiomata or palmar erythema, were present.

Semicolons, Continued

He has very little or no wrist flexion; however, he does have some wrist extension.

His urine was infected with 4+ bacteria; of course, this patient has had a chronic urinary tract infection.

3. Use a semicolon to separate items in a series when one or more of the phrases in a series contain an internal comma. This is often necessary in medical transcription when multiple prescriptions (drugs, dosages, and instructions) are dictated.

    Histalog-stimulated gastric analysis revealed fasting free HCl 40 mEq/L; 15 minutes, 75 mEq/L; 30 minutes, 70 mEq/L; 45 minutes, 55 mEq/L; 60 minutes, 53 mEq/L.

    I examined her underwear today; they are of a heavy stretch type, they contain 12% spandex, and portions of her brassiere panels contain 16% spandex.

    The patient is a 16-year-old gravida 1, para 0, menarche at age 13, whose last normal menstrual period was March 11, who had a positive beta hCG; previous to that, normal menstrual cycles every 8 days.
    (Here, the semicolon is needed for clarity simply because the sentence is so complex and has so many commas.)

Worksheet

In the following sentences, place semicolons in place of the commas where appropriate, and circle the semicolons.

1. There is no family history of renal lithiasis, gout, or bone or joint disease, however, he is adopted.

2. Allergy to sulfa, her mouth breaks out from this.

3. Patient says he voids about 15 times during the day and at least every 2 hours at night, most of the time, it is more than that.

4. The foreskin has been freed up, however, adhesions recur.

5. Bladder was left intact, not removed, it was very tiny and scarred in.

6. Physical examination was significant for grade 2/4 left flank and left lower abdominal tenderness, otherwise, physical examination was within normal limits.

7. Test results were within normal limits with the following important exceptions: serum iron was 45, which is low, TIBC was 433, which is high, and percent iron saturation was 10, which is low.

8. She has been seen in second opinion, her insurance requires that.

9. There was no esophageal stricture, instead, the distal esophagus seemed soft and mobile and permitted easy passage of the 10 mm esophagoscope.

10. X-rays show a large deviation at the metatarsophalangeal joint of the great toe, otherwise, there are no specific signs of degenerative arthritis.

11. There was no obvious instability, however, because of the persistent pain, an x-ray was taken.

12. She had some evidence of subluxation by history, at least, she describes these episodes.

13. The patient indicated he may have fractured the same hand in the past, however, he did not seek treatment at that time.

14. His potassium was 5.0 and sodium 136, chloride was 102 with a total CO_2 of 27.

15. This 65-year-old man is admitted to the hospital drunken but with multiple premature ventricular beats, this is the primary reason.

Worksheet Continues

Worksheet, Continued

16. Her medications include Medrol 4 mg, one tablet a day, Lasix 20 mg a day, Micro-K 10 mEq q.d., #28, as well as Zantac 150 mg p.o. b.i.d., #14, doxycycline 100 mg p.o. q.d. x 14 days, verapamil 80 mg, #30, and Proventil inhaler 2 puffs q.i.d., 2 inhalers, 6 refills.

17. There is no periareolar hair, however, she has a well-developed male escutcheon. (This female patient has hyperthyroidism.)

18. MEDICATIONS: Allopurinol 100 mg b.i.d., Lasix 160 mg a.m., 120 mg p.m., Feldene 20 mg q.a.m., Metamucil 2 tablespoons h.s., Darvocet-N 100, one every 4 to 6 hours p.r.n. pain, Dalmane 15 mg h.s., nitroglycerin 0.4 mg sublingually p.r.n. chest pain, Micro-K 10 mEq 1 to 3 times per day, Cardizem 60 mg q.i.d., and Isordil 30 mg q.i.d.

19. There was some mild bleeding from the tenaculum site, otherwise, the procedure was performed without complication.

20. The dog was removed from the house with no change in the patient's symptoms, indeed, there was some progression of his symptoms.

Hyphens

Next to commas, hyphens probably cause more confusion and frustration than any other mark in the English language, possibly because there are so few hard and fast rules for their use. In general, they are probably overused, especially since the trend today is to use fewer hyphens rather than more.

Hyphens are used to connect words together, either temporarily or permanently. Temporary hyphens help prevent ambiguity and clarify meanings. Compound adjectives used before a noun fall into this category. Some words, such as *mother-in-law*, are permanently hyphenated.

Compound adjectives. In general, use a hyphen when two or more words are used as a single modifier before a noun. In many cases, it is helpful to say the adjective-noun phrase with each modifying word alone. For example, if you are considering the phrase 18-year-old white female, *white* obviously modifies *female* and so can be used alone, but *18 female, year female,* or *old female* do not make much sense. (It is unlikely that a physician would dictate *old female* without the specific age.)

Another technique that is sometimes helpful is to mentally insert the word *and* between each adjective. For example, read the phrase as *18 and year and old and white female.* The only adjective that makes sense read that way is *white*; the others obviously need to be read as a unit.

Hyphens in Compound Modifiers

1. Hyphenate compounds that consist of a noun plus a present or past participle (the *-ing* or *-ed* forms of a verb) when the compound is used as an adjective and precedes the noun it modifies. These are often called temporary compounds because the words form a compound for a specific function but are not permanently joined.

   The patient had steroid-induced moon facies.

   Provisional diagnosis was an aldosterone-producing tumor.

   I would be very hesitant to give her sulfonamide-based diuretics or any sulfa-type drugs in the future. (Sulfonamide-based is a noun-adjective compound. Compounds including the suffix *-type* are always hyphenated, thus sulfa-type.)

   Histalog-stimulated gastric analysis revealed fasting free HCl 40 mEq/L; 15 minutes, 75 mEq/L; 30 minutes, 70 mEq/L; 45 minutes, 55 mEq/L; 60 minutes, 53 mEq/L.

   The patient has had asthma, basically exercise-induced, since age 2.

Hyphens, Continued

2. Use a hyphen in adjective compounds that consist of an adverb not ending in *-ly* plus a present or past participle when the compound precedes the noun it modifies.

> This well-developed, well-nourished patient complains of chronic, unremitting cough.
> The patient is well developed and well nourished.

> This well-known politician collapsed as he was debating his opponent on *Face the Nation*.
> *But:* This patient is well known to me.

> On examination today, there is a well-healed 1.25 cm scar on the left lower lip.
> *Note:* Although you will see later that English measurement dimensions (*a jagged 2-inch scar*) used as modifiers are hyphenated, the hyphen is usually omitted when the dimension is expressed as a metric whole number or a metric whole number plus fraction, as in *1 cm scar* or *1.25 cm scar* above.

> Prescription was written for the above-mentioned medications.

> ABDOMEN: Well-healed inguinal herniorrhaphy scar.

> I have seen the above-named patient for several visits since her colonoscopy.

Note: Do not use a hyphen in adverb-adjective combinations when the adverb ends in *-ly*.

> The patient complained of an intensely painful lesion on her lower back.

> The squamous cell carcinoma was excised, and clearly delineated margins were noted on frozen section.

Note: Be careful that you do not mistake an adjective ending in *–ly* for an adverb.

> The patient had a ghostly-white complexion.
> (*Ghostly* is an adjective.)

3. Use a hyphen in adjectival compound phrases preceding the nouns they modify.

> An end-to-end anastomosis was performed.
> (*But:* The anastomosis was performed end to end.)

> He has developed dark-colored lesions in the edge of a burn scar overlying the clavicle.

> Follow-up cystogram was performed that revealed a moderate postvoid residual and a left-sided bladder diverticulum.

Hyphens, Continued

Double-voided a.m. urine specimen showed specific gravity of 1.014 with an osmolality of 602, sodium of 174 mEq/L, and creatinine of 43 mg/dl.

A high-pitched holosystolic murmur was heard over the precordium. (*Note*: Most *high-* and *low-* adjectival compounds are hyphenated.)

4. Use a hyphen in a noun-adjective or adjective-noun compound when it precedes the word it modifies.

    It is difficult to overdose on water-soluble vitamins.
    But: Vitamin C is water soluble.

    The diagnosis was low-renin hypertension.
    Meaning: The hypertension was associated with low levels of renin.
    But: His hypertension was associated with low renin activity.
    Meaning: Renin activity was low, not activity was low renin.

    The patient lives in a second-floor apartment and has been having trouble getting up the stairs due to shortness of breath.
    But: The patient's apartment is on the second floor.

    The infant was placed on high-frequency jet ventilation.
    But: The infant was placed on jet ventilation at a high frequency.

    The patient has been using metered-dose inhalers for her chronic obstructive pulmonary disease.

    Optional: Chest x-ray was suspicious for small-cell (or small cell) lung cancer.
    But giant cell carcinoma; large cell carcinoma; basal cell carcinoma

5. Hyphenate a combination of two nouns used as a unit to modify a noun when they precede the noun they modify.

    A good physician-patient relationship is essential.

    The risk-benefit ratio was explained to the patient and her family.

    Note: It would be improper to use virgules (slash marks) in the above examples; virgules indicate a separation, not a joining.

6. Hyphenate compounds consisting of two or more adjectives used coordinately or as conflicting terms whether they precede the noun or follow the predicate as an adjective complement.

    The patient has a long history of manic-depressive episodes.

Hyphens, Continued

The Central Columbia Cardiology group participated in a double-blind study of Cardura, an antihypertensive.

The HIV antigen study was false-positive.

The Cardura study protocol was double-blind.

7. Use a hyphen to form all compounds beginning with the prefixes *all-*, *self-*, and *ex-* whether they precede or follow the noun.

The patient reported to the emergency department after having been beaten up by her ex-husband.

The following impressions are not all-inclusive and are tentative at best.

The patient appeared self-assured, but I believe this was just a front.

8. Hyphenate adjective compounds indicating color when the two words are of equal weight.

The child had blue-black bruises on his back and the backs of his legs.
(*But:* The skin lesions were reddish tan.) (*Reddish* and *tan* are not equal.)

The patient's green contact lenses made her eyes appear blue-green.

9. Hyphenate a compound modifier in which the first word is a number or letter when it precedes the noun it modifies.

This ninth-grade young man was injured this afternoon at football practice.

I explained to the patient that recovery was a two-way process; I had to do my part, but he had to comply with my instructions.

The patient had a 4-week history of intermittent headaches.

There was a 30-pack-year history of cigarette smoking.

The patient claims to have had a 3- to 4-month interval with no symptoms, only to relapse 2 weeks ago.

DIAGNOSIS: A 4 cm V-shaped laceration, radial aspect of left index finger, sutured.

Hyphens, Continued

10. Hyphenate a compound modifier consisting of an abbreviation followed by a word.

    The allergic reaction may be an IgE-mediated reaction.

    It is my impression that the patient has probable NSAID-induced peptic ulcer disease.

    She was placed in immobilization and started on quad-strengthening exercises.

Hyphens with Prefixes

1. Hyphenate a compound modifier consisting of a prefix followed by a capitalized word, an abbreviation, a number, or a letter.

    The patient is a member of the pro-Serbian forces who stepped on a land mine and was sent to the United States for reconstructive surgery.

    The patient has a long history of non-Hodgkin's lymphoma.

    Anti-RNA antigen was not detected on the lab study.

2. Use a hyphen after a prefix if the prefix applies to a following phrase rather than a single word. Similarly, use a hyphen after a word that modifies a phrase.

    The pathology report revealed non-small-cell lung cancer.

    Note: References are inconsistent when hyphenating phrases such as in the examples above. One well-respected medical dictionary has *non-small cell lung cancer* in one location, but *small-cell lung cancer* in another and *small cell lung cancer* in yet another. The rules above, however, are widely accepted; also, you should be consistent in typing a phrase the same way each time in a report.

    Style Note: In a phrase such as *non–small-cell carcinoma*, if your word processor allows it, you may use an en dash for the first hyphen and a regular hyphen for the second. Similarly, when a word modifies an entire phrase, an en dash may be used instead of a hyphen.

3. A hyphen is occasionally used after a prefix or before a suffix when omitting the hyphen would result in a combination of two of the same vowels or three of the same consonants (e.g., *semi-independent, salpingo-oophorectomy, shell-like, post-traumatic*). However, the use of a hyphen to avoid the combination of two vowels or consonants is rapidly declining. It is best to consult an English or medical dictionary for the proper use or non-use of a hyphen with such compounds.

Hyphens, Continued

4. Sometimes hyphens are used after prefixes for clarity or ease of pronunciation when two or more prefixes are appended to a single word.

    non–small-cell carcinoma
    non-insulin-dependent diabetes mellitus

Hyphens in Compound Nouns

1. Hyphenate a combination of two nouns of equal weight used as a single noun.

    Chemotherapy-radiotherapy is outlined below.

2. Use a hyphen with most noun-preposition compounds.
   (*Note:* Refer to the latest edition of a good collegiate dictionary if uncertain.)

    The patient started out as a looker-on to a fight but somehow ended up being punched by an unknown assailant.

    There was a tie-up in surgery that delayed Mr. Franklin's operation for four hours.

    But: workup, checkup, flareup, onlooker, passerby

   Note: *Webster's Collegiate Dictionary* lists *follow-up* (with a hyphen) as a noun and an adjective and *follow up* as a verb. While the *American Heritage Dictionary* lists *followup* as an acceptable alternative to *follow-up* as both noun and adjective, *followup* is not yet widely used. There are some practitioners who use *followup* as a noun and *follow-up* as an adjective. The verb form, however, is always two words (i.e., *follow up*) as is the verb form of *work up*, *check up*, and *flare up*, the latter usually used in the past tense form (e.g., *His fever flared up*). *Workup, checkup*, and *flareup* are not used as adjectives.

3. Hyphens are used with some compounds in which the first word is a possessive. Check a dictionary if you are unsure whether to hyphenate.

    The patient came in wanting to have "something done about my crow's-feet."

Hyphens with Spelled-out Numbers

1. Hyphenate spelled-out fractions used as adjectives but not as nouns, compound ordinal and cardinal numbers when written out, and spelled-out numerals from 21 to 99 (ninety-nine, thirty-three).

    The I.V. bag was two-thirds full.

Hyphens, Continued

"Ninety-first birthdays don't come around too often," the patient stated.

Forty-five patients were enrolled in the study to receive Cardura and another 45 to receive the placebo.

Note: If two or more hyphenated compounds are used consecutively and contain the same base, you may omit the base in all but the last compound. For nonhyphenated compounds, however, most medical language authorities do not approve of omitting the base and using a hyphen after the prefix, although certain nonmedical publishing references accept the practice.

The first-, second-, and third-shift nurses all had trouble satisfying this difficult patient.

The patient has 10- and 12-year-old brothers.

But: Preoperative and postoperative (*not* pre- and postoperative) laboratory studies were unremarkable.

Hyphens with Numbers or Letters

1. Use a hyphen to indicate the space or spaces between one vertebra and another and between some letter-letter, number-letter, and letter-number compounds (such as lab tests). Hyphenate a number-word compound. Numbers followed by *-odd* are hyphenated.

   Diagnostic studies were performed including electrocardiogram, CPK-MB via electrophoresis, and chemistry-21.

   Myelogram revealed a herniated disk at L5-S1.

   On spirometry, FEV-1 achieves 3.24 L or 72% of predicted after 12% improvement with bronchodilator; FEV-1/FVC ratio was mildly increased at 85 instead of predicted 82.

   The patient would only admit that she was 40-odd years old.

Note: The use of a hyphen to signify a range between one number and another is universally accepted, though many prefer to write the word *to.*

   She was discharged on Toradol 10 mg 3-4 times a day as needed.

Note: The physician dictates the word *to* between the numbers. The word *to* means from one number up to but not including the second number; *through* means from one number up to and including the second number. A hyphen may never be substituted for the word *through* in a range of numbers.

Hyphens, Continued

Hyphens to Avoid Ambiguity

1. Use a hyphen to avoid ambiguity or confusion in meaning of a phrase.

    A large-bore needle was selected.

2. Use a hyphen after a prefix when, if omitted, the word would have a different meaning.

    I am going to re-treat this patient with prednisone because of a good but incomplete response to the previous treatment.
    Also: re-create, re-perfusion

When Not to Use Hyphens

Most prefixes are joined to roots *without* the use of a hyphen. These prefixes include *ante-, anti-, bi-, co-, contra-, counter-, de-, extra-, infra-, inter-, intra-, micro-, mid-, non-, over-, pre-, post-, pro-, pseudo-, re-, semi-, sub-, super-, supra-, trans-, tri-, ultra-, un-,* and *under.* This rule is most frequently abused with the prefixes *non-* and *un-.* Don't fall prey to this mistake. A common exception is when the last letter of the prefix is the same as the first letter of the root word, resulting in confusion if a hyphen is omitted (*anti-inflammatory*).

The following suffixes are not preceded by a hyphen unless foregoing a hyphen would create an awkward combination of repetitive letters: *-fold, -hood, -less, -like, -wise.*

   cardiacwise, formless, gluelike, threefold

Do not hyphenate groups of words commonly considered a unit or names of disease entities used as modifiers.

grand mal seizures	hyaline membrane disease
basal cell carcinoma	sickle cell disease

Hyphens to Mark Word Division

Probably every printed publication (newspapers, magazines, and so forth) uses hyphens to divide words at the end of a line. End-of-line hyphenation and full-justified line format are discouraged in medical reports because reports are easier to read and meaning is more readily conveyed without divided words. If your teacher or supervisor endorses end-of-line hyphenation, be sure to consult reputable English and medical dictionaries or spellers for correct hyphenation. The automatic hyphenation inserted by most word processors is probably the least useful and most error-prone feature.

176

Worksheet

Place hyphens correctly in the following sentences, and circle the hyphens. Some sentences may not need hyphens.

1. This youngish, 20 odd year old female was admitted in acute distress.

2. The patient claims to have followed an 800 calorie diet for the last 3 months but with no weight loss.

3. I recommended a high fiber diet.

4. A 3 cm incision was made over the seventh rib.

5. He is to use his thigh length TED hose on his left lower extremity.

6. The albumin globulin ratio was 4.5 over 1.5 or 3.0.

7. X rays of the abdomen showed small air fluid levels and one dilated loop of small bowel.

8. The patient is a 28 year old African American male admitted with an infected human bite on the right hand.

9. HEENT was remarkable only for a high arched palate and moist mucous membranes.

10. I recommended that the patient discontinue regular aspirin and placed her on Ecotrin, an enteric coated aspirin, instead.

11. She does have a high pitched systolic murmur of mitral insufficiency at the apex of the heart.

12. IMPRESSION: Right sided pleural effusion, most likely on the basis of congestive heart failure.

13. There is a grade 2 to 3 low pitched aortic ejection systolic murmur heard best during expiration.

14. It is doubtful that the last mentioned diagnosis adequately explains the full range of the patient's symptoms.

15. The subject is a normally developed and somewhat overweight white male.

16. Scalp hair is normally distributed and gray.

Worksheet Continues

Worksheet, Continued

17. In 8 weeks we will do the full blown treadmill stress test and based on that will make the final modification of his exercise program.

18. The above captioned patient was examined by me on this date for determination of disability benefits.

19. Apparently this man had two previous episodes of left sided ureteral colic followed by spontaneous passage of stones.

20. Recommendations: Clean voided midstream urine for culture and sensitivity.

21. The patient is agreeable with this and is admitted to the hospital for the above mentioned procedure.

22. A clean voided urine showed 15 to 20 white blood cells per high power field, 8 to 10 red cells, 4+ occult blood, 1+ protein, negative for sugar, pH 5.5.

    (*Note*: *High power* is an adjective noun compound.)

23. The mucus secreting cells are anaplastic and appear rounded.

24. The patient presented with a 6 month history of progressive shortness of breath and a 35 pound weight loss.

25. Fine needle aspiration revealed well differentiated small cell carcinoma.

26. CHEST: Decreased breath sounds in the lower one third of the left lung field with dullness to percussion and end inspiratory wheezes on the left.

27. Thirty odd stones were found in the gallbladder on dissecting it on the side table.

28. This is a 34 year old lady who comes to the clinic today with a long standing history of hypothyroidism, for which she has taken Cytomel in the past.

29. Fine needle aspiration revealed what was thought to be a Hürthle cell adenoma.

30. The patient states she had been taking a 2000 calorie ADA diet.

31. PLAN: Discontinue hydrochlorothiazide and birth control pills to end possible drug induced hyperglycemia.

Worksheet Continues

Worksheet, Continued

32. The patient is to receive nutritional counseling on a 1200 calorie ADA diet.

33. CHIEF COMPLAINT: Elevated blood sugars, uncontrolled by high dose outpatient insulin.

34. NPH and regular insulin will be given on a split dose b.i.d. dosing regimen.

35. The patient is a 67 year old Mexican American female.

36. This is a 19 year old female college student who is seen with reference to vulvar pain and urinary burning of 2 to 2 $1/2$ days' duration.

37. The patient is to take Tylenol No. 3, one or two tabs q.4 6h. p.r.n. for pain.

38. PELVIC EXAMINATION: Vaginal cuff is negative; cul de sac is free.

39. On examination, there is a second degree cystourethrocele with loss of urethrovesical angle.

40. Her heavy bleeding decreased the hematocrit to the 26 28% range.

41. The patient is a para 3, 2 0 1 2, Rh negative woman in her 36th week of pregnancy.

42. The patient is admitted for work up of possible adult onset diabetes mellitus.

43. The vagina is well epithelialized with good support.

44. This 14 year old white male is seen for follow up of his acne.

45. Dr. Alexander, an allergist, is board certified.

46. The patient was thought to have infected eczema or gram negative toe web infection.

47. X rays showed mild demineralization but no definite osteomyelitis.

48. The patient is to call me in a week for follow up.

49. She is concerned that this represents a flare up of her chronic lupus erythematosus.

50. She is not pregnant or breast feeding.

Colons

The colon is used to call attention to what follows, which may be an explanation, a list, a summary, or a quotation. The first letter after a colon need not be capitalized, but it frequently is in medical reports, especially if it begins a quotation or a clause.

Note: A single sentence generally should not contain more than one colon. In medical reports, however, colons are often used after headings, and the colon after a heading does not count as part of the sentence.

His symptoms include all of the following: dyspnea on exertion, fatigue, and productive cough.

Laboratory studies were as follows: White count was 10.4 with 61% segmented neutrophils and 6 banded neutrophils.

HEART: The heart sounds are strong on auscultation.

DIAGNOSIS:
Brain, biopsies x 2: gliosis.

DIAGNOSIS:
Brain, biopsy: astrocytoma, grade 3 (glioblastoma multiforme).

Tumor contour: Infiltrative. Vascular invasion: None demonstrated.

Duodenum: No ulcerations identified.

Lungs: Vascular congestion, mild.

Lungs: The left lung weighs 620 g.

HEENT: Eyes PERRLA.

Recommendations include the following: Push fluids for next several days; discontinue hydrochlorothiazide and birth control pills; start Micronase 2.5 mg q.d.

A colon is used between numbers in time references, but not in military time.

She was seen in the emergency department at 3:30 a.m. because of diaphoresis and weakness.

The code was called at 12:55 on the afternoon of February 6.

The patient was admitted at 1420 hours.

Colons, Continued

A colon is used between titles and subtitles and in scriptural references.

The Language of Medicine: Its Evolution, Structure, and Dynamics

H&P: A Nonphysician's Guide to the Medical History and Physical Examination

John 3:16

A colon is used after the salutation in a business letter and after "Re" (regarding).

Re: Patient Leroy Anderson, #000-00-0000

Dear Dr. Jones:

Worksheet

Place colons in the following sentences where appropriate, then circle the colons.

1. PHYSICAL EXAMINATION Heart Regular rate and rhythm.

2. Estimated blood loss 750 cc for the total procedure.

3. Pathologically the following types of tumors are observed solitary and multiple polyps, adenomas, multiple polyposis, leiomyoma, neuroma.

4. PAST HISTORY Hospitalizations None. Surgery None. Serious medical illnesses None.

5. Test results were within normal limits with the following important exceptions serum iron was 45, which is low; TIBC was 433, which is high; and percent iron saturation was 10, which is low.

6. Epstein-Barr nuclear antigen was positive at 140.

7. Examination of the right knee reveals the following genu valgum 7 degrees, Q angle 19 degrees, anterior and posterior drawer signs negative.

8. Antinuclear antibody proved to be positive at 1160.

9. Panel was negative other than 1400 for antithyroid microsome.

10. Differential diagnoses include the following

    a. Hypersensitivity pneumonitis.

    b. Mycoplasma pneumonia.

    c. Less likely candidates appear to be Wegener's granulomatosis, Goodpasture's syndrome, sarcoidosis.

11. LABORATORY DATA Arterial blood gases pH 7.28, PCO_2 29, PO_2 85, bicarbonate 13.

12. She has been n.p.o. since 100 p.m.

13. Examination showed recurrence of the retinal detachment with an open retinal break at about the 530 position.

Apostrophes

The apostrophe is used to show possession, to indicate omitted letters in a contraction, and to form some plurals.

1. Use an apostrophe to form the **possessive** of a noun, including acronyms and all-capital abbreviations.

    > I saw Dr. Gal's patient today.
    > *Compare:* This is a patient of Dr. Richard Gal.

    > The patient comes in with a six weeks' bleeding spell.
    > *Compare:* . . . bleeding of six weeks.
    >   . . . six-week bleeding spell.

    > The EKG's reading was apparently postponed.
    > *Compare:* Reading of the EKG was apparently postponed.

    > I asked Social Services to get the patient's daughter's address so that I could discuss her mother's condition.

    > The patient has a past history of Hodgkin's lymphoma.

2. Use an apostrophe to form the **possessive adjective** in units of time and money.

    > I prescribed Dilantin 200 mg per day (approximately 4 mg/kg per day) for a 6 months' trial period.

    > He describes intermittent, rather severe left arm pain of about 2 to 3 weeks' duration.

    > Fundus examination showed evidence of a previously placed scleral buckle from about 2 to 10 o'clock, reinforced with a radial sponge at 5 o'clock.

3. Use an apostrophe to indicate the **plurals** of lowercase abbreviations with and without periods (but not all-capital abbreviations), lowercase letters, numbers, and symbols spoken of as such, or words spoken of as words when -*s* alone would be confusing.

    > wbc's   rbc's   5's   +'s   serial K's   and's

4. Use an apostrophe in **contractions.**

    Style Note: Although many oppose the use of contractions (words or numbers) in medical reports, a significant number see no problem with using contractions of words in such reports.

    > I've scheduled the patient for a sleep-deprived EEG.

Apostrophes, Continued

He's never been told by others that he has any associated unusual movements of the hand or mouth to suggest automatisms.

There's been no significant change in the frequency of the dizzy spells.

It's hard for him to focus, read, and watch television.

5. Use an apostrophe with a **singular possessive eponym,** if dictated. See the Style Note, below.

Biopsy of the lesion on his chest revealed malignant melanoma, Clark's level 3.

Examination revealed positive Brudzinski's and Kernig's signs.

Hodgkin's disease was diagnosed several years ago.

Romberg's test was negative.

Style Note: There is a movement by some within the medical transcription profession to minimize the use of the possessive form with eponyms, although apostrophes are correctly dictated and transcribed in examples such as those above. As always, we recommend that you transcribe what the dictator says, unless it is incorrect.

No medical dictionary has completely eliminated the use of the possessive form of single eponyms used as modifiers, although you will find that dictionaries vary on which eponyms take the possessive form and which do not. It is recommended that you consult a reputable medical dictionary or seek your supervisor's opinion on whether to use the possessive form of an eponym.

The possessive form of eponyms with surgical instruments was eliminated long ago.

A Kocher clamp was then utilized for mobilization.

The piriformis muscle was reattached to the fossa with three Bunnell sutures.

The distal end of the hole was radialized with the Acufex rasp.

As test, procedure, and disease entity modifiers, however, the use of the possessive varies. Generally, hyphenated or compound eponyms do not take the possessive form when used to modify diseases, tests, procedures, or the like. Similarly, eponyms preceded by the articles *a, an,* or *the* generally do not take the possessive form.

Osgood-Schlatter disease was diagnosed when she was ten and taking ballet.

The Down syndrome child she bore in her late 40s died last year.

Apostrophes, Continued

Misuse of the Apostrophe

Many people confuse the distinction between possessives and contractions. Two trouble spots in particular are *its* vs. *it's*, and *who's* vs. *whose*. The following examples demonstrate the proper use of *its* and *whose*.

Ultrasonography revealed a complex renal cyst, but CT scan showed the cyst to be simple in **its** complexity. (Shows possession; is not a contraction for *it is*)

I have explained the procedure, **its** intended objectives, and **its** possible complications thoroughly to the patient and his wife.

Because of **its** increasing size, the possibility of malignancy of the thyroid had to be considered.

The patient, **whose** task it is to keep a food diary, reports no correlation between food intake and resultant headache. (*Whose* shows possession and is not a contraction for *who is*)

When asked **whose** home she preferred to stay in, the child indicated a preference for the mother.

Do not use an apostrophe to indicate the plural of all-capital abbreviations or numerals, including years.

His ABGs were within normal limits.

Serial EKGs performed on subsequent days showed a slight left axis deviation.

The patient had an open cholecystectomy in the late 1980s.

She reports that she went through menopause in her late 30s.

Worksheet

Insert an apostrophe where appropriate in the following sentences, and circle the apostrophes.

1. He is to return to the office in ten days time.

2. Its apparent that the patient does not understand the medication regimen Ive prescribed.

3. The lesion was approximately 1 cm and located at about 5 o clock on the glenoid rim.

4. The patient is seen for possible release of Dupuytrens contracture.

5. The patients general health has been quite good.

6. Shes had no hematuria, and its been a week since her last bleeding episode.

7. There was no pain over McBurneys point.

8. The patient experienced excruciating left flank pain radiating down into the left groin and testicle, chills, nausea, vomiting, and slight urinary burning, all of about 2 hours duration.

9. I think wed better attempt to bring this stone down with a snare before he gets enough local edema to obstruct completely or gets into trouble with a red-hot ascending pyelonephritis.

10. PLAN: He is to be admitted on an elective basis at the convenience of the parents schedule.

11. SOCIAL HISTORY: Hes married, retired, has two children.

12. External genitalia normal for the childs age.

13. Because of its increasing size, the possibility of malignancy had to be considered.

14. The patient, a 50-year-old black woman, presented with a 4 to 6 weeks history of episodes of postprandial epigastric distress.

15. Under the operating microscope I was able to dilate Whartons duct on the right, and after dilatation the gland resumed its normal size.

16. Ive referred her to your office to further assess whether the Azulfidine or Crohns is the source of her fever.

Worksheet Continues

Worksheet, Continued

17. The radiologists impression was that there was a soft tissue mass in the terminal ileum; my impression was that this could possibly be a Meckels, although this would be very unusual.

18. Im considering possible excision of Mortons neuromas at the patients left forefoot area if shes having persistent symptomatology.

19. He states hed never had this pain occur before, and its not occurred since.

20. CHIEF COMPLAINT: Precordial-type squeezing chest pain radiating to left shoulder and left arm, unrelieved for approximately 24 hours duration.

21. All of these drugs are prescription items and are vital to maintenance of her chronic emphysema and its associated cardiac arrhythmias.

22. Stent will be removed in about one months time.

23. On exam hes a pleasant young man whos in no acute distress.

24. The patients addition of serial 7s was within normal limits.

Periods, Question Marks, Exclamation Points

Periods indicate an even more decisive pause in speech or thought than commas or semicolons. Periods are used to separate main (independent) clauses that are not closely related to each other, in some abbreviations, and as a decimal point.

When using a word processing program to create a document that is not proportionately spaced, end-of-sentence marks should be followed by two spaces. With proportional spacing, the computer or word processor automatically inserts slightly more space following end-of-sentence punctuation marks than following words and other punctuation marks, so only one space is typed.

All other punctuation marks are followed by a single space.

1. Use a period to end a declarative or slightly imperative sentence.

    Total abdominal hysterectomy was performed.

    Check vital signs and neurologic status every hour on the hour for 24 hours.

2. Use periods to end some abbreviations and within other abbreviations.

    I also sent stool for *C. difficile,* which was negative, and ordered an upper GI with a small-bowel series.

    The patient was kept n.p.o. for 12 hours after the procedure.

    The patient is taking Minipress 5 mg t.i.d. and Catapres 1 mg b.i.d.

3. Periods are used as decimal points in metric numbers.

    The patient had a total protein of 5.4, albumin level 3.2, chloride 106, and total bilirubin 1.2.

    The patient was given atropine 0.5 mg and intubated with a 7.5 ET tube.

    The specimen measures 1.5 mm x 3.0 mm x 0.5 mm.

Question marks. Question marks are used after direct questions but not after indirect questions.

    "What are the risks of this procedure?" the patient asked.

Question marks are rarely used in medical dictation except to indicate the uncertainty of a statement, fact, or value. When used in this context, the question mark is enclosed in parentheses. The dictator may indicate this by saying, "query," "question," or more specifically "parenthesis question mark parenthesis."

MICROSCOPIC DIAGNOSIS: Segment of small bowel showing transmural acute inflammation (perforation?) with extensive serosal fibrosis.

POSTOPERATIVE DIAGNOSIS: Valvar and supravalvar aortic and pulmonary stenosis, (?) Williams syndrome.

AP, lateral, and oblique x-rays of the right hand reveal what appear to be residuals of a well-healed (?) fracture with a large ball of mature callus.

Exclamation points. Exclamation points are used after emphatic interjections and after other expressions to show surprise or disbelief. Exclamation points are rarely used in medical dictation; when they are, it is for the latter reason.

The patient screamed, "Help me!"

The patient growled at the attendant, "I want this I.V. out and I want it out *now*!"

Dashes, Parentheses, Brackets, Slashes, Ellipses

A dash (—) is used to indicate a break in thought, to set off a parenthetical expression for emphasis or clarity, and to set off an introductory series. Do not use a dash in place of a colon.

DIAGNOSIS: Transurethral resection of the prostate—well-differentiated adenocarcinoma of the prostate gland.

The serum electrolytes—sodium, potassium, chloride, and CO_2—should always be done postoperatively in a patient with abdominal pain.

2. **Parentheses** ( ) are used to set off parenthetical expressions, enclose supplementary material or illustrative matter, or to enclose figures or letters used for enumeration within a paragraph or sentence.

Note: When enumerating lists in a column (as in diagnoses), the numbers are followed by periods. Do not use a combination of a period and parentheses when enumerating.

The patient has one small colonic polyp with a history of (1) Hemoccult-positive stools, (2) fatigue, and (3) a URI.

The serum electrolytes (sodium, potassium, chloride, and CO_2) should always be done postoperatively in a patient with abdominal pain.

A partial problem list at this time would include (1) vomiting, (2) heartburn, (3) recently irregular periods, (4) mood swings.

PROVISIONAL ANATOMIC DIAGNOSIS:
   1. Bilateral bronchopneumonia.
   2. Malignant tumor of unknown primary, with metastases to:
      a. Periaortic lymph nodes.
      b. Left and right lungs.
      c. Carinal lymph nodes.
   3. Past history of bladder carcinoma.
   4. Myocardial hypertrophy with left ventricular thickening.
   5. Splenic hypertrophy.

Medications at the time of discharge include:
1. Maalox/Mylanta 30 cc p.o. p.c. and h.s.
2. Zyloprim 300 mg p.o. q.d.
3. Lorelco 2 tabs p.o. b.i.d. with meals.
4. Questran $1^1/_2$ scoops p.o. b.i.d.
5. $FeSO_4$ 300 mg 1 p.o. b.i.d.
6. Restoril 30 mg p.o. h.s. p.r.n.

Dashes, Parentheses, Brackets, Slashes, Ellipses, Continued

Punctuation Note: When a sentence ends with an expression in parentheses, the period follows the closing parenthesis without any intervening space. If parentheses are used to enclose a complete sentence in isolation, the period goes inside the closing parenthesis.

3. **Brackets** ([ ]) replace parentheses within parentheses and set off insertions in quoted matter.

   He would make remarks like, "I wanted to perform [a certain] procedure, but the PRO would not approve it, so I had to perform another procedure which I did not feel was in the patient's best interest."

4. A **slash** or **virgule** (/) is used to represent *per*, *and*, and *or* and to divide material. It is used between terms to indicate that either term is applicable, such as *and/or*. Note, however, that many experts do not consider *and/or* to be an acceptable construction. If dictated by a physician though, you would type as dictated. Also, do not confuse a construction in which either term is applicable with a construction in which both terms are equal and equally applicable; such a compound uses a hyphen.

   A slash is used between numbers when the word "over" is dictated. Do not use a slash for hemoglobin and hematocrit even if dictated; separate the terms and place the value for each with the term.

   The patient's blood pressure was 120/70.

   But not: Hemoglobin/hematocrit 16/32. (Dictated)
   Transcribe: Hemoglobin 16, hematocrit 32.
   Hint: Do not space before or after the slash when it is used between terms or numbers.

5. **Ellipsis points** (. . .) are rarely used in medical reports and should not be used unless dictated. They indicate an omission within a quotation or reference or mark a reflective pause or hesitation. Within a sentence ellipsis points are properly typed as three periods with a space before and after each point. If a comma precedes the use of ellipsis points, it may be left in or omitted (, . . .). If the ellipsis points are used at the end of a sentence, they are preceded by a period that follows the final word (. . . .)

6. **Quotation marks** are used in medical dictation to quote words, phrases, or sentences of the patient or a speaker.

   "Kids" is how Dr. Brownstone, the pediatric endocrinologist, refers to his patients.

   The patient stated that she feels "weepy" and "floppy" on the new medication.

7. Periods always go inside single or double quotation marks.

Worksheet

Insert dashes where needed in the following sentences and circle them.

1. History is impossible because he denies everything he's fine, no problem, and so it's difficult to know what problems he has.

2. DIAGNOSIS: Meningitis could be viral.

3. Three weeks ago the following diagnoses hepatic insufficiency with cirrhosis secondary to alcohol abuse, prostatic hypertrophy, chronic obstructive lung disease, and hiatal hernia were made.

4. She was instructed to call if blood sugars run less than 80 or greater than 300 she will be checking these at home.

Insert parentheses where needed in the following sentences and circle them.

5. Electrolytes sodium, potassium chloride and CO_2 were all within normal limits.

6. DIAGNOSIS: Chronic I.V. intravenous drug user.

7. The patient's confabulation indicated to me that 1 he had little insight into his situation and 2 his judgment was grossly impaired.

8. It is my feeling that acute urticaria in our definition an urticaria that has been present for less than 3 months should not be evaluated for cause unless that cause is apparent, but rather should be treated only with drug therapy.

Insert slashes where needed in the following sentences and circle them.

9. Electrocardiograms, Holter monitor, and exercise stress results for Sally will be dictated or manually and or machine generated.

10. The patient is an obese, well-oriented, cooperative female who has a temperature of 100.3°F, pulse 88, respiratory rate 20, and blood pressure 142 90.

11. The FEV-1 FVC was 0.78 (101% of predicted).

Worksheet, Continued

Insert periods where needed in the following sentences and circle them.

12. O&P studies were done to rule out *G lamblia*

13. The patient will continue on Vicodin tabs 1 or 2 for pain qid prn and return to see me in three weeks, sooner if pain does not remit

14. Specimen is a 70 x 35 x 35 cm gallbladder with a smooth surface and a lumen that measures up to 03 cm in diameter.

Insert quotation marks (and any associated commas) where needed in the following sentences and circle them.

15. Patient presents with the chief complaint I have a sore on my right hip.

16. He said I can't walk normal.

17. The patient states that she vomits phlegm.

18. Today the patient indicated that his left knee is the same.

Insert question mark and periods where needed in the following sentences, and change lower case to upper case where appropriate. Circle your edits.

19. If Dr Gleason ordered bed rest for the patient, why is he still going to work three days a week is he equating part-time work with bed rest

20. Diagnosis is unknown at this time is patient malingering

Insert exclamation marks, any associated commas and quotation marks, and change lower case to upper case where needed in the following sentences. Circle your edits.

21. Save me the patient was screaming to the paramedics in the ambulance all the way to the hospital don't let me die

22. The patient shouted no way when I asked if he would consider a vasectomy rather than subject his wife to a tubal ligation

Section 3.
Anatomy & Physiology

Body Organization

Fill in the blanks with the appropriate answers. Some answers may require more than one word.

1. Body planes are imaginary, flat surfaces that divide the body into parts. The three main body planes are the _____ plane, the _____ plane, and the _____ plane.

2. When a patient stands erect, eyes forward, with arms at the sides and feet and palms directed forward, this is known as the _____ position.

3. The two principal body cavities are the _____ and the _____.

4. The term that denotes an upward orientation is called _____.

5. The term that denotes downward orientation and means *toward the feet* is called _____.

6. The term that means *toward the front of the body* is _____.

7. The term that means *toward the back of the body* is _____.

8. The term that means *toward the midline* is _____.

9. The term that means *toward the side* is _____.

10. The term that describes *away from the midline* is _____.

11. The term that describes *toward the midline* is _____.

12. The term that means *within the body* is _____.

13. The term that means *toward the body surface* is _____.

14. The term *axillary* refers to the _____.

15. The term *celiac* refers to the _____.

16. The term *cervical* refers to the _____.

17. The term *inguinal* refers to the _____.

18. The term *cephalic* refers to the _____.

19. The term *gluteal* refers to the _____.

20. The term *occipital* refers to the _____.

21. The abdomen may be divided into four _____.

195

Anatomy & Physiology of Cells and Tissues

Fill in the blanks with the appropriate answers. Some answers may require more than one word.

1. The portion of the protoplasm outside the nucleus of a cell is called the

   _____.

2. The _____ complex packages secretions for export from

   the cell and produces lysosomes.

3. The movement of ions from regions of higher to lower concentration is known as

   _____.

4. _____ is the process by which a substance is forced through

   a membrane by hydrostatic pressure.

5. The process of white cells ingesting other substances is _____.

6. The duplication of chromosomes prior to cell division is termed _____,

   and the division of cytoplasm to form two cells is termed _____.

7. Tissues are made up of _____.

8. Epithelial cells are classified according to their shape as _____,

   _____, and _____.

9. Any structure that is differentiated to produce a secretion may be called a (an)

   _____.

10. Tissue that consists of bundles or sheets of long, narrow cells arranged in parallel and having

    the capacity to shorten under appropriate stimulation is _____.

11. The muscle found only in the heart is called _____ muscle.

12. _____ tissue is specialized to transmit neural impulses.

13. _____ are tiny hairlike organelles projecting from the

    surfaces of many types of cells that help to move materials outside the cell.

Anatomy and Physiology of the Integumentary System

Fill in the blanks with the appropriate answers. Some answers may require more than one word.

1. The skin, its hair, glands, and nails are collectively known as the_____ system.

2. The tiny openings on the skin surface are called _____.

3. _____ glands secrete water and some wastes from the skin.

4. Skin consists of two main layers: the _____ and the _____ .

5. Hair is found on all skin surfaces of the human body except the _____ and the _____.

6. Sebaceous glands are also known as _____ glands.

7. The main purpose of the sweat glands is to regulate _____.

8. The white, moon-shaped, crescentic area on the actively growing fingernail or toenail is called the _____.

9. Cells producing pigment granules are made up of a protein called _____.

10. Sweat glands release _____ water onto the skin surface.

11. The part of the hair that is visible is called the _____ ; the part below the skin surface is the _____.

12. The yellowish pigment in the skin of Asian people is caused by _____.

13. The subcutaneous layer contains a variable amount of fat, also called _____ tissue.

14. The band of epidermis at the base and side of the nail plate is the _____.

15. A structural protein found in the skin and connective tissue is_____.

16. The exposed red portion of the upper or lower lip is the _____ border.

A&P of the Integumentary System, Continued

Choose the correct answer in each of the following multiple-choice questions. Write your answer in the space provided next to the number of the question.

_____ 17. A black pigment formed by melanocytes in the epidermis is known as:
  a. keratin
  b. stratum
  c. collagen
  d. melanin

_____ 18. The outermost layer of the epidermis is known as the:
  a. corium
  b. stratum corneum
  c. sebum
  d. epithelium

_____ 19. The oily substance secreted by sebaceous glands is called:
  a. lipogen
  b. sebum
  c. kcratin
  d. collagen

_____ 20. Each hair grows within a sac called the:
  a. sebaceous gland
  b. stratum corneum
  c. hair follicle
  d. cuticle

_____ 21. A horny cell is filled with:
  a. fat
  b. fluid
  c. collagen
  d. keratin

_____ 22. Which of the following is NOT a function of the skin?
  a. helps excrete excess water and body wastes
  b. acts as a barrier against unfriendly microorganisms
  c. prevents stimulation of nerve endings upon injury
  d. produces vitamin D

_____ 23. A hair fiber is composed of:
  a. albumin
  b. keratin
  c. collagen
  d. epithelium

_____ 24. A toenail that has been removed takes how long to grow back completely?
  a. 2 to 4 months
  b. 5 to 8 months
  c. 9 to 12 months
  d. 12 months or longer

Anatomy & Physiology of the Urinary System

Arrange the following anatomic structures in order to show the formation and pathway of urine. Begin with the renal artery.

renal artery	ureter	calices
glomerulus	renal tubules	Bowman capsule
urethra	renal pelvis	bladder
renal artery	hilum	urethral meatus

1. renal artery
2. _____
3. _____
4. _____
5. _____
6. _____
7. _____
8. _____
9. _____
10. _____
11. _____

Fill in the blanks with the correct answer. Some answers may require more than one word.

12. The hormone that serves as a chemical messenger from the brain to the distal tubules and collecting ducts of the kidneys is the _____ hormone.

13. Urine is composed of about 96% _____.

14. A structure that regulates blood pressure in the kidney is the _____ apparatus.

15. Each kidney contains more than a million microscopic units which are called

    _____.

16. The bladder can hold approximately _____ mL of urine.

17. The urge to urinate occurs when the bladder reaches approximately _____ mL of urine.

18. The renal tubules and collecting ducts return most of the filtrate to the blood by a process called

    _____.

A&P of the Urinary System, Continued

Choose the correct answer in each of the following multiple-choice questions. Write your answer in the space provided next to the number of the question.

_____ 19. Which of the following structures is a temporary storage sac for urine?
    a. bladder
    b. ureters
    c. kidneys
    d. glomerules

_____ 20. Which of the following best describes the renal cortex?
    a. structure through which urine passes into the minor calices
    b. muscular sac that serves as a reservoir for urine
    c. central urine collecting basin in the kidney
    d. outer region of the kidney

_____ 21. A ball-shaped collection of capillaries in the kidney is called a:
    a. nephron
    b. glomeruli
    c. calix
    d. meatus

_____ 22. A hormone secreted by the kidneys to stimulate production of red blood cells is:
    a. antidiuretic hormone
    b. erythropoietin
    c. follicle-stimulating hormone
    d. renin

_____ 23. What substance appears in the urine following the breakdown of hemoglobin?
    a. bilirubin
    b. blood
    c. iron
    d. glucose

_____ 24. The hormone that is synthesized, stored, and secreted by the kidneys, and which raises blood pressure by indirectly narrowing blood vessels, is:
    a. antidiuretic hormone
    b. erythropoietin
    c. follicle-stimulating hormone
    d. renin

_____ 25. The function of the renal vein is:
    a. filtration
    b. to bring blood to the kidneys
    c. to carry blood away from the kidneys
    d. reabsorption

_____ 26. A waste product of muscle metabolism excreted in the urine is:
    a. blood urea nitrogen
    b. creatinine
    c. bilirubin
    d. iron

Anatomy & Physiology of the Male Reproductive System

Arrange the following anatomic structures in order to show the formation and pathway of spermatozoa. Begin with the sperm cells.

spermatogenic cells   seminal vesicles   seminiferous tubules
urethra   vas deferens   ejaculatory duct
                                      epididymis

1. spermatogenic cells

2. _____

3. _____

4. _____

5. _____

6. _____

7. _____

Fill in the blanks with the correct answer. Some answers may require more than one word.

8. The prepuce is more commonly known as the _____.

9. _____ glands is another name for the bulbourethral glands.

10. The sensitive tip of the penis is the _____.

11. The main components of semen are _____ and _____.

12. The male gonad that produces spermatozoa and male hormones is otherwise known as the _____.

13. The area between the anus and the scrotum in the male is called the _____.

14. The narrow tube that carries sperm from the epididymis into the body and toward the urethra, and which is severed in the vasectomy procedure, is known as the _____.

15. Spermatogenesis is the _____ of sperm.

A&P of the Male Reproductive System, Continued

Choose the correct answer in each of the following multiple-choice questions. Write your answer in the space provided next to the number of the question.

_____ 16. The purpose of the prostate gland is to:
   a. lubricate the penis
   b. support the parenchyma
   c. secrete fluid to aid motility of sperm
   d. temporarily store sperm cells

_____ 17. The hormone responsible for secondary sex characteristics in men is:
   a. testosterone
   b. androgen
   c. progestin
   d. gonadotropin

_____ 18. The hair-like process on a sperm cell that makes it motile is called:
   a. fimbria
   b. villus
   c. cilium
   d. flagellum

_____ 19. Which structure serves as a cooling unit for sperm?
   a. prostate gland
   b. scrotum
   c. seminal vesicles
   d. epididymis

_____ 20. Which hormone stimulates development of the seminiferous tubules and promotes sperm production?
   a. follicle-stimulating hormone
   b. androgen
   c. testosterone
   d. luteinizing hormone

_____ 21. Where are sperm produced?
   a. in the seminal vesicles
   b. in the prostate gland
   c. in the corpus callosum
   d. in the seminiferous tubules

_____ 22. How many sperm are present in the normal ejaculate?
   a. hundreds
   b. thousands
   c. hundreds of thousands
   d. millions

Anatomy & Physiology of the Gastrointestinal System

Arrange the following anatomic structures in order to show the pathway of digestion. Begin with the oral cavity.

oral cavity · pharynx · duodenum · sigmoid colon
transverse colon · stomach · ileum · jejunum
descending colon · esophagus · cecum · anus
ascending colon · rectum

1. oral cavity
2. _____
3. _____
4. _____
5. _____
6. _____
7. _____
8. _____
9. _____
10. _____
11. _____
12. _____
13. _____
14. _____

Fill in the blanks with the correct answer. Some answers may require more than one word.

15. The _____ serves as a common passageway for air moving from the nose to the trachea and for food moving from the oral cavity to the stomach.

16. The opening that leads from the mouth and into the oropharynx is called the _____.

17. Two sphincters in the wall of the anal canal guard the anal opening. These are called the _____ sphincter and the _____ sphincter.

18. The pancreas is both an _____ and an _____ gland.

19. Saliva is released from three glands: the _____, the _____, and the _____.

20. Millions of tiny, microscopic _____ line the walls of the small intestine.

A&P of the Gastrointestinal System, Continued

Match the anatomy words in the left column with their correct definitions in the right column.

____ 21. colon

____ 22. deglutition

____ 23. appendix

____ 24. bile

____ 25. common bile duct

____ 26. duodenum

____ 27. bowel

____ 28. ileum

____ 29. sigmoid colon

____ 30. esophagus

____ 31. stomach

____ 32. pharynx

____ 33. gallbladder

____ 34. liver

____ 35. jejunum

____ 36. feces

____ 37. insulin

____ 38. pancreas

____ 39. anus

____ 40. bilirubin

____ 41. cecum

____ 42. parotid

____ 43. enzyme

____ 44. amino acids

____ 45. mastication

____ 46. saliva

A. lower part of the colon shaped like an S.

B. organ that stores bile

C. another term for the large intestine

D. first part of the large intestine

E. digestive juice produced by salivary glands

F. organ that produces insulin

G. swallowing

H. pigment in bile

I. salivary gland near the ear

J. blind pouch hanging from the first part of the colon

K. another word for "throat"

L. hormone that transports sugar into cells

M. chemical that speeds up reactions between substances

N. digestive juice made in the liver

O. building blocks of proteins

P. second part of the small intestine

Q. third part of the small intestine.

R. tube connecting the throat and stomach

S. organ that receives food from the esophagus

T. first part of the small intestine

U. another word for "intestine"

V. opening of digestive tract to outside of the body

W. chewing

X. carries bile from liver and gallbladder to duodenum

Y. another word for "stool"

Z. organ that secretes bile and destroys old red cells

A&P of the Gastrointestinal System, Continued

Choose the correct answer in each of the following multiple-choice questions. Write your answer in the space provided next to the number of the question.

_____ 47. The hormone that stimulates the gallbladder to contract and release bile is:
   a. insulin
   b. lipase
   c. cholecystokinin
   d. maltase

_____ 48. The liver removes excess glucose from the bloodstream, storing it in liver cells as:
   a. pepsin
   b. fatty acids
   c. glycogen
   d. triglycerides

_____ 49. The parotid gland is located:
   a. near the ear
   b. behind the liver
   c. under the tongue
   d. next to the pancreas

_____ 50. The substance produced by the stomach that is necessary for digestion is:
   a. hydrochloric acid
   b. dentin
   c. amylase
   d. chyme

_____ 51. The vermiform appendix:
   a. digests cellulose in vegetables
   b. serves as a vestigial structure
   c. stores vital appendicoliths
   d. incubates bacteria that can break down food particles

_____ 52. Which of the following is NOT a function of the large intestine?
   a. absorption of sodium and water
   b. incubation of bacteria
   c. elimination of wastes
   d. storage of iron and other vitamins

_____ 53. What is the function of a sphincter?
   a. to close a passage
   b. to act as a catalyst
   c. to release nutrients
   d. to open a valve

_____ 54. Most chemical digestion takes place within the:
   a. mouth
   b. duodenum
   c. small bowel
   d. large bowel

206

Anatomy & Physiology of the Musculoskeletal System

Match the anatomy words in the left column with their correct definitions in the right column.

____ 1. acetabulum	A. process on temporal bone
____ 2. disk	B. round process on each side of ankle joint
____ 3. fossa	C. rubbery connective tissue
____ 4. periosteum	D. growth center at end of bone
____ 5. sinus	E. bone formation process
____ 6. trochanter	F. socket where thigh bone joins pelvis
____ 7. xiphoid process	G. narrow portion of sternum
____ 8. tubercle	H. the end of a long bone
____ 9. vertebra	I. small round process on a bone
____ 10. sulcus	J. ribs 8 through 12
____ 11. acromion	K. knuckle-like process at end of bone near joint
____ 12. styloid process	L. large process below neck of femur
____ 13. condyle	M. area of fusion of two pubic bones
____ 14. calcium	N. ribs 11 and 12 specifically
____ 15. tuberosity	O. membrane around bones
____ 16. epiphysis	P. shaft of a long bone
____ 17. olecranon	Q. opening in bones where vessels enter and exit
____ 18. false ribs	R. groove-like depression
____ 19. floating ribs	S. plate-like structure between vertebrae
____ 20. epiphyseal plate	T. cavity within bone
____ 21. foramen	U. large round process on a bone
____ 22. cartilage	V. elbow
____ 23. diaphysis	W. point of the shoulder
____ 24. malleolus	X. mineral in bone
____ 25. pubic symphysis	Y. back bone
____ 26. ossification	Z. shallow bone cavity

A&P of the Musculoskeletal System, Continued

Fill in the blanks with the correct answer. Some answers may require more than one word.

27. Metacarpals are found in the _____.

28. Metatarsals are found in the _____.

29. The _____ is the thigh muscle that extends the knee.

30. In the hip, the head of the _____ fits into the _____.

31. The _____ joint connects the shoulder bone and the collar bone.

32. The joint between the wrist and forearm is the _____ joint.

33. A sac-like, fluid-filled cavity situated in places where friction would otherwise develop

    is known as a _____.

34. The supporting ligaments that cross each other in the knee are known as the anterior and

    posterior _____ ligaments.

Choose the correct answer in each of the following multiple-choice questions. Write your answer in the space provided next to the number of the question.

___ 35. The temporomandibular joint is the area of connection between:
   a. the temporal bone and the mastoid process
   b. the temporal bone and mandibular bone
   c. the mandible and the maxilla
   d. the mandibular bone and the styloid process

___ 36. What is the best definition for *articulation?*
   a. the place of union between two or more bones
   b. the ability to move a joint freely and without pain
   c. the junction of tendon and muscle
   d. circular movement around a central point

___ 37. What is the medical term for the place where muscle is attached to stationary bone?
   a. insertion
   b. origin
   c. belly
   d. abductor

___ 38. What is the medical term for muscle that is smooth?
   a. tendinous
   b. visceral
   c. striated
   d. fascicular

A&P of the Musculoskeletal System, Continued

_____ 39. The medical name for the shoulder blade is:
    a. clavicle
    b. olecranon
    c. sternum
    d. scapula

_____ 40. The medical name for the tailbone is:
    a. coccyx
    b. sacrum
    c. vertebra
    d. lamina

_____ 41. The longest bone in the body is the:
    a. humerus
    b. tibia
    c. fibula
    d. femur

_____ 42. The posterior part of the pelvis is called the:
    a. ilium
    b. ileum
    c. ischium
    d. pelvic girdle

_____ 43. The patella is the:
    a. ankle bone
    b. kneecap
    c. wrist bone
    d. collar bone

_____ 44. An immovable joint is called a(n):
    a. amphiarthrosis
    b. diarthrosis
    c. anklylosis
    d. synarthrosis

_____ 45. How many thoracic vertebrae does the average person have?
    a. 7
    b. 12
    c. 13
    d. 15

_____ 46. How many pairs of ribs does the average person have?
    a. 8
    b. 10
    c. 12
    d. 15

____ 47. The axial skeleton consists of the:
   a. upper and lower extremities, pectoral girdle, pelvic girdle
   b. cervical spine, thoracic spine, lumbar spine, sacrum, coccyx
   c. skull, extremities, pelvic girdle, vertebral column
   d. skull, vertebral column, ribs, sternum

____ 48. A band of fibrous tissue that connects bones or cartilages is a:
   a. ligament
   b. muscle
   c. joint
   d. tendon

____ 49. A lamina is a:
   a. platelike structure
   b. bulbous projection
   c. depressed area
   d. grated surface

____ 50. Muscles that cannot be controlled voluntarily are known as:
   a. striated muscles
   b. smooth muscles
   c. skeletal muscles
   d. voluntary muscles

____ 51. The occipital bone is found in the:
   a. vertebral column
   b. upper extremities
   c. skull
   d. lower extremities

____ 52. Which of the following is NOT part of the bony skeleton?
   a. dendrite
   b. tubercle
   c. facet
   d. dens

____ 53. The large muscle of the buttocks is the:
   a. gastrocnemius
   b. adductor longus
   c. gracilis
   d. gluteus maximus

____ 54. Which of the following muscles rotates the humerus and moves the arm?
   a. quadriceps
   b. latissimus dorsi
   c. trapezius
   d. zygomatic

Anatomy & Physiology of the Cardiovascular System

Arrange the following anatomic structures in order to show the pathway of circulation. Begin with the venae cavae.

left ventricle	venae cavae	pulmonary vein
aorta	left atrium	right ventricle
aortic valve	right atrium	tricuspid valve
pulmonary valve	mitral valve	pulmonary artery

1. venae cavae
2. _____
3. _____
4. _____
5. _____
6. _____
7. _____
8. _____
9. _____
10. _____
11. _____
12. _____

Fill in the blanks with the correct answer. Some answers may require more than one word.

13. The sac surrounding the heart is called the _____.

14. The four chambers of the heart are the _____, the
_____, the _____,
and the _____.

15. The largest artery of the body is the _____.

16. The _____ is known as the pacemaker of the heart.

17. The period of relaxation of the heart is _____.

18. The volume of blood pumped by one ventricle during one beat is known as the

_____.

19. The test that traces and displays the electrical potentials of the heart is known as the

_____.

20. The alternate expansion and recoil of an artery is the _____.

A&P of the Cardiovascular System, Continued

Choose the correct answer in each of the following multiple-choice questions. Write your answer in the space provided next to the number of the question.

_____ 21. The smallest blood vessel is a(n):
    a. capillary
    b. arteriole
    c. venule
    d. artery

_____ 22. The blood vessel that carries oxygenated blood is the:
    a. capillary
    b. venule
    c. vein
    d. artery

_____ 23. The amount of blood pumped by one ventricle in one minute is called the:
    a. arterial pulse
    b. cardiac output
    c. ejection fraction
    d. stroke volume

_____ 24. The "good" cholesterol is the:
    a. LDL
    b. VDL
    c. HDL
    d. VLDL

_____ 25. Purkinje fibers are found in the:
    a. left atrium
    b. myocardium of the ventricles
    c. endocardium of the atria
    d. bundle of His

_____ 26. The valve that is located between the left upper and lower chambers of the heart is the:
    a. pulmonary
    b. mitral
    c. triscuspid
    d. bicuspid

_____ 27. Oxygen is carried to the brain by the:
    a. carotid arteries
    b. pulmonary arteries
    c. aortic vein
    d. jugular vein

_____ 28. The artery most used by healthcare workers to measure the pulse is the:
    a. carotid
    b. radial
    c. ulnar
    d. jugular

Anatomy & Physiology of the Pulmonary System

Arrange the following anatomic structures in order to show the pathway of air movement. Begin with the nose.

nares	alveoli	pharynx
bronchioles	trachea	nasal cavities
larynx	bronchi	lung capillaries

1. nares
2. _____
3. _____
4. _____
5. _____
6. _____
7. _____
8. _____
9. _____

Fill in the blanks with the correct answer. Some answers may require more than one word.

10. The smallest branches of the bronchi are called _____.

11. At least 100 times more _____ is present in expired air than in the environmental air we inspire.

12. The _____ is the membrane that surrounds each lung.

13. There are (number) _____ divisions of the lungs known as _____.

14. The midline region of the lung where vessels, nerves, lymph tissue, and bronchial tubes enter and exit is called the _____.

15. Air enters the blood stream through the _____ of the lung.

16. Air sacs and small bronchioles together are called the _____.

17. The muscle separating the chest and abdomen is the _____.

18. The _____ is the layer of pleura that is closest to the lung tissue.

19. A space between two ribs is known as a(n) _____.

A&P of the Pulmonary System, Continued

Choose the correct answer in each of the following multiple-choice questions. Write your answer in the space provided next to the number of the question.

_____ 20. The flap of cartilage that covers the opening of the larynx is the:
    a. glottis
    b. epiglottis
    c. voice box
    d. vocal cords

_____ 21. The right lung in the average patient has how many lobes?
    a. one
    b. two
    c. three
    d. four

_____ 22. Air expelled to equalize the pressure of the lungs is known as what kind of air?
    a. apical
    b. exhaled
    c. bronchial
    d. tracheal

_____ 23. The hairlike processes projecting from the free surface of a cell that help keep mucus moving through the respiratory structures are called:
    a. cilia
    b. bronchioles
    c. villi
    d. alveoli

_____ 24. The normal number of complete respirations per minute is:
    a. 5 to 7
    b. 8 to 10
    c. 12 to 20
    d. 16 to 25

_____ 25. Inhaled air contains approximately how much oxygen?
    a. 3 percent
    b. 12 percent
    c. 16 percent
    d. 21 percent

_____ 26. In the region of the mediastinum, the trachea divides into two structures called:
    a. bronchi
    b. lobes
    c. branches
    d. alveoli

_____ 27. Mucous cells within the lining of lungs produce how much mucus daily?
    a. one teaspoon
    b. one ounce
    c. one cup
    d. one pint

214

Anatomy and Physiology of the Endocrine System

Match the terms in the left column with their correct definitions in the right column.

_____ 1. cortisol

_____ 2. ACTH

_____ 3. thyroxine

_____ 4. oxytocin

_____ 5. prolactin

_____ 6. catecholamines

_____ 7. corticosteroids

_____ 8. somatotropin

_____ 9. vasopressin

_____10. triiodothyronine

_____11. estrogen

_____12. norepinephrine

_____13. testosterone

_____14. luteinizing hormone

_____15. thyroid-stimulating hormone

_____16. progesterone

_____17. androgen

_____18. electrolyte

_____19. glucagon

_____20. steroid

_____21. hormone

_____22. insulin

_____23. calcitonin

_____24. estradiol

_____25. homeostasis

_____26. sympathomimetic

A. increases metabolism in cells; also called T_4

B. growth hormone

C. noradrenaline

D. male hormone produced by the testes

E. group name for lipids that contain a hydrogenated ring system; adrenocortical hormone is one of them

F. hormones derived from amino acids; epinephrine is one

G. estrogen produced by the ovaries

H. produced by islet cells; lowers blood sugar

I. hormone excreted by adrenal cortex that increases blood sugar

J. male hormone produced by testes; testosterone is one

K. mimics the effect of the sympathetic nervous system

L. hormones produced by adrenal cortex; mineralo-corticoid is one

M. tendency of an organism to maintain constant internal environment

N. hormone that prepares uterus for pregnancy

O. hormone which stimulates the adrenal cortex

P. hormone that promotes milk secretion

Q. hormone that lowers blood calcium

R. ionized substance found in blood and tissues

S. hormone that stimulates ovulation in females

T. antidiuretic hormone

U. thyrotropin

V. female hormone produced by the ovaries and adrenal cortex

W. substance produced by endocrine gland; acts to modify the structure or function of other organs

X. increases metabolism in cells; also called T_3

Y. hormone produced by islet cells of pancreas; increases blood sugar by conversion of starch to glucose

Z. hormone that stimulates contractions of the uterus

A&P of the Endocrine System, Continued

Choose the correct answer in each of the following multiple-choice questions. Write your answer in the space provided next to the number of the question.

____27. Which gland fits the definition for both exocrine and endocrine?
    a. thyroid
    b. adrenal
    c. pituitary
    d. pancreas

____28. The adrenal glands are located:
    a. at the base of the skull
    b. in the anterior neck
    c. behind the stomach
    d. on top of the kidneys

____29. Epinephrine and norepinephrine help the body to:
    a. lower the blood calcium level
    b. cope with stress
    c. stimulate growth at puberty
    d. ripen ova and generate spermatazoa

____30. The pituitary gland is located:
    a. within the sella turcica
    b. adjacent to the liver
    c. within the islets of Langerhans
    d. below the thyroid structures

____31. Which of the following are NOT part of the endocrine system?
    a. thyroid and parathyroid glands
    b. ovaries and testes
    c. adrenal cortex and adrenal medulla
    d. lacrimal and mammary glands

____32. Which gland begins to atrophy and stops functioning in most people by age 30?
    a. pineal
    b. thymus
    c. pituitary
    d. suprarenal

____33. How many parathyroid glands do most people have?
    a. one
    b. two
    c. three
    d. four

____34. The thyroid cartilage is also called:
    a. Adam's apple
    b. Sandstrom gland
    c. the substernal notch
    d. the palatine protuberance

Anatomy and Physiology of the Female Reproductive System

Match the terms in the left column with their correct definitions in the right column.

____ 1. adnexa	A.	lips of the female external genitalia
____ 2. endometrium	B.	structures located within the breasts
____ 3. labia	C.	period of time immediately following delivery
____ 4. estrogen	D.	external female genitalia
____ 5. menopause	E.	organ of metabolic interchange between fetus and mother
____ 6. mammary glands	F.	lining of the uterus
____ 7. placenta	G.	period of fetal development
____ 8. menarche	H.	glands on either side of vaginal orifice
____ 9. cul-de-sac	I.	giving birth
____10. cervical os	J.	onset of menses
____11. myometrium	K.	cessation of menses
____12. Bartholin	L.	mouth of cervix
____13. vulva	M.	membrane covering vagina
____14. gestation	N.	fallopian tubes and ovaries
____15. perineum	O.	tube extending from uterus to external genitalia
____16. ovulation	P.	hormone produced by the ovaries
____17. postpartum	Q.	the region between the rectum and uterus
____18. vagina	R.	muscle layer of the uterus
____19. hymen	S.	release of egg from ovary
____20. parturition	T.	area between anus and vagina
____21. puerperium	U.	fingerlike ends of fallopian tubes
____22. clitoris	V.	gestation from conception through second month
____23. chorion	W.	gestation from the third month to birth
____24. fimbriae	X.	organ homologous with penis in the male
____25. embryo	Y.	membrane surrounding embryo but part of placenta
____26. fetus	Z.	period during complete involution of the uterus

A&P of the Female Reproductive System, Continued

Choose the correct answer in each of the following multiple-choice questions. Write your answer in the space provided next to the number of the question.

_____ 27. The long fingerlike projections at the distal ends of the fallopian tubes are called:
    a. flagellum
    b. graafian follicles
    c. fimbriae
    d. cilia

_____ 28. The tissue between the rectum and the vagina is called the rectovaginal:
    a. fistula
    b. septum
    c. perineum
    d. peroneum

_____ 29. The placental hormone is called:
    a. human chorionic gonadotropin
    b. follicle-stimulating hormone
    c. luteinizing hormone
    d. prolactin

_____ 30. The hormone responsible for the development and maintenance of secondary female sex characteristics:
    a. estrogen
    b. progestin
    c. progesterone
    d. growth hormone

_____ 31. Climacteric usually occurs around ages:
    a. 12 to 14
    b. 18 to 21
    c. 30 to 35
    d. 48 to 52

_____ 32. Conception normally occurs:
    a. in the fallopian tube
    b. in the placenta
    c. in the uterus
    d. in the ovary

_____ 33. Skene glands are located:
    a. near the cervix
    b. around the nipple
    c. at the vaginal orifice
    d. around the urethra

_____ 34. The purpose of the lactiferous ducts is to:
    a. facilitate movement of the fertilized ovum
    b. enclose each ovum within the ovary
    c. carry milk within the breast
    d. move sperm through the vaginal canal

A&P of the Female Reproductive System, Continued

____35. How many vessels does the normal umbilical cord contain?
   a. one
   b. two
   c. three
   d. four

____36. The subdivisions on the uterine surface of the placenta are called:
   a. cotyledons
   b. partitions
   c. labyrinths
   d. yolk sacs

____37. The main portion of the uterus is called the:
   a. fundus
   b. corpus
   c. cervix
   d. endometrium

____38. The recesses formed between the vaginal wall and cervix are known as:
   a. glands
   b. labia
   c. rugae
   d. fornices

____39. The part of the follicle that remains behind in the ovary after the ovum ruptures is the:
   a. fimbriated end
   b. zygote
   c. graafian follicle
   d. corpus luteum

____40. For the first few days after childbirth, the mammary glands produce a fluid called:
   a. colostrum
   b. mother's milk
   c. lactated Ringer's
   d. meconium

____41. How many sperm does it take to fertilize an ovum?
   a. one
   b. hundreds
   c. thousands
   d. millions

____42. Which of the following is NOT a ligament of the female reproductive tract?
   a. round
   b. cardinal
   c. volar
   d. broad

Anatomy and Physiology of the Ears, Nose, and Throat

Match the anatomy words in the left column with their correct definitions in the right column.

_____ 1. cochlea

_____ 2. uvula

_____ 3. pharynx

_____ 4. pinna

_____ 5. cuspids

_____ 6. enamel

_____ 7. incisors

_____ 8. oval window

_____ 9. palate

_____ 10. incus

_____ 11. saliva

_____ 12. malleus

_____ 13. rugae

_____ 14. pulp

_____ 15. organ of Corti

_____ 16. dentin

_____ 17. ossicle

_____ 18. utricle

_____ 19. naris

_____ 20. conchae

_____ 21. stapes

_____ 22. nasal septum

_____ 23. tympanic membrane

_____ 24. taste buds

_____ 25. olfactory cells

_____ 26. auditory meatus

A. communication between middle and inner ears

B. nostril

C. the four front teeth

D. responsible for smell and taste

E. soft tissue within a tooth

F. fleshy structure that hangs from the palate

G. structure associated with maintaining equilibrium

H. anvil

I. auditory canal

J. the flap of the ear

K. stirrup

L. bony structures projecting from lateral walls of nose

M. tissue underlying the enamel of a tooth

N. auditory receptor in cochlea of inner ear

O. roof of mouth

P. throat

Q. eardrum

R. hard, outer layer of teeth

S. canine teeth

T. digestive juice

U. organ that contains hearing-sensitive receptor cells

V. ridges on palate

W. hammer

X. small bone

Y. able to distinguish sweet, sour, salty, and bitter

Z. wall dividing the nasal cavities

Anatomy of the Ears, Nose, and Throat, Continued

Choose the correct answer in each of the following multiple-choice questions. Write your answer in the space provided next to the number of the question.

_____ 27. Collections of lymph tissue in the oropharynx are called:
    a. tonsils
    b. uvulae
    c. adenoids
    d. alveoli

_____ 28. The channel that leads from the pinna to the eardrum is called the:
    a. eustachian tube
    b. auditory canal
    c. organ of Corti
    d. oval window

_____ 29. Collections of lymph tissue in the nasopharynx are called:
    a. bronchi
    b. adenoids
    c. alveoli
    d. cilia

_____ 30. Air-containing cavities in the bones around the nose are called:
    a. paranasal sinuses
    b. adenoids
    c. palatine tonsils
    d. alveoli

_____ 31. The pinna of the ear is also called the:
    a. eardrum
    b. ossicle
    c. auricle
    d. cochlea

_____ 32. The pharyngeal tonsils are more commonly known as the:
    a. adenoids
    b. palatine tonsils
    c. hypopharynx
    d. nasopharynx

_____ 33. The fine hairlike processes on the cells that line the walls of the nasal cavity are called:
    a. flagella
    b. villi
    c. cilia
    d. stubble

_____ 34. The eustachian tube connects the:
    a. middle ear and pharynx
    b. inner ear and maxillary sinuses
    c. tympanic membrane and larynx
    d. ethmoid sinuses and ear canal

Anatomy and Physiology of the Eyes

Match the anatomy words in the left column with their correct definitions in the right column.

_____ 1. ciliary body

_____ 2. cones

_____ 3. sclera

_____ 4. macula

_____ 5. iris

_____ 6. pupil

_____ 7. retina

_____ 8. cornea

_____ 9. rods

_____10. optic nerve

_____11. lens

_____12. vitreous humor

_____13. posterior chamber

_____14. aqueous humor

_____15. anterior chamber

_____16. choroid layer

_____17. conjunctiva

_____18. fovea centralis

_____19. optic chiasm

_____20. lacrimal apparatus

_____21. suspensory ligaments

_____22. fundus

A. nerve cell layer containing rods and cones

B. vascular layer of eye between retina and sclera

C. point at which optic nerve fibers cross in the brain

D. membrane of eyelids and covering most of anterior eye

E. area in retina that is the region of clearest vision

F. structure that contains the fovea centralis

G. attach the lens to the ciliary muscle

H. bends light rays to bring them into focus on retina

I. area in front of iris containing aqueous humor

J. area behind iris that contains the aqueous humor

K. clear tissue over the anterior portion of the eyeball

L. receptor cells responsible for color and central vision

M. fluid in the eye chambers produced by ciliary body

N. colored portion of the eye

O. retinal receptor cells essential for vision in dim light

P. structure that connects the choroid and iris

Q. gelatinous material behind lens of eye

R. tear duct system

S. carries impulses from the retina to the brain

T. dark opening of the eye through which light passes

U. white of the eye

V. posterior, inner part of the eye

A&P of the Eyes, Continued

Choose the correct answer in each of the following multiple-choice questions. Write your answer in the space provided next to the number of the question.

_____ 23. The process by which the curvature of the lens is increased to permit focusing on close objects is called:
    a. accommodation
    b. refraction
    c. flexion
    d. reflexion

_____ 24. The error that results when the globe of the eye is abnormally short in length from front to back so that vision is better for distant objects is:
    a. astigmatism
    b. hyperopia
    c. myopia
    d. presbyopia

_____ 25. A mydriatic does what to the eye?
    a. anesthetizes the eye structures
    b. paralyzes eye movement
    c. dilates the pupil
    d. colors the sclera to help locate foreign bodies

_____ 26. The lens of the eye is:
    a. concave
    b. convex
    c. biconvex
    d. biconcave

_____ 27. The structure that contains muscles to adjust the shape and thickness of the lens is the:
    a. pupil
    b. lens
    c. retina
    d. ciliary body

_____ 28. Which of the following is NOT a true statement about the vitreous humor?
    a. maintains the shape of the eyeball
    b. helps refracts light rays
    c. transforms light to nerve impulses
    d. does not replace itself

_____ 29. An error that causes the light to focus unevenly or diffusely across the retina so that part of the visual field is in focus while other parts are not is:
    a. presbyopia
    b. astigmatism
    c. hyperopia
    d. myopia

Anatomy and Physiology of the Nervous System

Match the anatomy words in the left column with their correct definitions in the right column.

_____ 1. pia mater

_____ 2. sensory nerves

_____ 3. efferent nerves

_____ 4. gyrus

_____ 5. cauda equina

_____ 6. dura mater

_____ 7. brain stem

_____ 8. afferent nerves

_____ 9. thalamus

_____ 10. hypothalamus

_____ 11. sulcus

_____ 12. synapse

_____ 13. receptor

_____ 14. nerve

_____ 15. cerebellum

_____ 16. cerebrum

_____ 17. medulla oblongata

_____ 18. cerebral cortex

_____ 19. neurotransmitter

_____ 20. neuron

_____ 21. ventricle

_____ 22. cerebrospinal fluid

_____ 23. myelin sheath

_____ 24. meninges

_____ 25. central nervous system

_____ 26. axon

A. outer layer of the meninges

B. controls sleep, appetite, temperature, pituitary

C. space through which nerve impulses are transmitted

D. part of brain that coordinates muscular activity

E. consists of axons and dendrites in bundles

F. carry messages to the brain and spinal cord

G. reservoir-like cavity filled with cerebrospinal fluid

H. part of brain that controls autonomic nervous system

I. nerve cell

J. fissure

K. fatty tissue around axon of nerve cell

L. spinal nerves at the level of L2

M. carries nerve impulses away from cell body

N. the delicate inner membrane of the meninges

O. the brain and spinal cord

P. chemical messenger

Q. carry impulses away from the brain and spinal cord

R. organ that receives nerve stimulations

S. a convolution

T. also known as sensory nerves

U. part of brain that controls voluntary movements

V. main relay center of the brain

W. three membranes surrounding brain and spinal cord

X. connects cerebrum with spinal cord

Y. fluid that circulates in brain and spinal cord

Z. gray matter of the brain

A&P of the Nervous System, Continued

Choose the correct answer in each of the following multiple-choice questions. Write your answer in the space provided next to the number of the question.

_____ 27. A large interlacing network of nerves is known as a:
   a. neuron
   b. plexus
   c. dendrite
   d. gyrus

_____ 28. Recognition of one's temporal, spatial, and personal relationships to the environment is referred to as:
   a. stereognosis
   b. orientation
   c. neuroglia
   d. automatism

_____ 29. Blood vessels that selectively let certain substances enter the brain tissue and keep other substances out are collectively called the:
   a. blood-brain barrier
   b. placental barrier
   c. arteriovenous barrier
   d. autonomic barrier

_____ 30. The function of the pons is to:
   a. help maintain balance, posture, and muscular tone
   b. control muscles of the heart and respiratory center
   c. process thought, judgment, memory, and association
   d. bridge cerebellum and cerebrum with the rest of brain

_____ 31. The peripheral nervous system consists of:
   a. 12 pairs of spinal nerves and 12 pairs of cranial nerves
   b. 6 pairs of spinal nerves and 15 pairs of cranial nerves
   c. 15 pairs of cranial nerves and 8 pairs of spinal nerves
   d. 12 pairs of cranial nerves and 31 pairs of spinal nerves

_____ 32. A cranial suture is:
   a. a thin membrane that connects skull bones
   b. an area of the brain that has been oversewn
   c. a very fine monofilament sewing thread
   d. a longitudinal fissure

_____ 33. The Broca area of the brain is responsible for:
   a. vision
   b. hearing
   c. speech
   d. body movement

A&P of the Nervous System, Continued

_____ 34. The olfactory nerve is responsible for the sense of:
   a. sight
   b. touch
   c. hearing
   d. smell

_____ 35. The ligament that connects each vertebra to the next is the:
   a. ligamentum flavum
   b. ligamentum arcuatum mediale
   c. ligamentum conoideum
   d. ligamentum lumbocostale

_____ 36. The spinal cord is located within the vertebral canal and is continuous with the:
   a. cerebral aqueduct
   b. corpus callosum
   c. diencephalon
   d. medulla oblongata

_____ 37. Respiratory rate, body temperature, and heart rhythm are controlled mainly by the:
   a. central nervous system
   b. autonomic nervous system
   c. peripheral nervous system
   d. sympathetic nervous system

_____ 38. Which of the following is NOT a brain wave?
   a. delta
   b. theta
   c. zeta
   d. beta

_____ 39. The area of skin supplied by one spinal nerve through both of its rami is called a:
   a. pyramidal tract
   b. dermatome
   c. neurotransmitter
   d. synaptic knob

_____ 40. All of the following are lobes of the cerebral cortex EXCEPT:
   a. transverse
   b. occipital
   c. frontal
   d. parietal

_____ 41. The spinal cord terminates at the:
   a. first and second lumbar vertebrae
   b. second and third lumbar vertebrae
   c. third and fourth lumbar vetebrae
   d. fourth and fifth lumbar vertebrae

_____ 42. The fluid-filled cavities within the brain are called:
   a. aqueducts
   b. meninges
   c. ventricles
   d. horns

_____ 43. What part of the brain is sensitive to pain?
   a. interventricular foramen
   b. inferior horn
   c. dura mater
   d. lateral recess

_____ 44. Which cranial nerve is responsible for the sense of smell?
   a. I
   b. III
   c. V
   d. VII

_____ 45. Fissures are deep grooves that divide:
   a. the sulci
   b. the cranial sutures
   c. the spinal canal
   d. the cerebrum into quadrants

_____ 46. A muscular contraction occurring in response to a sensory stimulus is called a:
   a. reflex
   b. tic
   c. fast twitch
   d. shock

_____ 47. The adult brain weighs about:
   a. 1 pound
   b. 3 pounds
   c. 5 pounds
   d. 7 pounds

_____ 48. Between the pia mater and the dura mater is a delicate meshwork of connective tissue called the:
   a. diencephalon
   b. midbrain
   c. brain stem
   d. arachnoid

_____ 49. Each axon in the peripheral nerves is covered by a fine membrane called the neurilemma, or sheath of:
   a. Scarpa
   b. Neumann
   c. Schwann
   d. Henle

Anatomy and Physiology of the Immune System

Select one of the following terms that matches the definition.

antibodies　helper cell　suppressor cell　thymus
interferons　plasma cell　vaccination　tonsils
killer cell　T cell　natural immunity　adenoids
macrophage　toxin　passive immunity　spleen
interleukin　immunoglobulins　acquired immunity　lymph nodes

1. stationary lymph tissue along lymph vessels　　lymph nodes

2. formation of antibodies after exposure to antigen　　_____

3. large phagocyte found in lymph nodes and other tissues　　_____

4. T-cell lymphocyte that inhibits activity of B cell lymphocytes　　_____

5. a poison　　_____

6. introduction of altered antigen to produce immunity　　_____

7. protein that stimulates growth of T cell lymphocytes and activates immune response　　_____

8. T cell that aids B cell to recognize antigens and stimulate antibody production　　_____

9. organ near the stomach that produces, stores, and eliminates blood cells　　_____

10. inborn ability to fight disease　　_____

11. masses of lymph tissue in the nasopharynx　　_____

12. immunity administered by ready-made immune bodies　　_____

13. organ in the mediastinum that produces T cell lymphocytes　　_____

14. masses of lymph tissue in the back of the oropharynx　　_____

15. T cells that destroy foreign cells and bacteria　　_____

16. a cell that secretes antibody　　_____

17. IgA, IgE, IgG, IgM, IgD　　_____

18. lymphocyte formed in the thymus gland　　_____

19. antiviral proteins secreted by T cells　　_____

20. proteins that destroy antigens　　_____

A&P of the Immune System, Continued

Choose the correct answer in each of the following multiple-choice questions. Write your answer in the space provided next to the number of the question.

_____ 21. Lymph nodes are located in all of the following areas EXCEPT:
   a. the neck
   b. the groin
   c. the mediastinum
   d. the ankles

_____ 22. A lymphatic organ which is important to the immune process but gets smaller as one ages is:
   a. the spleen
   b. the adenoids
   c. the tonsils
   d. the thymus

_____ 23. The large lymph vessel in the chest that receives lymph from below the diaphragm empties into the:
   a. axillary duct
   b. cystic duct
   c. thoracic duct
   d. hepatic duct

_____ 24. Two of the immune globulins are:
   a. IgL and IgG
   b. IgA and IgD
   c. IgH and IgE
   d. IgM and IgF

_____ 25. Which of the following is NOT a function of the spleen?
   a. storage of gamma globulin
   b. filtration of microorganisms
   c. activation of lymphocytes
   d. destruction of old red blood cells

_____ 26. Approximately what percent of the population is plagued with respiratory allergies?
   a. 10 percent
   b. 15 percent
   c. 20 percent
   d. 25 percent

Section 4.
Medical Terminology

General Suffixes and Prefixes

Match each prefix or suffix in the left column with a related word or phrase on the right.

_____ 1. -tomy

_____ 2. -graphy

_____ 3. oligo-

_____ 4. -logy

_____ 5. super-

_____ 6. inter-

_____ 7. -uria

_____ 8. -pathy

_____ 9. post-

_____10. -plasia

_____ 11. -algia

_____ 12. -osis

_____ 13. -rrhea

_____ 14. meno-

_____ 15. crypto-

_____ 16. myco-

_____ 17. mono-

_____ 18. poly-

_____ 19. hema-

_____ 20. intra-

_____ 21. hyper-

_____ 22. nephro-

_____ 23. -opsy

_____ 24. ichthyo-

_____ 25. -ectomy

_____ 26. myelo-

A. scanty or deficient

B. after

C. fungal

D. development or formation

E. more than one; many

F. pertaining to menses

G. denoting a painful condition

H. cutting or incision

I. disease

J. to view

K. excision of part or all of an organ

L. pertaining to the spinal cord

M. above or excessive

N. hidden or concealed

O. a condition, usually abnormal

P. one or single

Q. pertaining to flow or discharge

R. higher than normal

S. the process of writing or recording

T. pertaining to the kidneys

U. pertaining to the blood

V. between

W. the science or study of

X. within

Y. pertaining to urine

Z. pertaining to a fish

General Suffixes and Prefixes, Continued

Match each prefix or suffix in the left column with a related word or phrase on the right. Some terms match more than one prefix/suffix.

_____ 27. -plexy		A. false
_____ 28. myo-		B. without
_____ 29. neo-		C. denoting plastic surgery
_____ 30. infra-		D. pertaining to muscle
_____ 31. pseudo-		E. pertaining to tissue
_____ 32. dys-		F. around
_____ 33. -genesis		G. outside
_____ 34. exo-		H. pertaining to the use of an instrument
_____ 35. -odynia		I. pertaining to abnormal enlargement
_____ 36. -lysis		J. below normal
_____ 37. a(n)-		K. new
_____ 38. -oma		L. situated below or beneath
_____ 39. histo-		M. painful or difficult
_____ 40. -plasty		N. a stroke or seizure
_____ 41. -genic		O. with or together
_____ 42. -scopy		P. resembling
_____ 43. -ptosis		Q. bad
_____ 44. -oid		R. produced by
_____ 45. -megaly		S. large
_____ 46. ante-		T. destruction
_____ 47. con-		U. pain
_____ 48. peri-		V. before or forward
_____ 49. macro-		W. sagging
_____ 50. mal-		X. tumor or mass
_____ 51. pro-		Y. condition of producing or forming
_____ 52. hypo-		

Plurals

Write one correct plural form of each of the following words. Some may have more than one acceptable plural.

1. biopsy   biopsies

2. alveolus   _____

3. fingerbreadth   _____

4. brother-in-law   _____

5. ovary   _____

6. teaspoonful   _____

7. foramen   _____

8. allergy   _____

9. arthritis   _____

10. phalanx   _____

11. adnexa   _____

12. neuroma   _____

13. leiomyoma   _____

14. diverticulum   _____

15. cornu   _____

16. bursa   _____

17. apex   _____

18. appendix   _____

19. bruit   _____

20. calix   _____

21. criterion   _____

22. contrast medium   _____

23. cervix   _____

24. humerus   _____

25. chondroma   _____

Plurals, Continued

26. atrium _____

27. cul-de-sac _____

28. fundus _____

29. urinalysis _____

30. Pap smear _____

31. forceps _____

32. lumen _____

33. epididymis _____

34. ganglion _____

35. axilla _____

36. fibula _____

37. os _____

38. fistula _____

39. lentigo _____

40. vas _____

41. anastomosis _____

42. salpinx _____

43. larynx _____

44. varix _____

45. exanthema _____

46. epiphysis _____

47. thorax _____

48. ellipse _____

49. retina _____

50. femur _____

Slang Terms

There are many brief forms, slang, and special terms associated with medicine. Test your knowledge of medical slang by writing out the proper translations.

1. bili   bilirubin

2. fluoro _____

3. retic _____

4. chem _____

5. echo _____

6. primip _____

7. cysto _____

8. DC'd _____

9. trach _____

10. dig ("dij") _____

11. coag _____

12. fib (bone) _____

13. ca (or CA) _____

14. procto _____

15. lytes _____

16. cath _____

17. mets _____

18. diff _____

19. nitro _____

20. peds _____

21. 'crit _____

22. lap chole _____

23. meds _____

24. 'tic _____

25. multip _____

Credentials, Degrees, & Organization Abbreviations

Credentials, academic degrees, and professional organization abbreviations are often used in the world of medicine. Translate the following abbreviations. In the event an abbreviation has more than one translation, just give one. NOTE: A *(c)* represents a credential; *(d)* represents a degree; and *(o)* is for an organization.

1. BS (d)   Bachelor of Science degree

2. AAMA (o) _____

3. RRA (c) _____

4. PA-C (c) _____

5. AHIMA (o) _____

6. AMA (o) _____

7. AS (d) _____

8. RN (c) _____

9. ART (c) _____

10. MAT (d) _____

11. BFA (d) _____

12. AAMT (o) _____

13. BSN (d) _____

14. CMA-A (c) _____

15. CMA-C (c) _____

16. CMT (c) _____

17. HCFA (o) _____

18. HIMSS (o) _____

19. JCAHO (o) _____

20. LPN/LVN (c) _____

21. RPT (c) _____

22. MA (d) _____

23. BA (d) _____

24. MBA (d) _____

25. MD (d) _____

26. MPA (d) _____

27. MSW (d) _____

28. ADA _____

Measurement, Dosage, and Time Abbreviations

Translate the abbreviations and brief forms below using their English definitions.

1. a.c.　　before meals
2. ad lib.
3. a.m.
4. b.i.d.
5. C.
6. cc
7. cm
8. cm³
9. d
10. dL
11. EU
12. F.
13. fL
14. ft.
15. g
16. gm
17. gr.
18. hr.
19. h.s.
20. IM (or I.M.)
21. IU
22. IV (or I.V.)
23. J
24. K
25. kg
26. km
27. L
28. lb.
29. m
30. mA
31. mcg
32. MCi

Measurement, Dosage, and Time Abbreviations, Continued

33. mCi _____

34. mEq _____

35. mEq/L _____

36. mg _____

37. mg/cc _____

38. mg/dL _____

39. mg/kg _____

40. mIU _____

41. mL _____

42. mm _____

43. mm Hg _____

44. mmol _____

45. mOsm _____

46. mU _____

47. ng _____

48. n.p.o. _____

49. o.d. _____

50. oz. _____

51. pg _____

52. p.m. _____

53. p.o. _____

54. p.r.n. _____

55. q. _____

56. q.a.m. _____

57. q.h.s. _____

58. q.i.d. _____

59. q.o.d. _____

60. q.p.m. _____

61. q.6h. _____

62. s _____

63. SL _____

64. t.i.d. _____

65. U _____

General Medical Terminology Challenge

Choose the correct answer in each of the following multiple-choice questions. Write your answer in the space provided next to the number of the question.

____ 1. On which portion of the upper extremity are the fingers located?
   a. proximal
   b. inferior
   c. distal
   d. lateral

____ 2. What is the name for the horizontal plane that divides the body into the upper and lower portions?
   a. transverse
   b. frontal
   c. sagittal
   d. proximal

____ 3. Which of the following terms is another word for the directional term "inferior"?
   a. proximal
   b. lateral
   c. caudal
   d. distal

____ 4. Which of the following best describes adduction?
   a. bending part of the body in any direction
   b. moving part of the body toward the midline
   c. moving part of the body away from the midline
   d. rotating any part of the body

____ 5. The instrument that measures blood pressure is called a (an):
   a. stethoscope
   b. sphygmomanometer
   c. stress test
   d. electrocardiogram

____ 6. A solution is dictated as "one to one hundred." How should this be transcribed?
   a. 1-100
   b. 1 to 100
   c. 1-2-100
   d. 1:100

____ 7. Which of the following medical reports usually has the highest priority in transcription?
   a. history and physical
   b. consultation
   c. discharge summary
   d. operative report

____ 8. Which of the following best defines the term *eponym?*
   a. A word based on the name of a person
   b. A word that means the same as another
   c. A word that sounds like another
   d. A word that is spelled like another but has a different meaning

General Medical Abbreviations

The abbreviations and brief forms below are those commonly found in standard H&Ps, consultations, and discharge summary reports. Translate them in full.

1. ADLs   activities of daily living

2. PMH (subheading) _____

3. AV nicking _____

4. Ob/Gyn *or* ob/gyn _____

5. CC (subheading) _____

6. GI _____

7. LUQ _____

8. CVA (2 def.) _____

9. CVS _____

10. AP _____

11. DTRs _____

12. EBL _____

13. e.g. _____

14. EKG _____

15. JVD _____

16. ENT _____

17. etc. _____

18. SOAP _____

19. TMs _____

20. G (pregnancy) _____

21. CCU _____

22. GU _____

23. RLQ _____

24. URI _____

25. HPI (subheading) _____

26. ICU _____

General Medical Abbreviations, Continued

27. i.e. _____

28. JV pulse _____

29. EOM _____

30. lab _____

31. UTI _____

32. LLQ _____

33. CNS _____

34. meds _____

35. BP _____

36. OR _____

37. P (pregnancy) _____

38. temp _____

39. P&A _____

40. PE (subheading) _____

41. PERRLA _____

42. A&P _____

43. PMI _____

44. ROS (subheading) _____

45. HEENT _____

46. RUQ _____

47. ED (or ER) _____

48. T&A _____

49. PA _____

50. H&P _____

Integumentary System Terminology Challenge

Match each of the prefixes and suffixes in the left column with a related term in the right column. Some terms match more than one prefix/suffix.

____ 1. trich-	A. skin
____ 2. squamo-	B. nail
____ 3. hidro-	C. burning
____ 4. myco-	D. hair
____ 5. xantho-	E. fungus
____ 6. -derma	F. yellow
____ 7. xero-	G. sebum
____ 8. unguo-	H. white
____ 9. adipo-	I. black
____ 10. diaphoro-	J. scaly
____ 11. causo-	K. horny
____ 12. cutaneo-	L. red
____ 13. sebo-	M. plant
____ 14. pilo-	N. fat
____ 15. onycho-	O. sweat
____ 16. steato-	P. dry
____ 17. albino-	Q. profuse sweating
____ 18. dermato-	
____ 19. melano-	
____ 20. lipo-	
____ 21. kerato-	
____ 22. ichthyo-	
____ 23. leuko-	
____ 24. erythemo-	
____ 25. phyto-	

Integumentary System Terminology Challenge, Continued

Choose the correct answer in each of the following multiple-choice questions. Write your answer in the space provided next to the number of the question.

_____ 26. Another term for *bedsore* is:
  a. aphthous ulcer
  b. decubitus ulcer
  c. penetrating ulcer
  d. trophic ulcer

_____ 27. A nevus is a:
  a. wart
  b. pimple
  c. blister
  d. mole

_____ 28. Another word for *wart* is:
  a. keratosis
  b. verruca
  c. herpes zoster
  d. vitiligo

_____ 29. Itching is also known as:
  a. hives
  b. urticaria
  c. allergic diathesis
  d. pruritus

_____ 30. Ringworm of the body is termed:
  a. tinea capitis
  b. tinea pedis
  c. tinea pubis
  d. tinea corporis

_____ 31. Which of the following terms describes a condition where the skin appears abnormally dimpled?
  a. le Bouveret
  b. cri du chat
  c. peau d'orange
  d. cafe au lait

_____ 32. Erythema is:
  a. blue-to-black areas on the skin
  b. redness of the skin
  c. white patches on the skin
  d. yellow coloration to the skin

_____ 33. *Alopecia* is another word for:
  a. a lack of melanin in the skin
  b. the half-moon shaped white area at the nail base
  c. hair loss
  d. milk-white patches on the skin

Urinary System Terminology Challenge

Translate the following word combinations into medical terms that relate to the urinary tract. An (n) following the word means "noun"; an (adj) means "adjective."

  1. ribs + vertebral bodies (adj)   costovertebral

  2. outside + body (adj) _____

  3. around + urethra (adj) _____

  4. semen + cyst (n) _____

  5. night + urination (n) _____

  6. ureter + stone formation (n) _____

  7. kidney + stone formation (n) _____

  8. pain + urination (n) _____

  9. testis + excision (n) _____

10. negative + holding (n) _____

11. ureter + bladder (adj) _____

12. kidney + study of (n) _____

13. prostate + inflammation (n) _____

14. blood + urination (n) _____

15. bladder + endoscopic examination (n) _____

16. renal pelvis + kidney + inflammation (n) _____

17. urine + stone formation (n) _____

18. above + pubis (adj) _____

19. calix + dilatation (n) _____

20. glomerulus + kidneys + inflammation (n) _____

21. kidney + stone + incision (n) _____

22. water + kidney + disease process (n) _____

23. scanty + urine (adj) _____

24. stone + crushing (n) _____

25. ketones + urine (n) _____

26. much + thirst (n) _____

Urinary System Terminology Challenge, Continued

Choose the correct answer in each of the following multiple-choice questions. Write your answer in the space provided next to the number of the question.

____ 27. Which of the following words means *inflammation of the urinary bladder?*
    a. pyovesiculitis
    b. cytology
    c. cystitis
    d. dysuria

____ 28. Which term designates a small, poorly functioning kidney?
    a. atopic
    b. ectopic
    c. enteric
    d. atrophic

____ 29. All of the terms below mean "to pass urine" EXCEPT:
    a. void
    b. urinate
    c. masticate
    d. micturate

____ 30. Which term is used to describe the backward flow of urine?
    a. reflux
    b. efflux
    c. reflex
    d. retroflex

____ 31. Uncontrollable passage of drops of urine, particularly just after voiding, is known as:
    a. oliguria
    b. incontinence
    c. dribbling
    d. anuria

____ 32. A problem initiating the flow of urine is termed:
    a. incontinence
    b. hesitancy
    c. prematuria
    d. dysuria

____ 33. The term *urolithiasis* literally means:
    a. ureteral stone
    b. kidney stone
    c. renal stone
    d. urine stone

____ 34. Hyposthenuria is a condition in which the urine is:
    a. markedly reduced in volume
    b. low in the bacteria normally found in urine
    c. reduced in particulate matter
    d. low in specific gravity

Male Reproductive System Terminology Challenge

Match each of the prefixes and suffixes in the left column with a related term in the right column. Some terms match more than one prefix/suffix.

_____ 1. gono-	A. seed
_____ 2. balano-	B. spermatozoa
_____ 3. -stomy	C. twisted or swollen vein
_____ 4. -genesis	D. water
_____ 5. zoo-	E. hidden
_____ 6. testo-	F. cold
_____ 7. spermo-	G. prostate gland
_____ 8. orchio-	H. male
_____ 9. vaso-	I. formation
_____10. varico-	J. animal life
_____11. -pexy	K. epididymis
_____12. -one	L. glans penis
_____13. andro-	M. duct
_____14. epididymo-	N. monster
_____15. crypto-	O. fixation
_____16. hydro-	P. hormone
_____17. semino-	Q. new opening
_____18. terato-	R. testicle
_____19. orchido-	
_____20. prostato-	
_____21. cryo-	

Genitourinary System Abbreviations

Translate the following abbreviations and brief forms.

1. ADH   antidiuretic hormone
2. VCUG   _____
3. HD   _____
4. PKU   _____
5. CAPD   _____
6. UA   _____
7. CRF   _____
8. GU   _____
9. TURP   _____
10. ESWL   _____
11. CVA   _____
12. WBCs   _____
13. BPH   _____
14. C&S   _____
15. IVP   _____
16. KUB   _____
17. UTI   _____
18. BUN   _____
19. pH   _____
20. RBCs   _____
21. SG   _____
22. ESRD   _____
23. cath   _____
24. UPJ   _____
25. ARF   _____

Gastrointestinal System Terminology Challenge

Match each of the prefixes and suffixes in the left column with a related term on the right. Some terms match more than one prefix/suffix.

_____ 1. cheilo-

_____ 2. colo-

_____ 3. procto-

_____ 4. pharyngo-

_____ 5. hepato-

_____ 6. oro-

_____ 7. duodeno-

_____ 8. ceco-

_____ 9. sigmoido-

_____ 10. celio-

_____ 11. colono-

_____ 12. pancreato-

_____ 13. bucco-

_____ 14. peritoneo-

_____ 15. laparo-

_____ 16. jejuno-

_____ 17. stomato-

_____ 18. gastro-

_____ 19. esophago-

_____ 20. bili-

_____ 21. litho-

_____ 22. steato-

_____ 23. amylo-

_____ 24. ileo-

_____ 25. chole-

_____ 26. entero-

A. peritoneum

B. abdomen or belly

C. cecum

D. bile

E. small intestine

F. cheek

G. esophagus

H. lip

I. throat

J. fat

K. colon or large intestine

L. stomach

M. anus

N. stone

O. ileum

P. duodenum

Q. sigmoid colon

R. liver

S. pancreas

T. mouth

U. jejunum

V. starch

W. esophagus

Gastrointestinal System Terminology Challenge, Continued

The suffix *-itis* refers to inflammation. Change each of the entries below to indicate inflammation of the anatomic structure.

27. jejunum   jejunitis

28. kidney   _____

29. colon   _____

30. duodenum   _____

31. esophagus   _____

32. gallbladder   _____

33. ileum   _____

34. liver   _____

35. stomach   _____

36. pancreas   _____

37. appendix   _____

38. peritoneum   _____

39. common bile duct _____

40. spleen   _____

41. bowel   _____

42. stomach + intestines _____

43. tongue   _____

44. pharynx   _____

45. rectum   _____

Gastrointestinal Terminology Challenge, Continued

Choose the correct answer in each of the following multiple-choice questions. Write your answer in the space provided next to the number of the question.

_____ 46. The term for the serosal membrane that lines the abdominopelvic walls is:
   a. perineum
   b. pterion
   c. peronia
   d. peritoneum

_____ 47. A papilla is a:
   a. tiny hair-like projection
   b. nipple-like elevation
   c. ridge
   d. blind pouch

_____ 48. Which of the following is the medical term for a rumbling, gurgling noise in the stomach and intestines?
   a. borborygmus
   b. belch
   c. flatus
   d. eructation

_____ 49. Choose the best definition for the word _celiac_.
   a. pertaining to the stomach
   b. pertaining to the small intestine
   c. pertaining to part of the large intestine
   d. pertaining to the abdomen

_____ 50. The adjective that describes a fluid wave in the abdomen is:
   a. ascetic
   b. acidic
   c. asthenic
   d. ascitic

_____ 51. Rugae are:
   a. projections
   b. contractions
   c. rings
   d. wrinkles

_____ 52. Postprandial pain is experienced after:
   a. waking
   b. sleeping
   c. eating
   d. belching

_____ 53. The movement that propels food from the esophagus to the stomach is termed:
   a. peristalsis
   b. deglutition
   c. absorption
   d. digestion

Gastrointestinal System Abbreviations

Translate the following abbreviations and brief forms.

1. alk phos   alkaline phosphatase

2. GE reflux   _____

3. BE   _____

4. SGOT   _____

5. LFTs   _____

6. PUD   _____

7. UGI   _____

8. GE junction   _____

9. EGD   _____

10. NG   _____

11. GB   _____

12. ALT   _____

13. GI   _____

14. IBD   _____

15. AST   _____

16. LDH   _____

17. CAT scan   _____

18. ERCP   _____

19. n.p.o.   _____

20. NSAIDs   _____

21. BRAT diet   _____

22. SGPT   _____

23. TPN   _____

24. CBD   _____

Musculoskeletal System Terminology Challenge

Match each of the prefixes and suffixes in the left column with a related term or phrase on the right.

_____ 1. -ankylo-	A. behind or in back of
_____ 2. -asthenia	B. a convex curvature
_____ 3. burso-	C. weakness
_____ 4. calcaneo-	D. pertaining to the hand bones
_____ 5. claviculo-	E. wedge-shaped
_____ 6. cranio-	F. pertaining to the lower jaw bone
_____ 7. -desis	G. pertaining to an arm bone
_____ 8. dorsi-	H. pertaining to the hip bone
_____ 9. ethmo-	I. pertaining to the upper jaw bone
_____ 10. costo-	J. a concave curvature
_____ 11. spheno-	K. pertaining to the skull
_____ 12. humero-	L. pertaining to marrow or the spinal cord
_____ 13. ilio-	M. slippage
_____ 14. kypho-	N. stiff, crooked, bent, fused
_____ 15. -olisthesis	O. pertaining to the bones of the toes or fingers
_____ 16. lordo-	P. related to the cord to which muscle is attached
_____ 17. malleolo-	Q. generation or formation
_____ 18. mandibulo-	R. bound or fused
_____ 19. maxillo-	S. pertaining to an extremity
_____ 20. metacarpo-	T. pertaining to a sac of fluid near a joint
_____ 21. myelo-	U. pertaining to the process on each side of the ankle
_____ 22. myo-	V. sieve-like
_____ 23. patello-	W. pertaining to the sole of the foot
_____ 24. phalango-	X. pertaining to the collar bone
_____ 25. -physis	Y. pertaining to the larger leg bone
_____ 26. plant-	Z. twisted or crooked
_____ 27. acro-	AA. pertaining to the ribs
_____ 28. scolio-	BB. pertaining to the kneecap
_____ 29. teno-	CC. pertaining to muscle
_____ 30. fibulo-	DD. pertaining to the heel bone
_____ 31. tibio-	EE. pertaining to a smaller leg bone

Musculoskeletal System Terminology Challenge, Continued

Determine the proper prefixes to complete the medical terms below.

32. excess movement in a joint   hypermobility

33. anti-inflammatory drug type   _____ - steroidal

34. incomplete dislocation   _____ - luxation

35. bursa between acromion and capsule of shoulder joint   _____ - acromial

36. improper position   _____ - alignment

37. below the kneecap   _____ - patellar

38. not supplied with blood   _____ - vascular

39. happened again   _____ - current

40. reduction in size due to disuse   _____ - trophy

41. inflammation of parts surrounding a joint   _____ - arthritis

42. between the shoulder blades   _____ - scapular

43. shaped improperly   _____ - formed

44. within the abdomen   _____ - abdominal

45. above the pubis   _____ - pubic

46. abnormal pigmentation   _____ - coloration

47. to make susceptible   _____ - dispose

48. outside the dura mater   _____ - dural

49. rendering unable   _____ - abling

50. in the center of the thorax   _____ - thoracic

51. an excess degree of extension   _____ - extension

Give the Latin equivalent for each of the English terms below.

52. muscle   musculus

53. tendon   _____

54. nerve   _____

55. bone   _____

56. condyle   _____

57. ligament   _____

58. articulation   _____

Musculoskeletal System Terminology Challenge, Continued

Choose the correct answer in each of the following multiple-choice questions. Write your answer in the space provided next to the number of the question.

____ 59. Flexion means:
   a. movement away from the midline of the body
   b. movement toward the midline of the body
   c. bending a limb
   d. straightening a limb

____ 60. The prefix *rhabdo-* means:
   a. bumpy
   b. development
   c. fibrous
   d. rod-shaped

____ 61. An abnormal inward curvature of the spine is known as
   a. kyphosis
   b. lordosis
   c. scoliosis
   d. ankylosis

____ 62. Which of the following is the word for webbed digits?
   a. pseudodigitalia
   b. anomaly
   c. syndactyly
   d. symbiosis

____ 63. Fibromyalgia (fibro+myalgia) is a condition that affects:
   a. bones
   b. joints
   c. ligaments
   d. muscles

____ 64. The prefix *synov-* means:
   a. watery flow
   b. crooked
   c. synovium
   d. cartilage

____ 65. Bending the foot backward or upward is an act of:
   a. dorsiflexion
   b. rotation
   c. extension
   d. adduction

Musculoskeletal System Abbreviations

Translate each of the following abbreviations.

1. ACL   anterior cruciate ligament

2. DTRs _____

3. BKA _____

4. C spine _____

5. VMO _____

6. PT _____

7. L5-S1 _____

8. DJD _____

9. D spine _____

10. AKA _____

11. EMG _____

12. T spine _____

13. Fx _____

14. L spine _____

15. DIP _____

16. LS spine _____

17. ORIF _____

18. PIP _____

19. DC (physician) _____

20. RA _____

21. DO (physician) _____

22. ROM _____

23. SLR _____

24. FABERE (test) _____

25. TENS (unit) _____

26. CTS _____

Cardiovascular System Terminology Challenge

Identify the noun from which each of the following adjectives is derived.

1. diabetic   diabetes
2. ischemic
3. hypotensive
4. venous
5. myocardial
6. dyspneic
7. arterial
8. ventricular
9. precordial
10. atrial
11. ductal
12. basilar
13. apical
14. aortic
15. embolic
16. valvular
17. varicose
18. occlusive
19. luminal
20. aneurysmal
21. cyanotic
22. sternal
23. stenotic
24. dysrhythmic
25. regurgitant
26. congestive
27. systolic
28. diastolic
29. arrhythmic

Cardiovascular System Terminology Challenge, Continued

Enter the proper medical term(s) for the phrases below. Some answers require more than one word.

30. abnormally slow heartbeat   bradycardia

31. narrowing or stricture of a vessel   _____

32. irregular heartbeat   _____

33. high blood pressure   _____

34. pertaining to the heart and vessels   _____

35. abnormally high cholesterol   _____

36. heart attack   _____

37. enlargement   _____

38. process of tissue death   _____

39. tracing of electrical potential of heart   _____

40. sensation of vibration over the heart   _____

41. severe plaque formation in the arteries   _____

42. blood clot   _____

43. vena saphena magna   _____

44. closure of a blood vessel   _____

45. area of dead tissue   _____

46. open (not blocked)   _____

47. pain, weakness in legs on walking   _____

48. fluctuating high blood pressure   _____

49. repair of heart valve   _____

Cardiovascular System Terminology Challenge, Continued

Choose the correct answer in each of the following multiple-choice questions. Write your answer in the space provided next to the number of the question.

_____ 50. What word defines the contraction phase of the heartbeat?
  a. circulation
  b. exhalation
  c. systole
  d. diastole

_____ 51. The syndrome called "tetralogy of Fallot" consists of how many conditions?
  a. three
  b. two
  c. five
  d. four

_____ 52. Which term refers to the muscular organ that maintains circulation?
  a. core
  b. cor
  c. corps
  d. chord

_____ 53. The terms S_1, S_2, S_3, and S_4 refer to:
  a. ejection fractions
  b. cardiac sounds
  c. rib spaces
  d. locations of cardiac arteries

_____ 54. The prefix _phlebo-_ means:
  a. vein
  b. rhythm
  c. chest
  d. oxygen

_____ 55. An uncomfortable sensation in the chest related to cardiac arrhythmias is:
  a. palpation
  b. palliation
  c. papillation
  d. palpitation

_____ 56. The prefix _athero-_ means:
  a. vessel
  b. bluish tinge
  c. fatty degeneration
  d. valve

_____ 57. The prefix _brady-_ means:
  a. fast
  b. slow
  c. arm
  d. heart

Cardiovascular System Abbreviations

Translate each of the following abbreviations and brief forms.

1. ACE inhibitor   angiotensin-converting enzyme

2. PDA _____

3. LVH _____

4. ASD _____

5. CTR _____

6. LDL _____

7. MR (disease) _____

8. PND _____

9. cardiac cath _____

10. EKG _____

11. PTCA _____

12. JVD _____

13. CPK _____

14. AV (two def.) _____

15. VLDL _____

16. CVP _____

17. A_2 _____

18. MVP _____

19. DSA _____

20. DVT _____

21. SBE _____

22. ECG _____

23. regurg _____

24. CCU _____

25. ETT _____

26. HDL _____

27. CHF _____

260

Cardiovascular System Abbreviations, Continued

28. LDH _____

29. CVS _____

30. LV _____

31. ASCVD _____

32. MI _____

33. CABG _____

34. MUGA (scan) _____

35. DOE _____

36. NSR _____

37. P$_2$ _____

38. PAC _____

39. AF _____

40. PMI _____

41. CAD _____

42. t-PA _____

43. PVC _____

44. echo _____

45. S-A _____

46. ECC _____

47. CHD _____

48. VAD (device) _____

49. CPR _____

50. VSD _____

51. VT _____

52. BBB _____

53. RVH _____

54. CVC (line) _____

Pulmonary System Terminology Challenge

Translate the following word combinations into medical terms that relate to the respiratory system. An (n) following the word means "noun"; (adj) means "adjective"; (v) means "verb."

  1. bronchus + lung (adj)   bronchopulmonary

  2. lung + specialist (n) _____

  3. back + front (adj) _____

  4. larynx + trachea (adj) _____

  5. trachea + esophagus (adj) _____

  6. bronchus + widen (v) _____

  7. heart + lung (adj) _____

  8. nose + throat (n) _____

  9. immune + defective (n) _____

10. bronchus + endoscopy (n) _____

11. bronchus + spasm (n) _____

12. mediastinum + endoscopy (n) _____

13. pleura + pain (n) _____

14. chest + incision (n) _____

15. epiglottis + inflammation (n) _____

16. lobe + excision (n) _____

17. trachea + larynx + inflammation (n) _____

18. blood + chest (n) _____

19. spitting + blood (n) _____

20. absence + breathing (n) _____

21. windpipe + incision (n) _____

22. breathing + measurement (n) _____

23. nose + throat + inflammation (n) _____

24. absence + smell (n) _____

25. lungs + dust + process (n) _____

Pulmonary System Terminology Challenge, Continued

Provide a simple definition for each of the following terms.

26. diaphoresis   perspiration

27. eupnea _____

28. aspiration _____

29. respiration _____

30. intrinsic _____

31. refractory _____

32. effusion _____

33. dyspnea _____

34. pleural _____

35. apnea _____

36. stridor _____

37. sibilant _____

38. wheeze _____

39. paroxysmal _____

40. pneumothorax _____

41. thrombus _____

42. acidosis _____

43. hyperpnea _____

44. necrosis _____

45. hypercapnia _____

Pulmonary System Terminology Challenge, Continued

Choose the correct answer in each of the following multiple-choice questions. Write your answer in the space provided next to the number of the question.

_____ 46. Listening to sounds within the body is:
    a. auscultation
    b. palpation
    c. percussion
    d. bronchoscopy

_____ 47. The prefix *telo-* means:
    a. voice
    b. dust
    c. particulate
    d. complete

_____ 48. Sputum is best described as:
    a. material expelled from the nares
    b. material expelled from the mouth
    c. material expelled from the sinuses
    d. material expelled from the chest

_____ 49. An accumulation of air or gas within the pleural cavity is known as:
    a. hemothorax
    b. hydrothorax
    c. pneumothorax
    d. pyothorax

_____ 50. The prefix *spiro-* means:
    a. spiral
    b. circular
    c. breathing
    d. upright

_____ 51. The term *purulent* pertains to:
    a. itching
    b. pus
    c. inflammation
    d. clotting

_____ 52. Difficulty breathing except in the upright position is termed:
    a. orthopnea
    b. trachypnea
    c. dyspnea
    d. apnea

_____ 53. A rale is a:
    a. snap
    b. crackle
    c. pop
    d. grating sound

Pulmonary System Abbreviations

Translate each of the following abbreviations.

1. A&P   auscultation and percussion

2. RD _____

3. V/Q scan _____

4. ARDS _____

5. IMV _____

6. CXR _____

7. FEV _____

8. DPT (injection) _____

9. ET tube _____

10. PPD _____

11. DOE _____

12. FEV_1 _____

13. PEEP _____

14. SOB _____

15. RUL _____

16. LLL _____

17. COPD _____

18. URI _____

19. PCP _____

20. FEF_{25-75} _____

21. PFTs _____

22. PND _____

23. FEF _____

24. ABGs _____

25. RLL _____

26. LUL _____

27. FVC _____

28. TB _____

29. P&A _____

30. AFB _____

31. RAD _____

Endocrine System Terminology Challenge

Match each of the prefixes and suffixes in the left column with a related term in the column on the right.

_____ 1. gonado-

_____ 2. -tropin

_____ 3. toco-

_____ 4. eu-

_____ 5. pan-

_____ 6. adeno-

_____ 7. thyro-

_____ 8. cortico-

_____ 9. dipso-

_____10. crino-

_____11. estro-

_____12. homeo-

_____13. lacto-

_____14. tetra-

_____15. -agon

_____16. -ine

_____17. stero-

_____18. somato-

_____19. glyco-

_____20. oxy-

_____21. tri-

_____22. toxico-

_____23. physo-

_____24. pituitar-

_____25. adreno-

A. to act upon

B. female

C. milk

D. thyroid

E. all

F. sugar

G. a substance

H. poison

I. pituitary

J. four

K. body

L. three

M. growing

N. childbirth

O. adrenal gland

P. sex glands

Q. solid substance

R. acid

S. normal

T. sameness

U. gland

V. secrete

W. outer region

X. to gather together

Y. thirst

Endocrine System Terminology Challenge, Continued

Choose the correct answer in each of the following multiple-choice questions. Write your answer in the space provided next to the number of the question.

_____ 26. Polyphagia means:
    a. excessive sweating
    b. excessive talking
    c. excessive movement
    d. excessive eating

_____ 27. Greater than normal serum potassium is termed:
    a. hypernatremia
    b. hypercalcemia
    c. hyperchloridemia
    d. hyperkalemia

_____ 28. Euthyroid refers to a person whose thyroid gland:
    a. is functioning normally
    b. is hyperactive
    c. is hypoactive
    d. has been surgically removed

_____ 29. A state of stability maintained in the body is called:
    a. equilibrium
    b. syncope
    c. homeostasis
    d. balance

_____ 30. Acromegaly means:
    a. moon facies
    b. enlargement of the thyroid gland
    c. protrusion of the eyeballs
    d. enlargement of the extremities

_____ 31. Myxedema literally means:
    a. rapid enlargement
    b. mucus swelling
    c. mixed swelling
    d. combined water

_____ 32. A pathological protrusion of the eyeballs is termed:
    a. exophthalmia
    b. exophthalmitis
    c. exophthalmoplegia
    d. exophthalmos

_____ 33. The combining form _andro-_ means:
    a. androgen
    b. male
    c. sex
    d. testis

Endocrine System Abbreviations

Translate each of the following abbreviations and brief forms. *(Note: Some endocrinology terms, particularly those related to diabetes mellitus, are becoming obsolete. However, it is still important for medical transcriptionists to know them since they are still used by some physicians.)*

1. ACTH   adrenocorticotropic hormone

2. FSH _____

3. IDDM _____

4. BMR _____

5. SIADH _____

6. DM _____

7. FBS _____

8. OGTT _____

9. GH _____

10. ADH _____

11. hGH _____

12. PTH _____

13. AODM _____

14. K _____

15. TSH _____

16. MSH _____

17. TFTs _____

18. NIDDM _____

19. 17-OH _____

20. GTT _____

21. PRL _____

22. RIA _____

23. DI _____

24. Na _____

25. LH _____

Female Reproductive System Terminology Challenge

Match each of the prefixes and suffixes in the left column with a related word or phrase in the right column. Some terms match more than one prefix/suffix.

____ 1. culdo-	A.	to bear
____ 2. amnio-	B.	labor
____ 3. mammo-	C.	muscle tumor
____ 4. phoro-	D.	act of turning
____ 5. -arche	E.	egg
____ 6. ante-	F.	breast
____ 7. primi-	G.	cul-de-sac
____ 8. colpo-	H.	menses
____ 9. nati-	I.	birth
____ 10. -parous	J.	vulva
____ 11. -gravida	K.	beginning
____ 12. -tocia	L.	uterus
____ 13. nulli-	M.	pregnancy
____ 14. -version	N.	amnion
____ 15. -cyesis	O.	first
____ 16. -myoma	P.	none
____ 17. oo-	Q.	vagina
____ 18. metro-	R.	milk
____ 19. masto-	S.	forward
____ 20. vagino-		
____ 21. meno-		
____ 22. galacto-		
____ 23. episio-		
____ 24. vulvo-		
____ 25. hystero-		

Female Reproductive System Terminology Challenge, Continued

Divide each word into its root words and define.

26. hysterectomy   uterus + cutting out (surgical removal of uterus)

27. estrogen   _____

28. dysplasia   _____

29. cystocele   _____

30. oligomenorrhea   _____

31. vesicovaginal   _____

32. mastectomy   _____

33. postcoital   _____

34. leukorrhea   _____

35. menarche   _____

36. multiparous   _____

37. gestation   _____

38. endometriosis   _____

39. dyspareunia   _____

40. intermenstrual   _____

41. galactorrhea   _____

42. toxemia   _____

43. curettage   _____

44. cephalopelvic   _____

45. episiotomy   _____

46. gynecology   _____

47. culdocentesis   _____

48. hysterosalpingogram   _____

49. endocervicitis   _____

50. oophoritis   _____

51. neonatology   _____

52. myometrium   _____

53. primigravida   _____

54. pyosalpinx   _____

55. retroflexion   _____

Female Reproductive System Terminology Challenge, Continued

Choose the correct answer in each of the following multiple-choice questions. Write your answer in the space provided next to the number of the question.

_____ 56. Which of the following is the proper word for false pregnancy?
   a. pseudocyesis
   b. negative gravidarum profundosis
   c. cyophoria
   d. ectopic

_____ 57. Which of the following is the medical term for the condition where the uterine lining grows outside of the uterus and implants on tubes and ovaries?
   a. endometriosis
   b. choriocarcinoma
   c. hematocolpos
   d. fibroidosis

_____ 58. A woman gives birth to twins prematurely. Twin A is still in an incubator, but twin B has been discharged home. This is the woman's third pregnancy; her oldest child, the healthy product of a full-term delivery, is just entering third grade. The next youngest child is starting kindergarten but was born prematurely. Which of the following is the correct expression of this patient's obstetrical status?
   a. gravida 1, para 4
   b. gravida 3, para 1-3-0-4
   c. gravida 2, para 2-0-1-3
   d. gravida 4, para 4-0-0-4

_____ 59. The prefix _chorio-_ refers to the:
   a. fluid in which the developing embryo resides
   b. vascular organ that nourishes the developing embryo
   c. innermost embryonic membrane that holds the fetus
   d. outermost membrane surrounding the developing embryo

_____ 60. An orifice is:
   a. a sensitive organ of erectile tissue
   b. a developing embryo
   c. an opening
   d. a sex cell

_____ 61. A secundigravida woman has had how many pregnancies?
   a. none
   b. one
   c. two
   d. more than two

Female Reproductive System Abbreviations

Translate each of the following abbreviations and brief forms.

1. ab (or AB)   abortus or abortion

2. Ob or OB or ob   _____

3. A&P repair   _____

4. PKU   _____

5. BUS   _____

6. Ca or CA   _____

7. VBAC   _____

8. DUB   _____

9. AFP   _____

10. CS   _____

11. D&C   _____

12. DES (med)   _____

13. C-section   _____

14. ECC   _____

15. BSO   _____

16. L&D   _____

17. ERT   _____

18. PID   _____

19. EMB   _____

20. G   _____

21. gyn or Gyn   _____

22. CIS   _____

23. HSG   _____

24. IUD   _____

Female Reproductive System Abbreviations, Continued

25. IUP _____

26. CPD _____

27. primip _____

28. LMP _____

29. multip _____

30. NSVD _____

31. UTI _____

32. hCG _____

33. OCT _____

34. P _____

35. Pap smear _____

36. VD _____

37. peds _____

38. VCUG _____

39. FSH _____

40. PMS _____

41. LH _____

42. PROM _____

43. STD _____

44. TAH _____

45. UC _____

46. OCPs _____

47. FHT _____

48. EDC _____

49. path _____

Otorhinolaryngology Terminology Challenge

Match each of the prefixes and suffixes in the left column with a related word or phrase in the right column. Some terms match more than one prefix/suffix.

_____ 1. acou-

_____ 2. bucco-

_____ 3. cochleo-

_____ 4. adeno-

_____ 5. mastoido-

_____ 6. naso-

_____ 7. audito-

_____ 8. -otia

_____ 9. salpingo-

_____ 10. tonsillo-

_____ 11. audio-

_____ 12. denti-

_____ 13. oto-

_____ 14. gingivo-

_____ 15. auro-

_____ 16. -osmia

_____ 17. myringo-

_____ 18. rhino-

_____ 19. stapedo-

_____ 20. cheilo-

_____ 21. ossiculo-

_____ 22. odonto-

_____ 23. -acusis

_____ 24. phono-

_____ 25. tympano-

_____ 26. glosso-

A. tooth

B. eustachian tube

C. eardrum

D. tongue

E. ear

F. gums

G. condition of the ear

H. lip

I. ossicle

J. stapes

K. cochlea

L. adenoids

M. mastoid process

N. nose

O. voice

P. hearing

Q. cheek

R. smell

S. tonsils

Otorhinolaryngology Terminology Challenge, Continued

Translate the following word combinations into medical terms that relate to the ears, nose, and throat.

27. opposite + pinna of ear   antihelix

28. old + hearing   _____

29. eardrum + surgical repair   _____

30. behind + ear   _____

31. eardrum + incision   _____

32. stapes + excision   _____

33. hearing + test   _____

34. mastoid + inflammation   _____

35. ear + fungus   _____

36. ear + nose + voice box + specialist   _____

37. near + nose   _____

38. nose + flow   _____

39. sinus + inflammation   _____

40. out + breathing + action   _____

41. adenoids + tonsils + excision   _____

42. absence + smell   _____

43. lip + inflammation   _____

44. tooth + cheek   _____

45. gums + inflammation   _____

46. under/below + tongue   _____

47. straight + tooth + specialist   _____

48. mouth + throat   _____

49. palate + surgical repair   _____

50. salivary gland + stone   _____

51. mouth + inflammation   _____

52. throat + tonsils + inflammation   _____

Otorhinolaryngology Terminology Challenge, Continued

Choose the correct answer in each of the following multiple-choice questions. Write your answer in the space provided next to the number of the question.

_____ 53. What does *sublingual* mean?
    a. under the chin
    b. under the ear
    c. under the jaw
    d. under the tongue

_____ 54. Which of the following is the correct term for the tooth surface on the facial side, farthest from the median line?
    a. distal
    b. lingual
    c. buccal
    d. mesial

_____ 55. The medical term *cerumen* means:
    a. ringing in the ears
    b. ear wax
    c. dizziness
    d. bloody nose

_____ 56. The prefix *palato-* refers to which structure?
    a. palatine tonsils
    b. cheeks
    c. gums
    d. roof of the mouth

_____ 57. Which of the following is the best definition for a sinus?
    a. a groove-like depression
    b. one of the bones of the face
    c. a cavity within a bone
    d. a growth plate

_____ 58. Visual examination of the ear and tympanic membrane is carried out using what type of instrument?
    a. gastroscope
    b. laryngoscope
    c. otoscope
    d. ophthalmoscope

_____ 59. The suffix *-tresia* means:
    a. opening
    b. tightening
    c. contraction
    d. spasm

_____ 60. The medical term for the voicebox is the:
    a. pharynx
    b. trachea
    c. epiglottis
    d. larynx

Otorhinolaryngology Abbreviations

Translate each of the following abbreviations and brief forms.

1. AD   right ear

2. TMJ   _____

3. URI   _____

4. AU   _____

5. T&A   _____

6. EAC   _____

7. NSR   _____

8. HEENT   _____

9. AS   _____

10. ITE hearing aid _____

11. BOM   _____

12. EEA   _____

13. UPPP   _____

14. SCC   _____

15. SMR   _____

16. SOM   _____

17. ENT   _____

18. TMs   _____

Ophthalmology Terminology Challenge

Match each of the prefixes and suffixes in the left column with a related word or phrase in the right column. Some terms match more than one prefix/suffix.

___ 1. lacrimo-	A. eye
___ 2. oculo-	B. eye muscle
___ 3. palpebro-	C. pupil
___ 4. corneo-	D. lens
___ 5. cyclo-	E. tears
___ 6. blepharo-	F. conjunctiva
___ 7. irido-	G. sclera
___ 8. conjunctivo-	H. cornea
___ 9. dacryo-	I. gray
___ 10. aqueo-	J. dim
___ 11. papillo-	K. retina
___ 12. coro-	L. optic disk
___ 13. opto-	M. eyelid
___ 14. phako-	N. to turn
___ 15. retino-	O. iris
___ 16. ophthalmo-	P. water
___ 17. pupillo-	Q. old age
___ 18. kerato-	R. uvea
___ 19. sclero-	S. vision
___ 20. uveo-	T. double
___ 21. amblyo-	
___ 22. glauco-	
___ 23. diplo-	
___ 24. -opsia	
___ 25. presby-	
___ 26. -tropia	

Ophthalmology Terminology Challenge, Continued

Choose the correct answer in each of the following multiple-choice questions. Write your answer in the space provided next to the number of the question.

_____ 27. The term *scotoma* refers to a:
    a. tic
    b. blind spot
    c. opening
    d. receptor

_____ 28. The term *xerophthalmia* means:
    a. dry eyes
    b. excessive tearing
    c. night blindness
    d. light sensitivity

_____ 29. Night blindness is termed:
    a. diplopia
    b. nyctalopia
    c. presbyopia
    d. hyperopia

_____ 30. The medical term for sensitivity to light is:
    a. mydriasis
    b. nyctalopia
    c. scotoma
    d. photophobia

_____ 31. The medical term for a corneal transplant is:
    a. keratoplasty
    b. corneal abrasion
    c. photocoagulation
    d. corneoplasty

_____ 32. Inflammation of the vascular layer of the eye is termed:
    a. retinitis
    b. ophthalmitis
    c. uveitis
    d. conjunctivitis

_____ 33. To refract means to:
    a. amplify light rays
    b. break back
    c. bring forward
    d. take apart

_____ 34. The prefix *aniso-* means:
    a. unequal
    b. horny
    c. turned
    d. circular

Ophthalmology Abbreviations

Translate each of the following abbreviation and brief forms.

1. AZT   azidothymidine (also zidovudine)

2. OD   _____

3. PRP   _____

4. EOM   _____

5. Hg   _____

6. OU   _____

7. EOMI   _____

8. SLE   _____

9. VA   _____

10. OS   _____

11. IOL   _____

12. CMV retinitis   _____

13. IOP   _____

14. VF   _____

15. FB   _____

16. EENT   _____

17. HIV   _____

18. PERRLA   _____

Nervous System Terminology Challenge

Match each of the prefixes and suffixes in the left column with a related word or phrase in the right column.

_____ 1. -taxo	A. brain
_____ 2. -sthenia	B. referring to the cerebrum
_____ 3. cerebello-	C. referring to the thalamus
_____ 4. duro-	D. pertaining to nerve sheaths
_____ 5. encephalo-	E. deep sleep
_____ 6. glio-	F. referring to the pons
_____ 7. lepto-	G. spinal cord
_____ 8. myelo-	H. excessive sensitivity to pain
_____ 9. radiculo-	I. pertaining to the cerebellum
_____ 10. theco-	J. burning
_____ 11. vago-	K. strength
_____ 12. causo-	L. slight paralysis
_____ 13. -esthesia	M. pertaining to the dura mater
_____ 14. -lepsy	N. paralysis
_____ 15. -plegia	O. muscle
_____ 16. -phasia	P. order, coordination
_____ 17. -paresis	Q. referring to the meninges
_____ 18. lexo-	R. pertaining to the nerve root
_____ 19. ponto-	S. feeling
_____ 20. cerebro-	T. pertaining to the vagus nerve
_____ 21. comato-	U. word or phrase
_____ 22. thalamo-	V. seizure
_____ 23. -algesia	W. thin
_____ 24. myo-	X. speech
_____ 25. meningo-	Y. glue

Nervous System Terminology Challenge, Continued

Choose the correct answer in each of the following multiple-choice questions. Write your answer in the space provided next to the number of the question.

_____ 26. What is the word that means "unable to speak"?
   a. aphagia
   b. ataxia
   c. aphasia
   d. aphakia

_____ 27. Hemiplegia is best defined as:
   a. paralysis of all four extremities and usually the trunk
   b. paralysis of one-half of the body, either left or right
   c. paralysis of one-half of the body, either upper or lower
   d. paralysis of trunk and lower extremities

_____ 28. Which is the best definition of the term _innervation?_
   a. to give energy to
   b. to take energy from
   c. to activate a nerve
   d. to deactivate a nerve

_____ 29. Ataxia is:
   a. difficulty speaking
   b. nervous exhaustion
   c. purposeless movements of body parts
   d. failure of muscular coordination

_____ 30. What is one correct plural of _plexus?_
   a. plexi
   b. plexuses
   c. plexae
   d. plexa

_____ 31. Kinesiology is the study of:
   a. sleep
   b. seizures
   c. movement
   d. comas

_____ 32. _Syncope_ is another word for:
   a. fainting
   b. coma
   c. arousal
   d. wakefulness

_____ 33. _Word salad_ refers to what?
   a. using vulgar language
   b. incoherent speech
   c. inability to understand the spoken word
   d. inability of a literate person to recognize the written word

Nervous System Abbreviations

Translate each of the following abbreviations and brief forms.

1. ADD   attention deficit disorder

2. PET scan _____

3. AFP _____

4. CVA _____

5. MRI _____

6. CSF _____

7. RIND _____

8. ALS _____

9. DTRs _____

10. ADLs _____

11. EMG _____

12. VP shunt _____

13. LP _____

14. CNS _____

15. MS _____

16. NCV _____

17. PERRLA _____

18. ICP _____

19. EEG _____

20. TENS _____

21. TIA _____

22. CT scan _____

Psychiatric Terminology

Match each of the prefixes and suffixes in the left column with a related word or phrase in the right column. Some terms match more than one prefix/suffix.

_____ 1. schizo-

_____ 2. iatro-

_____ 3. -mania

_____ 4. -genic

_____ 5. mento-

_____ 6. -phobia

_____ 7. hypo-

_____ 8. para-

_____ 9. -phoria

_____ 10. philo-

_____ 11. somato-

_____ 12. psycho-

_____ 13. anxio-

_____ 14. auto-

_____ 15. hypno-

_____ 16. -leptic

_____ 17. hallucino-

_____ 18. neuro-

_____ 19. phreno-

_____ 20. -thymia

_____ 21. an-

_____ 22. cata-

A. treatment

B. split

C. deficient

D. body

E. sleep

F. seize

G. produced by

H. wander in the mind

I. abnormal

J. irrational fear

K. not

L. obsessive preoccupation

M. nerve

N. feeling

O. mind

P. down

Q. self

R. distress

S. love

Psychiatric Terminology, Continued

Choose the correct answer in each of the following multiple-choice questions. Write your answer in the space provided next to the number of the question.

_____ 23. Anxiety is:
   a. severe lack of responsiveness
   b. sadness or hopelessness
   c. fear of the unknown
   d. disassociation

_____ 24. The term *cyclothymia* literally means:
   a. recurring mind
   b. round body
   c. cyclical fear
   d. repeated loss

_____ 25. Which of the following is a medical doctor licensed to treat mental illness?
   a. physiatrist
   b. psychiatrist
   c. psychologist
   d. physiologist

_____ 26. A person with a fear of being outside in open spaces suffers from:
   a. arachnophobia
   b. agoraphobia
   c. aerophobia
   d. androphobia

_____ 27. A patient's external emotions or emotional response is termed:
   a. effect
   b. affect
   c. ego
   d. autism

_____ 28. Apathy is:
   a. hate
   b. love
   c. anger
   d. indifference

_____ 29. Bipolar means:
   a. big bear
   b. two extremes
   c. large pole
   d. companion

Psychiatric Abbreviations

Translate each of the following abbreviations and brief forms. (NOTE: The abbreviation *org.* denotes an organization.)

1. ADHD   attention-deficit hyperactivity disorder

2. THC   _____

3. NA (org.)   _____

4. SAD   _____

5. ECT   _____

6. GA (org.)   _____

7. CNS   _____

8. WISC (test)   _____

9. MMPI (test)   _____

10. OA (org.)   _____

11. PCP   _____

12. DTs   _____

13. TAT (test)   _____

14. OBS   _____

15. WAIS (test)   _____

16. MAO inhibitor   _____

17. EtOH   _____

18. AA (org.)   _____

19. IQ (test)   _____

20. DSM   _____

21. LSD   _____

Immune System, Genetics, & Oncology Terminology Challenge

Match each of the prefixes and suffixes in the left column with a related word or phrase in the right column. Some terms match more than one prefix/suffix.

_____ 1. carcino-

_____ 2. muta-

_____ 3. pleo-

_____ 4. -plasm

_____ 5. radio-

_____ 6. scirrho-

_____ 7. -oma

_____ 8. -plasia

_____ 9. apo-

_____10. fungo-

_____11. caco-

_____12. -blast

_____13. onco-

_____14. -therapy

_____15. epi-

_____16. ana-

_____17. papillo-

_____18. sarco-

_____19. cryo-

_____20. folliculo-

_____21. meta-

_____22. chemo-

_____23. fibro-

_____24. cautero-

_____25. plaso-

_____26. toxo-

A. upon

B. flesh

C. cancer

D. off

E. drug

F. fungus

G. cold

H. backward

I. genetic change

J. hard

K. treatment

L. formation

M. tumor

N. immature or embryonic

O. many

P. rays

Q. poison

R. beyond

S. burn

T. fibers

U. nipple

V. bad

W. small sacs

Immune System, Genetics, & Oncology Terminology Challenge, Continued

Choose the correct answer in each of the following multiple-choice questions. Write your answer in the space provided next to the number of the question.

_____27. Which of the following is the correct word for a new growth or tumor?
    a. oncoplasm
    b. neoplasm
    c. neoma
    d. hyperosis

_____28. Which of the following words literally means "stopping beyond"?
    a. metastasis
    b. ultracessation
    c. metamorphosis
    d. anabolism

_____29. The spreading process of a malignant tumor is called:
    a. cancer
    b. metastasis
    c. urticaria
    d. neoplasia

_____30. An opportunistic infection is an infection caused by:
    a. a microorganism not normally present in the body
    b. a microorganism following infection of another organism
    c. a microorganism that does not usually cause disease
    d. more than one microorganism

_____31. Tissue that is necrotic is:
    a. cancerous
    b. dead
    c. burned
    d. hard

_____32. Enlargement of the spleen is known as:
    a. splenomalacia
    b. splenomyelomalacia
    c. splenolysis
    d. splenomegaly

_____33. Which of the following is another term for Down syndrome?
    a. Hashimoto disease
    b. Turner syndrome
    c. tetralogy of Fallot
    d. trisomy 21

_____34. The prefix _immuno-_ means:
    a. poison
    b. protection
    c. shield
    d. injection

_____ 35. *Hypersensitivity reaction* is more commonly known as:
    a. allergy
    b. rheumatoid arthritis
    c. lupus erythematosus
    d. multiple sclerosis

_____ 36. The term *cystic* refers to:
    a. hard mass
    b. fluid-filled spaces
    c. diffuse
    d. ulcerated

_____ 37. *Dysplastic* refers to:
    a. localized tumor cells
    b. abnormal formation of cells
    c. new tumor growth
    d. dead tissue

_____ 38. *Schirrhous* means:
    a. soft
    b. solid
    c. hard
    d. semisolid

_____ 39. *Exenteration* refers to:
    a. destruction of tissue by electric current
    b. removal of tumor by biopsy
    c. removal of tumor and all surrounding tissue in body space
    d. removal of tumor along with surrounding tissue and lymph nodes

_____ 40. The word *anaplasia* literally means:
    a. backward growth
    b. soft tumor
    c. cold flesh
    d. benign formation

_____ 41. Adjuvant therapy is:
    a. treatment with drugs
    b. drug and radiation treatment
    c. radiation in small, repeated doses
    d. combination chemotherapy

_____ 42. The tumor staging system is known by which abbreviation?
    a. ABC
    b. TSS
    c. ATS
    d. TNM

Immune System, Genetics, & Oncology Abbreviations

Translate each of the following abbreviations and brief forms.

1. AIDS   acquired immunodeficiency syndrome
2. HIV   _____
3. LE   _____
4. RA   _____
5. SLE   _____
6. AZT   _____
7. T-4   _____
8. CMV   _____
9. TNM   _____
10. ddI   _____
11. EBV   _____
12. XRT   _____
13. histo   _____
14. HSV   _____
15. CMF   _____
16. MAI   _____
17. PCP   _____
18. T-8   _____
19. crypto   _____
20. toxo   _____
21. ZVD   _____
22. chemo   _____
23. bx   _____
24. Ca or CA   _____
25. CD4   _____
26. KS   _____
27. DNA   _____
28. mets   _____
29. RNA   _____

Radiology Imaging Terminology Challenge

Match each of the prefixes and suffixes in the left column with a word or phrase on the right. Some terms match more than one prefix/suffix.

_____ 1. xero-

_____ 2. -gram

_____ 3. fluoro-

_____ 4. letho-

_____ 5. iso-

_____ 6. therapeuto-

_____ 7. vivo-

_____ 8. mucoso-

_____ 9. radio-

_____ 10. -opaque

_____ 11. tomo-

_____ 12. cine-

_____ 13. echo-

_____ 14. -suppression

_____ 15. -therapy

_____ 16. -lucent

_____ 17. -graphy

_____ 18. sono-

_____ 19. scintillo-

_____ 20. intra-

_____ 21. pharmaceuto-

_____ 22. roentgeno-

_____ 23. ortho-

_____ 24. ultra-

_____ 25. brachy-

_____ 26. inter-

A. record

B. treatment

C. repeated sound

D. drug

E. spark

F. beyond

G. short

H. luminous or shine

I. between

J. sound

K. stop

L. cut

M. straight

N. dry

O. x-ray

P. death

Q. life

R. process of recording

S. within

T. obscure

U. same

V. movement

W. mucous membrane

Radiology Imaging Abbreviations

Translate each of the following abbreviations and brief forms.

1. Bq   becquerel
2. MHz   _____
3. rad   _____
4. US   _____
5. SPECT   _____
6. Gy   _____
7. KUB   _____
8. AP   _____
9. S/N ratio   _____
10. MRI   _____
11. Hz   _____
12. CAT   _____
13. R   _____
14. cGy   _____
15. T   _____
16. angio   _____
17. IVP   _____
18. PA   _____
19. Ba   _____
20. CT   _____
21. fluoro   _____
22. CXR   _____
23. PET (scan) _____
24. DI   _____
25. I   _____
26. Ga   _____

Radiology Imaging Abbreviations, Continued

27. DSA _____

28. RAO _____

29. LS spine _____

30. mCi _____

31. μC (also μCi) _____

32. kHz _____

33. MUGA (scan) _____

34. kV _____

35. decub _____

36. Tc _____

37. UGI _____

38. CINE _____

39. VQ _____

40. XRT _____

41. DVT _____

42. RVH _____

43. LVH _____

44. FLASH _____

45. PTCA _____

46. DTPA _____

47. CDI _____

48. HDR _____

49. Fx _____

50. CCK _____

51. GB _____

Laboratory and Pathology Abbreviations

Translate the following abbreviations and brief forms below.

1. ABGs   arterial blood gases

2. polys _____

3. B strep _____

4. WNL _____

5. ADH _____

6. ELISA _____

7. LDH _____

8. AFP _____

9. BUN _____

10. alk phos _____

11. QNS _____

12. RPR _____

13. ANC _____

14. pH _____

15. FEV _____

16. CEA _____

17. bands _____

18. FEF _____

19. ACT _____

20. ESR _____

21. Ca _____

22. LH _____

23. eos _____

24. AST _____

25. CF _____

26. HSV _____

27. SMAC _____

28. GPT _____

29. CO_2 _____

Laboratory and Pathology Abbreviations, Continued

30. $PaCO_2$ _____

31. ABO   _____

32. EKG   _____

33. Hgb   _____

34. CSF   _____

35. FTA   _____

36. basos   _____

37. DFA-TP (test)   _____

38. CK   _____

39. DNA   _____

40. IgE   _____

41. PT/PTT   _____

42. ECG   _____

43. DHEA   _____

44. AFB   _____

45. CPK-MM   _____

46. diff.   _____

47. TSH   _____

48. GM-CSF   _____

49. ERA   _____

50. A/G (ratio)   _____

51. EtOH   _____

52. FANA   _____

53. CBC   _____

54. Fe   _____

55. TORCH   _____

56. ASO (titer)   _____

57. FiO_2 _____

58. LE (prep)   _____

59. Cu   _____

Laboratory and Pathology Abbreviations, Continued

60. strep _____

61. CPK-MB _____

62. STD (screen) _____

63. PFTs _____

64. GTT _____

65. IgD _____

66. hCG _____

67. WBC/hpf _____

68. LDL _____

69. K _____

70. H&E (stain) _____

71. C&S _____

72. APTT _____

73. H. flu _____

74. T_3 _____

75. ANA _____

76. *E. coli* _____

77. VDRL _____

78. IgA _____

79. Hct _____

80. EBNA _____

81. IgG _____

82. PSA _____

83. Rh (factor) _____

84. FEV_1 _____

85. MCH _____

86. LDL/HDL (ratio) _____

87. *C. difficile* _____

88. FBS _____

89. L/S ratio _____

Laboratory and Pathology Abbreviations, Continued

90. lymphs _____

91. Pap _____

92. GGTP _____

93. MCV _____

94. HCO_3 _____

95. EBV _____

96. Na _____

97. LFTs _____

98. O&P _____

99. RNA _____

100. TB test _____

101. P _____

102. PaO_2 _____

103. SGPT _____

104. pCO_2 _____

105. CMV _____

106. RBC _____

107. PMNs _____

108. *S. aureus* _____

109. MCHC _____

110. pro time _____

111. STS _____

112. Hgb A_{1c} _____

113. monos _____

114. ALT _____

115. RAST _____

116. TPI _____

117. RF _____

118. OGTT _____

119. hpf _____

Laboratory and Pathology Abbreviations, Continued

120. PO_2 _____

121. TNTC _____

122. HIV _____

123. UA _____

124. SGOT _____

125. O_2 _____

126. SMA-20 _____

127. Cl _____

128. PTH _____

129. staph _____

130. H&H _____

131. IgM _____

132. segs _____

133. T_4 _____

134. TFT _____

135. Mg _____

136. ACTH _____

137. VMA _____

138. HZV _____

139. VLDL _____

140. stabs _____

141. CO_2 _____

142. WBC _____

143. TIBC _____

Section 5.
Pathophysiology

Pathophysiology of the Integumentary System

Match the terms in the left column with their correct definitions in the right column.

_____ 1. bulla	A. cutaneous defect extending into the dermis
_____ 2. macule	B. crust
_____ 3. petechia	C. hard, irregular layer of dried blood and matter on skin
_____ 4. purpura	D. scar
_____ 5. cicatrix	E. hypertrophic scar
_____ 6. nodule	F. thick-walled structure containing fluid or soft material
_____ 7. pustule	G. crust on a burn
_____ 8. comedo	H. blister
_____ 9. eschar	I. pin-head-sized red or purple macule
_____10. crust	J. flake of epidermis
_____11. vesicle	K. zone of fibrous tissue at site of injury
_____12. plaque	L. crack in the epidermis
_____13. excoriation	M. thin-walled sac containing inflammatory material
_____14. erosion	N. blackhead
_____15. ecchymosis	O. purple hemorrhage in the skin
_____16. telangiectasia	P. solid patch of skin elevation >1 cm in diameter
_____17. cyst	Q. discolored spot not elevated from the skin
_____18. papule	R. bruise
_____19. ulcer	S. thin-walled sac containing fluid
_____20. scar	T. surface defect from rubbing
_____21. pit	U. small depression in the skin
_____22. scab	V. small solid node
_____23. lichenification	W. solid patch of skin elevation less than 1 cm in diameter
_____24. keloid	X. dilation of small blood vessels visible in skin
_____25. fissure	Y. thickening, coarsening, and pigment change of skin
_____26. scale	Z. abrasion from scratching

Pathophysiology of the Integumentary System, Continued

Fill in the blanks with the correct answers. Some answers may require more than one word.

27. Atopic dermatitis is also known as _____.

28. _____ dermatitis results from contact with an irritant or allergen.

29. _____ is a spreading bacterial infection of the skin causing itching and crusted sores, usually caused by staph or strep.

30. Inflammation of the hair follicles is known as _____.

31. A deep solitary abscess is called a(n) _____.

32. Comedones, papules, pustules, and cysts are all manifestations of _____.

33. Urticaria is another word for the condition known as _____.

34. A person with a lot of of body hair has the condition _____.

35. A localized soft tissue infection with swelling, redness, pain, and fever is _____.

36. Tinea pedis is also known as _____.

37. A dermatosis consisting of reddish-purple thickened plaques of skin covered with silvery, adherent scales, most frequently located on the scalp, knees, and elbows and containing Munro micro-abscesses on microscopic examination, is suggestive of a diagnosis of ——————————————

    _____.

38. Herpes zoster is also known as _____.

39. _____ creates patches of depigmentation widely distributed over the skin, due to the destruction of pigment cells.

40. _____ is characterized by redness, swelling, heat, and pain.

41. Water retention or swelling is known as _____.

42. A person who is unable to produce any pigment is called a(n) _____.

43. Three of the most common skin cancers are squamous cell carcinoma, basal cell carcinoma, and malignant _____.

Pathophysiology of the Integumentary System, Continued

Choose the correct answer in each of the following multiple-choice questions. Write your answer in the space provided next to the number of the question.

_____ 44. Which type of burn is the most serious?
    a. third-degree burn
    b. second-degree burn
    c. first-degree burn
    d. blistering sunburn

_____ 45. When a zone of normally lax skin is picked up between thumb and finger and then released, it should flatten out again immediately. Failure of the skin to do so is:
    a. windmilling
    b. willowing
    c. tenting
    d. turgoring

_____ 46. A solar keratosis is caused by:
    a. scarring
    b. sun exposure
    c. irritation
    d. a burn

_____ 47. A fungal infection affecting a fingernail or toenail is:
    a. ichthyosis
    b. onychomycosis
    c. lichen planus
    d. aphthous stomatitis

_____ 48. A chronic but benign disease of the sebaceous glands is:
    a. eczema
    b. contact dermatitis
    c. canker sores
    d. seborrheic dermatitis

_____ 49. An autoimmune connective tissue disease characterized by a butterfly rash on the face is:
    a. atopic dermatitis
    b. scleroderma
    c. discoid lupus erythematosus
    d. superficial spreading malignant melanoma

_____ 50. Which of the following is NOT caused by a herpes virus?
    a. warts
    b. shingles
    c. genital herpes
    d. fever blisters

____ 51. Vitiligo is characterized by:
   a. large, clear blisters
   b. thickening of the epidermis
   c. areas of depigmentation
   d. intense itching

____ 52. A particularly severe form of cellulitis with bulla formation and often septicemia is:
   a. erysipelas
   b. impetigo
   c. Bowen disease
   d. Ehlers-Danlos syndrome

____ 53. Panniculitis is inflammation of the skin of the:
   a. fatty apron
   b. antecubital fossa
   c. back of the knee
   d. sole of the foot

____ 54. A small pearly nodule, often umbilicated and generally occurring in clusters about the lower trunk of the body and genitalia, is diagnostic of:
   a. dermatofibroma
   b. pyogenic granuloma
   c. molluscum contagiosum
   d. mycosis fungoides

____ 55. The most common type of birthmark is caused from:
   a. freckling
   b. viral infection in utero
   c. forceps injury
   d. dilated blood vessels

____ 56. Cat-scratch disease may be manifested by what kind of isolated lesion at the site of injury?
   a. papule or pustule
   b. boil or abscess
   c. furuncle or carbuncle
   d. petechiae or purpura

____ 57. Herpes simplex is manifested by clusters of painful:
   a. vesicles
   b. pustules
   c. blebs
   d. fissures

Pathophysiology of the Genitourinary System

Match the terms in the left column with their correct definitions in the right column.

_____ 1. pyuria

_____ 2. glycosuria

_____ 3. balanitis

_____ 4. hydronephrosis

_____ 5. calculus

_____ 6. frequency

_____ 7. hydroureter

_____ 8. uremia

_____ 9. nephrolithiasis

_____10. cystitis

_____11. epispadias

_____12. hyposthenuria

_____13. ureterovesical

_____14. prostatitis

_____15. ureteroscopy

_____16. cryptorchidism

_____17. phimosis

_____18. ureterolithiasis

_____19. varicocele

_____20. diverticulum

_____21. hypospadias

_____22. polyuria

_____23. urethritis

_____24. colic

_____25. dialysis

_____26. atrophic

A. distention of the ureter with urine

B. inflammation of the bladder

C. formation of urine with low specific gravity

D. constriction of the penile prepuce

E. herniation of mucous membrane lining

F. pertaining to the ureters and bladder

G. excess of urea and creatinine in the blood

H. white blood cells in the urine

I. examination of the ureters with an endoscope

J. urethral opening located on underside of penis

K. removal of waste products from the blood

L. inflammation of the urethra

M. stone in the kidney

N. acute pain

O. sugar in the urine

P. stone in the ureter

Q. excessive urine production

R. stone

S. enlarged veins of the testicle

T. increase in number of voidings

U. undescended testicle

V. inflammation of the glans penis

W. inflammation of the prostate

X. distention of the kidneys with urine

Y. urethral opening on the upper surface of penis

Z. withered

Pathophysiology of the Genitourinary System, Continued

Fill in the blanks with the correct answers.

27. Costovertebral angle pain accompanied by tenderness suggests disease within the

    _____.

28. A condition in which both kidneys are enlarged and cystic is _____ disease.

29. Acute inflammation of renal glomeruli, with failure to excrete nitrogen wastes, is known as

    _____.

30. Acute inflammation of the kidney tissue and the renal pelvis due to bacterial infection is

    _____.

31. Nonmalignant enlargement of the prostate that accompanies aging and produces varying degrees of urinary obstruction is a condition called_____.

32. An RPR test is done to screen for the disease _____.

33. Twisting of the _____ is a condition known as testicular torsion.

34. An intravenous _____ is a radiographic procedure performed to asses the urinary tract.

35. Inflammation of the triangular area of the bladder is called _____.

36. _____ is another name for the disease syphilis.

37. In _____ disease, immune complexes form in the glomerulus, often after a flu-like illness.

38. _____ is the mechanical purifying of blood when the kidneys do not function properly.

39. The four stages of syphilis are the primary stage, the secondary stage, the tertiary stage, and the _____ stage, in which spirochetes remain alive in the body but no signs or symptoms of infection occur after the secondary stage.

40. Changes in the concentration of dissolved minerals or other substances in the urine can lead to _____.

41. The flexible tube passed through the urethra into the bladder to drain urine is called a

    _____.

Pathophysiology of the Genitourinary System, Continued

Choose the correct answer in each of the following multiple-choice questions. Write your answer in the space provided next to the number of the question.

____ 42. Inadequate secretion of antidiuretic hormone results in a disease known as:
   a. diabetes insipidus
   b. diabetes mellitus
   c. brittle diabetes
   d. latent diabetes

____ 43. Routine hemodialysis is accomplished through:
   a. arteriovenous fistula
   b. renal medulla
   c. renal artery
   d. Bowman capsule

____ 44. A man is diagnosed as infertile based on what?
   a. he is impotent
   b. he has had a vasectomy
   c. he has a low sperm count
   d. he is unable to father a child with his wife

____ 45. Which is NOT a symptom of diabetes mellitus?
   a. polyphagia
   b. polymyalgia
   c. polydipsia
   d. polyuria

____ 46. The physician performs a digital rectal examination on the male patient to evaluate the pelvic walls and to check for evidence of tenderness or enlargement of the:
   a. sphincter
   b. hemorrhoids
   c. lower intestine
   d. prostate

____ 47. Which of the following is NOT a type of urinary incontinence?
   a. urge
   b. overflow
   c. burning
   d. stress

____ 48. Of the following conditions, which is a risk for cancer of the testes?
   a. post vasectomy
   b. prostatitis
   c. hydrocele
   d. cryptorchidism

Pathophysiology of the Gastrointestinal System

Match the terms in the left column with their correct definitions in the right column.

____ 1. anorexia	A. gas expelled per rectum
____ 2. diarrhea	B. a feeling as if one is going vomit
____ 3. ascites	C. prolonged esophageal tightening
____ 4. melena	D. loss of appetite
____ 5. hematochezia	E. twisting of intestine upon itself
____ 6. reflux	F. varicose veins in the anal region
____ 7. flatus	G. bright red blood per rectum
____ 8. dysphagia	H. dilated veins at lower end of esophagus
____ 9. colic	I. abnormal passageway near the anus
____10. jaundice	J. painful swallowing
____11. nausea	K. intestinal obstruction
____12. polyposis	L. abnormal outpouching in intestinal wall
____13. achalasia	M. spastic colon
____14. fistula	N. abnormal accumulation of fluid in the abdomen
____15. stomatitis	O. telescoping of the intestines
____16. diverticulum	P. erosion of tissue
____17. esophageal varices	Q. backward flow of solids and fluids
____18. ulcer	R. very loose stools
____19. cholelithiasis	S. protrusion of organ through muscle
____20. hemorrhoids	T. small growths protruding from colonic membrane
____21. hernia	U. inflammation of the oral structures with herpesvirus
____22. cirrhosis	V. tarry stools containing blood
____23. volvulus	W. degeneration of liver cells
____24. ileus	X. icterus
____25. irritable bowel syndrome	Y. gallstones
____26. intussusception	Z. acute abdominal pain

Pathophysiology of the Gastrointestinal System, Continued

Fill in the blanks with the correct answers. Some answers may require more than one word.

27. Diarrhea often results in rapid transit of food through the _____.

28. A patient with constipation is usually advised to eat foods that are high in _____

    _____.

29. _____ is a disease manifested by chronic inflammation of the colon with the presence of ulcers.

30. Inflammation of the liver caused by a virus is _____.

31. A diet high in animal fat, postulated to cause the production of certain carcinogens, is suspected of causing _____ cancer.

32. _____ is the medical term for vomiting.

33. Projectile vomiting in an infant during feeding is symptomatic for the condition _____

    _____ .

34. Peptic ulcers were once thought to be caused by stress and lifestyle. However, today we know that most peptic ulcers are caused by _____.

35. _____ is the burning sensation caused by the regurgitation of hydrochloric acid from the stomach into the esophagus.

36. A condition that occurs when the upper part of the stomach protrudes through the esophageal opening in the diaphragm, often causing symptoms of gastroesophageal reflux, is _____

    _____.

37. The pain that results when a gallstone blocks the excretion of bile is called biliary _____

    _____.

38. When a patient receives nourishment other than through the alimentary canal, it is referred to as _____ nutrition.

39. A fecalith is is a stonelike mass of hardened _____.

40. Fever, tachycardia, and rebound tenderness over McBurney point are symptomatic of _____

    _____ .

310

Pathophysiology of the Gastrointestinal System, Continued

Choose the correct answer in each of the following multiple-choice questions. Write your answer in the space provided next to the number of the question.

_____ 41. Which form of hepatitis is acute but self-limited and not likely to cause complications or serious sequelae?
   a. hepatitis A
   b. hepatitis B
   c. hepatitis C
   d. hepatitis D

_____ 42. In a patient with a bleeding peptic ulcer, one would expect the patient's stools to be:
   a. streaked with bright red blood
   b. clay-colored
   c. black
   d. chalky

_____ 43. A chronic relapsing disease that causes inflammation with diarrhea, cramping, and fever, and which affects the terminal ileum is:
   a. Crohn disease
   b. irritable bowel syndrome
   c. diverticulitis
   d. dysentery

_____ 44. A chronic disorder of the liver characterized by inflammation of secretory cells followed by nodular regeneration and fibrosis is named for which person?
   a. Lasègue
   b. Lhermitte
   c. Laugier
   d. Laënnec

_____ 45. Increase in pressure in the portal vein is known as:
   a. renal compression
   b. portacaval syndrome
   c. choledochocystitis
   d. portal hypertension

_____ 46. A 40-year-old overweight female with a long history of yo-yo dieting presents with severe, acute colicky pain in the right upper quadrant and epigastric area radiating through to her back. This is symptomatic of what digestive system disease?
   a. chronic pancreatitis
   b. acute cholecystitis
   c. chronic hepatitis
   d. acute appendicitis

Pathophysiology of the Gastrointestinal System, Continued

___47. Most cases of this disease occur in alcoholics or in persons with chronic biliary track disease such as cholelithiasis and cholecystitis:
   a. cirrhosis
   b. pancreatitis
   c. hepatitis
   d. peritonitis

___48. A common hernia of infancy in which the abdominal contents protrude at the navel is classified as a type of:
   a. hiatal hernia
   b. femoral hernia
   c. esophageal hernia
   d. abdominal hernia

___49. Transformation of normal esophageal squamous epithelium into columnar epithelium is characteristic of:
   a. esophageal reflux
   b. esophageal stricture
   c. Barrett esophagus
   d. esophageal varices

___50. A pancreatic tumor that produces excessive amounts of the hormone gastrin, thus causing hypersecretion of gastric acid, is characteristic of:
   a. Cronkhite-Canada syndrome
   b. Zollinger-Ellison syndrome
   c. Courvoisier-Terrier syndrome
   d. Budd-Chiari syndrome

___51. Which of the following is a pseudo-obstruction of the bowel?
   a. Ogilvie syndrome
   b. volvulus
   c. intussusception
   d. mechanical ileus

___52. The treatment of choice for peptic ulcer disease caused by *Helicobacter pylori* is:
   a. rest
   b. antibiotics
   c. ulcer diet
   d. antacids

___53. Congenital megacolon (dilatation and hypertrophy of the colon) is also known as:
   a. Treacher-Collins syndrome
   b. Zenker diverticulum
   c. Crohn disease
   d. Hirschsprung disease

Pathophysiology of the Musculoskeletal System

Select one of the following terms that matches the definition.

muscular dystrophy	osteomyelitis	osteoporosis	exostosis
arthritis	bunion	osteoarthritis	carpal tunnel syndrome
rheumatoid arthritis	sprain	ganglion cyst	Legg-Calvé-Perthes disease
dislocation	osteomalacia	Lyme disease	chondromalacia patellae
gout	tendinitis	talipes equinovarus	ankylosing spondylitis
Paget disease	strain	fibromyalgia	Osgood-Schlatter disease

1. inflammation of one or more joints _____

2. bacterial infection of bone _____

3. disease of tibial tubercle _____

4. avascular necrosis _____

5. inherited disease with muscular wasting and weakness _____

6. inflammation of tendon sheath _____

7. syndrome of musculoskeletal pain, weakness, fatigue _____

8. disease from urate crystal deposition _____

9. bony growth from surface of bone _____

10. decrease in bone density with thinning _____

11. clubfoot _____

12. abnormal swelling of joint between big toe and first metatarsal bone _____

13. degenerative joint disease _____

14. autoimmune inflammatory arthritis _____

15. progressive arthritis with stiff spine _____

16. compression of median nerve at wrist _____

17. trauma to joint with ligament injury _____

18. overstretching of muscle injury _____

19. cystic mass of tendon in wrist _____

20. displacement of bones at joint _____

21. arthritic disease from tick bite _____

22. softening of bone _____

23. degenerative disorder of bone _____

24. degeneration of cartilage of kneecap _____

Pathophysiology of the Musculoskeletal System, Continued

Fill in the blanks with the correct answers. Some answers may require more than one word.

25. Hallux valgus is a major deviation of the _____ joint of the great toe.

26. Low back pain often radiates down the leg in the distribution of the _____ nerve.

27. Range of motion in the shoulder is measured by testing _____ (drawing away from midline) and _____ (drawing toward midline).

28. _____ edema is painless swelling in the ankles and feet.

29. The medical term for bowleg is _____.

30. The lay term for the condition that is opposite of bowleg is _____, and _____ is the medical term.

31. _____ is the term that describes the sound made when rubbing together the ends of a fractured bone.

32. When a child's leg lengths are unequal and the normally straight vertical line of the spine is deviated laterally, the physician would likely suspect the child suffers from _____ _____.

33. A test that is performed to determine evoked and action potentials of the muscles is _____ _____.

34. A herniated nucleus _____ may produce shock-like pain radiating down an extremity with hypesthesia and paresthesia.

35. A forward displacement of one vertebra over another is _____.

36. _____ is a general term for an injury of any kind.

37. A fracture with more than two fragments that is accompanied by an open wound from which a fragment protrudes is termed a _____ fracture.

38. Failure of fracture fragments to knit together is termed _____.

39. About one-half of all reported occupational disease conditions are the consequence of repetitive trauma, termed _____ disorder.

Pathophysiology of the Musculoskeletal System, Continued

Choose the correct answer in each of the following multiple-choice questions. Write your answer in the space provided next to the number of the question.

____40. The most common cause of intervertebral disk herniation is:
   a. genetic defect
   b. congenital defect
   c. aging
   d. trauma

____41. The Lachman test is performed to check for:
   a. carpal tunnel syndrome
   b. back torsion
   c. neck pain
   d. knee injury

____42. Triple diapering, in which three diapers are stacked one on top of another and put on an infant, is a technique used to treat:
   a. dislocated hips
   b. talipes valgus
   c. talipes varus
   d. femur fractures

____43. A condition in which the first segment of the sacrum is not fused with the second and produces an additional articulated vertebra is a condition known as:
   a. sacralization
   b. lumbarization
   c. cervical rib
   d. spina bifida occulta

____44. A patient who twists the knee with the foot planted and subsequently develops pain, fluid in the joint space, crepitus, and a positive McMurray test probably has a:
   a. ruptured tendon
   b. torn meniscus
   c. torn muscle
   d. ruptured ligament

____45. Rickets is caused by deficiency of:
   a. calcium
   b. calciferol
   c. folic acid
   d. retinol

____ 46. Scheuermann disease is a condition affecting the:
   a. tibial tubercle
   b. capitellum of the humerus
   c. intervertebral cartilage
   d. carpal lunate

____ 47. Osteogenesis imperfecta, in which the patient has excessively fragile bones and abnormal dentin, arises from a hereditary defect in:
   a. connective tissue
   b. cartilage
   c. enchondral bone formation
   d. bone marrow

____ 48. Multiple myeloma is a malignant neoplasm of:
   a. connective tissue
   b. cartilage
   c. enchondral bone formation
   d. bone marrow

____ 49. Marie-Strumpell disease is also known as:
   a. gout
   b. ankylosing spondylitis
   c. hypertrophic osteoarthropathy
   d. myositis ossificans

____ 50. Which bone disease is caused by tuberculosis?
   a. Hand-Schüller-Christian disease
   b. Niemann-Pick disease
   c. Pott disease
   d. Gaucher disease

____ 51. Osteochondritis dissecans affects the:
   a. knees and elbows
   b. hips and shoulders
   c. ankles and wrists
   d. long bones of the leg

____ 52. A greenstick fracture in one in which:
   a. the lower fragment is displaced posteriorly
   b. the bone on one side is broken, the other bent
   c. the break extends in an oblique direction
   d. a small piece of bone is chipped off

Pathophysiology of the Cardiovascular System

Match the terms in the left column with their correct definitions in the right column.

____ 1. fibrillation	A. extra heart sound
____ 2. septal defect	B. failure of valve to prevent backflow during systole
____ 3. hypotension	C. inflammation of the lining of the heart
____ 4. pericarditis	D. restoration of heart to normal rhythm
____ 5. murmur	E. inflammation of the muscular wall of the heart
____ 6. aneurysm	F. rapid, ineffective heartbeats
____ 7. cardiomegaly	G. sweating
____ 8. insufficiency	H. chest pain due to myocardial ischemia
____ 9. angina pectoris	I. vascular sound synchronous with heartbeat
____ 10. ischemia	J. left ventricular failure with respiratory symptoms
____ 11. myocarditis	K. enlargement of the heart
____ 12. shock	L. abnormally twisted and swollen veins
____ 13. thrombophlebitis	M. heart disease caused by rheumatic fever
____ 14. pulmonary edema	N. inflammation of the sac surrounding the heart
____ 15. canalization	O. congenital malformation of the heart with 4 defects
____ 16. diaphoresis	P. leaky mitral valve
____ 17. bruit	Q. deficiency due to obstruction of a blood vessel
____ 18. flutter	R. hole between the atria or ventricles
____ 19. endocarditis	S. dislocated clot that blocks a blood vessel
____ 20. mitral valve prolapse	T. abnormal dilatation of a vessel
____ 21. varicosities	U. lower than normal blood pressure
____ 22. tetralogy of Fallot	V. device that maintains normal heart rate and rhythm
____ 23. rheumatic heart disease	W. venous inflammation associated with clot
____ 24. embolus	X. rapid, regular contractions of atria or ventricles
____ 25. cardioversion	Y. low systemic blood pressure with poor perfusion
____ 26. pacemaker	Z. opening of a new passage through an obstructed vessel

Pathophysiology of the Cardiovascular System, Continued

Fill in the blanks with the correct answers. Some answers may require more than one word.

27. Abnormalities in the heart at birth are called _____ anomalies.

28. A _____ exercise stress test is sometimes ordered to diagnose heart function.

29. A heart defect in the newborn which is commonly associated with rubella in the mother, in which blood flows from the aorta to the pulmonary artery, is known as _____.

30. A patient has _____ when fluid seeps out of capillaries into the lung alveoli in congestive heart failure.

31. Blockage of vessels in the lower extremities due to atherosclerotic disease is known as _____ _____ vascular disease.

32. Four areas of the anterior chest are designated according to the valves whose sounds are best heard there: the _____ area, the _____ area, _____ and _____ areas

33. Slowing of the pulse and conversion of arrhythmias to normal sinus rhythm can sometimes be accomplished by careful massage of the _____.

34. _____ venous distention is bulging of the neck veins.

35. A condition in which plaque completely occludes the lumen of an artery is known as arteriosclerosis _____.

36. Three-block_____ is diagnostic of stenosis of a major artery supply blood to an extremity.

37. When the aortic valve sound is the same intensity as the pulmonic valve sound on auscultation, it is said that _____ is equal to _____.

38. Hypertension is sustained elevation of arterial blood pressure above _____ mmHg systolic or _____ mmHg diastolic.

39. A _____ is a clot adherent to the wall of a heart chamber.

40. The three major classes of aneurysms are _____, _____, and _____.

Pathophysiology of the Cardiovascular System, Continued

Choose the correct answer in each of the following multiple-choice questions. Write your answer in the space provided next to the number of the question.

_____41. A complication that occurs when the right ventricle fails to pump enough blood to the lungs is known as
    a. cor pulmonale
    b. pulmonary edema
    c. pulmonary embolism
    d. myocardial infarction

_____42. Recurrent chest pain is often a sign of:
    a. Ludwig angina
    b. angina catarrhalis
    c. angina pectoris
    d. Plaut angina

_____43. The percentage of blood contained in a ventricle at the end of diastole that is ejected from the heart during the succeeding systole is the:
    a. hemodynamics
    b. ejection fraction
    c. cardiac impulse formation
    d. cardiothoracic ratio

_____44. Buerger disease is the eponymic name for:
    a. gargoylism
    b. temporal arteritis
    c. thromboangiitis obliterans
    d. periarteritis nodosa

_____45. Where is precordial chest pain felt?
    a. in the right upper quadrant
    b. in the epigastric and inferior thoracic region
    c. in either lower quadrant of the abdomen
    d. in the left chest radiating into the jaw or down the left arm

_____46. Pallor and numbness in the fingers and toes due to arteriolar constriction is symptomatic of what condition?
    a. Raynaud phenomenon
    b. Wolff-Parkinson-White syndrome
    c. Dupuytren contracture
    d. carpal tunnel syndrome

_____47. A person who smokes one-and-a-half packs of cigarettes per day for 24 years has smoked for how many pack-years?
    a. 12
    b. 24
    c. 36
    d. 48

Pathophysiology of the Cardiovascular System, Continued

_____48. Which of the following is NOT characteristic of arterial plaque?
    a. thick
    b. adherent
    c. white
    d. rubbery

_____49. Mönckeberg sclerosis is a disease that principally affects which structures?
    a. myocardium and endocardium
    b. valves of the heart
    c. arterial intima
    d. arterial media

_____50. A congenital anomaly involving defective formation of the interatrial septum causing left-to-right shunt is:
    a. atrial septal defect
    b. ventricular septal defect
    c. patent ductus arteriosis
    d. coarctation of the aorta

_____51. Mitral valve insufficiency is most commonly caused by:
    a. blunt trauma
    b. rheumatic heart disease
    c. diabetic neuropathy
    d. myocardial infarction

_____52. Which of the following is NOT a feature of tetralogy of Fallot?
    a. pulmonary stenosis
    b. overriding of the aorta
    c. valvular degeneration
    d. right ventricular hypertrophy

_____53. Popliteal artery injuries are often associated with blunt trauma to the:
    a. knee
    b. ankle
    c. thigh
    d. calf

_____54. Defective valves within leg veins can lead to:
    a. congestive heart failure
    b. varicose veins
    c. below-knee amputation
    d. above-knee amputation

_____55. Severe plaquing of the carotid arteries can lead to:
    a. myocardial infarction
    b. partial leg amputation
    c. cerebrovascular accident
    d. claudication

Pathophysiology of the Pulmonary System

Match the terms in the left column with their correct definitions in the right column.

____ 1. croup

____ 2. cystic fibrosis

____ 3. atelectasis

____ 4. bronchitis

____ 5. asthma

____ 6. pneumonia

____ 7. tuberculosis

____ 8. emphysema

____ 9. pneumothorax

____10. asbestosis

____11. anthracosis

____12. chronic obstructive pulmonary disease

____13. diphtheria

____14. pertussis

____ 15. bronchogenic carcinoma

____ 16. pneumoconiosis

____ 17. pulmonary abscess

____ 18. pulmonary embolism

____ 19. pulmonary edema

____ 20. pleural rub

____ 21. pleurisy

____ 22. hydrothorax

____ 23. pulmonary infarction

____ 24. silicosis

____ 25. empyema

A. asbestos particles in lungs

B. acute childhood respiratory syndrome

C. cancerous tumor arising from bronchus

D. inflammation of the bronchial passages

E. dust in the lungs with chronic infection and bronchitis

F. clot lodged in vessel of lung

G. infection of pharynx and trachea caused by *Bordetella*

H. glass dust in lungs

I. incomplete expansion of lung air sacs

J. fluid in pleural cavity

K. collection of pus in lungs

L. area of necrotic tissue in lung

M. hyperinflation of lung air sacs

N. accumulation of pus in pleural cavity

O. exocrine gland disease causing airway obstruction

P. inflammation of the pleura

Q. infectious lung disease caused by *Mycobacterium*

R. coal dust accumulation in lungs

S. spasm and narrowing of bronchi with thick mucus

T. fluid in air sacs and bronchioles

U. infection of respiratory tract with *Corynebacterim*

V. accumulation of air in pleural cavity

W. persistent obstruction of air flow through lungs

X. acute infection of alveoli causing loss of aeration

Y. sound made by friction between pleural surfaces

Pathophysiology of the Pulmonary System, Continued

Fill in the blanks with the correct answers. Some answers may require more than one word.

26. _____ is graded by the the number of pillows the patient requires in order to avoid respiratory distress.

27. More than _____ percent of patients with chronic bronchitis have a history of heavy cigarette smoking.

28. A measurement of partial pressures of oxygen and carbon dioxide in arterial blood is arterial _____.

29. Digital _____ is enlargement of the fingertips with elevation of proximal parts of nails due to chronic pulmonary disease.

30. Blue color of the skin, in particular of lips and nail beds, due to the presence of excess unoxygenated blood in the circulation is _____.

31. _____ tests are performed by means of finely calibrated instruments to measure the rate and volume of gas exchange in the respiratory system.

32. Irreversible dilatation of large bronchi due to chronic infection, obstruction, or autoimmune disease is called _____.

33. Another, more complex name for asthma is _____.

34. The primary cause of lung cancer is _____.

35. Divers who return to the surface of the water after diving deeply run the risk of developing _____.

36. An individual who has stopped breathing because of drowning, electrical shock, cardiac arrest, or other crisis, can often be kept alive by a set of human maneuvers known as _____.

37. A chronic asthmatic condition may result in increased _____ diameter of the chest.

38. Normal inspiration and expiration yield a faint sighing or whispering sound called _____ breathing.

39. _____ is a communicable bacterial lung disease that was once thought to be curable by medication but has now developed strains that are antibiotic-resistant.

Pathophysiology of the Pulmonary System, Continued

Choose the correct answer in each of the following multiple-choice questions. Write your answer in the space provided next to the number of the question.

____40. Brown lung disease, which is caused by cotton dust accumulation in the lungs, is known medically as:
   a. anthracosis
   b. asbestosis
   c. byssinosis
   d. silicosis

____41. A method to relieve a person from choking by applying thrusting pressure over the midepigastric area is the:
   a. Adson maneuver
   b. Kocher maneuver
   c. Valsalva maneuver
   d. Heimlich maneuver

____42. E to A change is otherwise known as:
   a. Hamman sign
   b. egophony
   c. pectoriloquy
   d. Ewart sign

____43. The vibration felt by the examiner when a patient speaks is called:
   a. vocal fremitus
   b. friction rub
   c. succussion splash
   d. percussion note

____44. Obtaining material from lung tissue via washing is called:
   a. pulmonary toilette
   b. pulmonary gavage
   c. bronchoalveolar lavage
   d. bronchoscopy

____45. The condition that causes inflammation and fibrinoid degeneration in the lungs, pulmonary hemorrhage within alveoli, and collagenous deposits in alveolar septa is:
   a. Boeck sarcoid
   b. Charcot-Leyden crystal disease
   c. Friedlander pneumonia
   d. Goodpasture syndrome

____46. Chronic productive cough lasting for at least three months in each of two successive years is diagnostic of:
   a. chronic bronchitis
   b. atelectasis
   c. bronchiectasis
   d. asthma

Pathophysiology of the Pulmonary System, Continued

_____47. About one-half of all cases of bronchiectasis occur in patients who have:
    a. reactive airways disease
    b. respiratory distress syndrome
    c. status asthmaticus
    d. cystic fibrosis

_____48. Increased anteroposterior diameter of the chest is referred to as:
    a. flail chest
    b. barrel chest
    c. pigeon breast
    d. funnel chest

_____49. Coccidioidomycosis, a granulomatous lung disease, is also called:
    a. East Coast fever
    b. Fort Bragg fever
    c. Rocky Mountain spotted fever
    d. San Joaquin valley fever

_____50. The five-year survival rate for bronchogenic carcinoma is:
    a. 5 to 10 percent
    b. 10 to 15 percent
    c. 15 to 20 percent
    d. 20 to 25 percent

_____51. Pulmonary sulcus tumor is also known as:
    a. Burkitt tumor
    b. Askin tumor
    c. Wilms tumor
    d. Pancoast tumor

_____52. Prolonged immobilization, surgery, childbirth, congestive heart failure, obesity, and advanced age are all risk factors for:
    a. pulmonary embolus
    b. pleural effusion
    c. pneumothorax
    d. hydrothorax

_____53. A respiratory problem in the premature baby in which lack of protein causes collapse of lung tissue is known as:
    a. pulmonary hypertension
    b. lobar atelectasis
    c. respiratory distress syndrome
    d. hyaline membrane disease

Pathophysiology of the Endocrine System

Match the terms in the left column with their correct definitions in the right column. Some definitions match more than one prefix/suffix.

_____ 1. Graves disease

_____ 2. Addison disease

_____ 3. hyperparathyroidism

_____ 4. pheochromocytoma

_____ 5. hyperthyroidism

_____ 6. hyperinsulinism

_____ 7. myxedema

_____ 8. diabetes mellitus

_____ 9. acromegaly

_____ 10. adrenal virilism

_____ 11. exophthalmos

_____ 12. hypothyroidism

_____ 13. hypoparathyroidism

_____ 14. dwarfism

_____ 15. thyrotoxicosis

_____ 16. Hashimoto disease

_____ 17. tetany

_____ 18. cretinism

_____ 19. hirsutism

_____ 20. diabetes insipidus

_____ 21. SIADH

_____ 22. Cushing syndrome

_____ 23. hypoglycemia

_____ 24. osteitis fibrosa cystica

_____ 25. ketoacidosis

_____ 26. gigantism

_____ 27. panhypopituitarism

_____ 28. DeQuervain disease

A. tumor of adrenal medulla

B. underactivity of the thyroid gland in children

C. extremity enlargement

D. decalcified bones susceptible to fractures and cysts

E. excessive secretion of antidiuretic hormone

F. excessive production of parathormone

G. abnormal overgrowth of body before puberty

H. lack of insulin to metabolize glucose

I. excessive hair on face and body

J. underactivity of the thyroid gland in adults

K. low blood sugar

L. development of antibodies to one's own thyroid

M. overactivity of the thyroid gland

N. congenital hyposecretion of growth hormone

O. accumulation of ketones in the body

P. secretion of excess cortisol from adrenal cortex

Q. bulging eyes

R. underactivity of the thyroid gland

S. unabating muscle spasm

T. excess secretion of insulin causing hypoglycemia

U. excessive output of adrenal androgens

V. deficient production of parathormone

W. insufficient secretion of vasopressin

X. hypofunction of the adrenal cortex

Y. deficiency of all pituitary hormones

Z. giant cell thyroiditis

Pathophysiology of the Endocrine System, Continued

Fill in the blanks with the correct answers. Some answers may require more than one word.

29. Hypoparathyroidism is manifested by positive presence of two signs: first, twitching of the face after percussion over the facial nerve in front of the ear, called _____ sign, and spastic contraction of the hand after application of a constructing arm cuff, known as _____ sign.

30. Congenital adrenal hyperplasia results in the deficiency of _____ and overproduction of _____ .

31. Thyrotoxicosis is also known by the eponymic name _____ disease.

32. _____ is a general term for the sum of all the chemical and electrical processes that occur in the living body.

33. Gelatinous matter predominates in a(n) _____ goiter.

34. A goiter is surgically removed during a _____.

35. An elevated _____ level is suspected in a woman with excess body hair and an enlarged thyroid.

36. The test that measures eyeball protrusion in hyperthyroidism is known as _____ _____ .

37. Radioactive _____ is administered orally and its uptake into the thyroid gland is measured as evidence of thyroid function.

38. Endemic goiter is caused by dietary _____ deficiency.

39. The brittle bones, kidney stones, and joint pains associated with hyperthyroidism are the result of too much of the mineral _____.

40. Adenomas are small, benign tumors that may affect a patient's thyroid function by causing _____.

41. _____ diabetes mellitus, which is more common in the obese and those over 40, can sometimes be controlled by diet and exercise alone.

42. Sluggish reflexes, dryness of hair and skin, constipation, and weight gain are all symptoms that may occur with the condition _____ .

Pathophysiology of the Endocrine System, Continued

Choose the correct answer in each of the following multiple-choice questions. Write your answer in the space provided next to the number of the question.

_____43. A goiter is related to:
    a. pituitary disease
    b. thyroid disease
    c. pancreatic disease
    d. adrenal disease

_____44. Myxedema is:
    a advanced hyperthyroidism in adults
    b. extreme hypothyroidism during infancy and childhood
    c. advanced hypothyroidism in adults
    d. extreme hyperthyroidism during infancy and childhood

_____45. Which of the following is NOT likely to be prescribed for the diabetic?
    a. iron
    b. exercise
    c. medication
    d. diet

_____46. The etiology of diabetes mellitus is:
    a. iatrogenic
    b. idiopathic
    c. overeating
    d. excessive fluid intake

_____47. Which of the following is NOT a potential complication of diabetes mellitus?
    a. nerve damage
    b. blindness
    c. cancer
    d. small vessel disease

_____48. Which of the following is a symptom of Cushing syndrome?
    a. acromegaly
    b. moon facies
    c. palpitations
    d. hypergonadism

_____49. Simmonds disease is also known as:
    a. panhypopituitarism
    b. papillary carcinoma
    c. follicular carcinoma
    d. congenital adrenal hyperplasia

Pathophysiology of the Endocrine System, Continued

_____50. Which condition is NOT an indication for thyroidectomy?
   a. hyperthyroidism
   b. hypothyroidism
   c. benign tumor
   d. cancerous tumor

_____51. A childhood tumor that develops from the nasopharynx, consisting of cystic masses filled with cloudy fluid that may compress the pituitary gland, is:
   a. craniopharyngioma
   b. chromophobe adenoma
   d. acidophil adenoma
   d. basophil adenoma

_____52. Chronic fibrous thyroiditis is also known as:
   a. Graves disease
   b. DeQuervain disease
   c. Hashimoto thyroiditis
   d. Riedel struma

_____53. Half of all thyroid cancers are:
   a. undifferentiated carcinoma
   b. well-differentiated adenocarcinoma
   c. follicular carcinoma
   d. papillary carcinoma

_____54. Conn syndrome is best described as:
   a. malignancy of the adrenal glands
   b. benign tumor of the adrenal glands
   c. adrenogenital hyperplasia
   d. primary aldosteronism

_____55. A buffalo hump is characteristic of an endocrine disease that affects the:
   a. pituitary
   b. parathyroids
   c. adrenals
   d. pancreas

_____56. Which of the following endocrine diseases can cause or exacerbate peripheral vascular disease?
   a. diabetes mellitus
   b. panhypopituitarism
   c. thyroid disease
   d. pancreatitis

Pathophysiology of the Female Reproductive System

Select one of the following terms that matches the definition.

cervicitis
ovarian cyst
adenomyosis
placenta previa
Down syndrome
mittelschmerz

fibroid
hydatidiform mole
abruptio placentae
choriocarcinoma
dermoid cyst

kernicterus
pelvic inflammatory disease
ectopic pregnancy
preeclampsia
Pap smear

1. benign neoplasm of uterine muscle _____

2. bacterial infection of uterus and tubes _____

3. fertilized ovum implanted outside of uterus _____

4. collection of fluid within a sac in the ovary _____

5. premature separation of placenta _____

6. brain deposition of bilirubin in neonate _____

7. scraping of cervical tissue for examination _____

8. abnormality of chromosome 13 _____

9. hypertrophy and enlarged glands of myometrium _____

10. abnormal pregnancy with pathologic ovum _____

11. malignant tumor of pregnant uterus _____

12. fluid and debris within a sac in the ovary _____

13. placental implantation over cervix or low in uterus _____

14. hypertension, proteinuria, edema of pregnancy _____

15. inflammation of the cervix _____

16. pain with ovulation _____

Pathophysiology of the Female Reproductive System, Continued

Fill in the blanks with the correct answers. Some answers may require more than one word.

17. A condition in which a term fetus is too large to be delivered through the mother's pelvic inlet is called _____.

18. Use of a machine to electronically record the infant's heart rate during labor is called _____ _____.

19. A _____ ovarian cyst is caused by endometriosis and is named for the thick brown fluid it contains.

20. Hemolytic disease of the newborn is also known as _____.

21. Preeclampsia that has progressed to seizure stage is then known as eclampsia or _____ _____ .

22. Two types of amenorrhea are primary (failure to start menses at puberty), and _____ _____ (cessation of menses that were previously normal).

23. The cul-de-sac is also known as the pouch of _____.

24. In one-third of patients with amenorrhea, the hormone _____, which is produced by the pituitary gland, is elevated.

25. Endometrial implants often appear as hemorrhagic cysts or "_____" lesions on the peritoneal surface.

26. Examination of the vaginal vault and the uterine cervix is carried out with the bivalved instrument known as a(n) _____.

27. A small yellowish mass consisting of dilated endocervical glands and usually appearing at the external cervical os is a _____ cyst.

28. If fertilization has not occurred, menses predictably begin (number) _____ days after ovulation.

29. The condition where a woman's bladder bulges through the vagina called a(n) _____ _____.

30. The group of distressing physical and emotional symptoms linked to shifting hormonal changes experienced by some women a week before the onset of menses is known as _____ _____.

31. During delivery, a device known as a _____ may be needed to grasp the baby and help pull it out of the birth canal.

Pathophysiology of the Female Reproductive System, Continued

Choose the correct answer in each of the following multiple-choice questions. Write your answer in the space provided next to the number of the question.

_____32. What color is the cervix during early pregnancy?
   a. pale or white
   b. blue
   c. strawberry (reddish)
   d. pink

_____33. What instrument is placed on the abdomen to auscultate fetal heart tones?
   a. fetoscope
   b. internal fetal monitor
   c. pelviscope
   d. Leopold stethoscope

_____34. Painful and difficult labor is known as:
   a. dyssynergia
   b. dysmetria
   c. dystocia
   d. dyskinesia

_____35. One or more benign lumps in the breast, typically more tender just before the onset of menses, is characteristic of:
   a. adenocarcinoma
   b. cystosarcoma phyllodes
   c. fibrocystic disease
   d. milk duct ectasia

_____36. Which of the following is NOT a function of the Pap smear?
   a. to detect infectious changes
   b. to identify inflammatory changes
   c. to determine hormonal effect
   d. to detect pregnancy

_____37. A chocolate cyst is characteristic of what disease?
   a. endometriosis
   b. adenomyosis
   c. leiomyomatosis
   d. cystadenomatosis

_____38. Which one of the following is NOT considered a normal menstrual period?
   a. three-day flow
   b. five-day flow
   c. seven-day flow
   d. nine-day flow

Pathophysiology of the Female Reproductive System, Continued

____39. During each menstrual cycle, a woman is fertile for approximately:
    a. 12 to 24 hours
    b. two to three days
    c. four to five days
    d. a week

____40. A benign, solid tumor of the breast that is firm, spherical, measures 1 to 5 cm in diameter, and typically occurs in younger women is a:
    a. fibroadenoma
    b. cyst
    c. ductal ectasia
    d. tubercle of Montgomery

____41. How long does the average case of cervical carcinoma take to metastasize?
    a. 6 to 12 months
    b. 1 to 3 years
    c. 3 to 5 years
    d. 5 to 10 years

____42. A complication of gonorrhea in women, marked by fever and right upper quadrant pain, is:
    a. Munro-Kerr syndrome
    b. Fitz-Hugh-Curtis syndrome
    c. Taussig syndrome
    d. Credé syndrome

____43. What type of abortion occurs when the product of conception is nonliving and is retained in the uterus for over two months?
    a. imminent
    b. incomplete
    c. missed
    d. inevitable

____44. The normal presentation of a fetus is:
    a. breech
    b. cephalic
    c. transverse
    d. shoulder

____45. According to the International Federation of Gynecologists and Obstetricians (FIGO), stage III cervical carcinoma is:
    a. invasion of the pelvic wall and lower third of the vagina, bladder, rectum, and extrapelvic structures
    b. carcinoma extending beyond the cervix but not to the pelvic wall or lower third of the vagina
    c. carcinoma in situ
    d. carcinoma invading the basement membrane but confined to the cervix

Pathophysiology of the Ears, Nose, and Throat

Enter the proper medical term(s) for the phrases below. Some answers require more than one word.

1. inflammation of middle ear   otitis media

2. infection of the mastoid antrum   _____

3. tooth decay   _____

4. white patches on oral mucosa   _____

5. inflammation of nasal mucous membranes   _____

6. inflammation of outer ear canal   _____

7. nosebleed   _____

8. inflammation of mouth with small ulcers _____

9. collection of cholesterol within a sac in the middle ear   _____

10. sore throat   _____

11. hardening of bony tissue of labyrinth of the ear   _____

12. sensation of room spinning with dizziness   _____

13. inflammation causing loss of voice   _____

14. visual exam of ear with instrument   _____

15. vibration source instrument   _____

16. disorder of labyrinth and elevated endolymph pressure in cochlea   _____

17. ringing in the ears   _____

18. birdshot-like enlarged lymph nodes in the neck   _____

19. bad breath   _____

20. runny nose   _____

21. common cold   _____

Pathophysiology of the Ears, Nose, and Throat, Continued

Fill in the blanks with the correct answers. Some answers may require more than one word.

22. The _____ maneuver can be used to test the mobility of the tympanic membranes when the patient swallows.

23. A benign neoplasm arising from connective tissue cells in the perineurium of the eighth cranial nerve is called an acoustic neuroma, also known as a vestibular _____

    _____.

24. Irregular nodules of the vocal cords which are more common in children are known as ____

    _____.

25. Swimmer's ear is a painful condition of the _____.

26. Three types of hearing loss are _____, which can happen with chronic otitis media; _____, which can happen with cochlear disease or trauma; and _____, which is caused by eighth nerve lesions and cerebrovascular disease.

27. A recurrent, often seasonal, inflammation of the nasal mucous membranes caused by inhaled materials is known as _____.

28. The measure of loudness of sound is the _____.

29. Massive overgrowths of chronically inflamed mucosa deep in the nose are called _____

    _____.

30. Small children are more prone to ear infections, especially otitis media, because their ear canals are _____ than an adult's.

31. Swelling due to engorgement of vessels is known as _____.

32. Irregularity of the patient's dental bite, where the teeth do not meet appropriately, is known as _____.

33. Severe inflammation with pus pockets of the gums is a condition known as _____

    _____.

34. Laënnec pearls and Curschmann spirals are small plugs of _____ formed in the bronchioles in asthma and expelled in the sputum.

Pathophysiology of the Ears, Nose, and Throat, Continued

Choose the correct answer in each of the following multiple-choice questions. Write your answer in the space provided next to the number of the question.

____35. The procedure in which the examiner shines a light in the patient's mouth in a darkened room to check for sinus blockage is called:
   a. transillumination
   b. slit lamp examination
   c. Valsalva maneuver
   d. Kocher procedure

____36. Acute sinusitis may be caused by:
   a. nose picking
   b. bacterial infection
   c. aspiration
   d. trauma

____37. Vertigo is caused by:
   a. fear of heights
   b. dysphonia
   c. alteration in consciousness
   d. labyrinthitis

____38. Dryness and scaling of the skin, excessive hair in the ear canal, or narrow ear canals may result in:
   a. external otitis
   b. otitis media
   c. impacted cerumen
   d. otosclerosis

____39. Which of the following is NOT a cause of laryngitis?
   a. bacterial infection
   b. viral infection
   c. abscessed teeth
   d. prolonged screaming

____40. Coarsely lumpy appearance of the tongue, caused by inflammation, is called:
   a. stippling
   b. cobblestoning
   c. boxcarring
   d. geographic tongue

____41. An external ear deformed by repeated or severe trauma, as in boxers and wrestlers, is called:
   a. otodactyly
   b. sundowning
   c. cauliflower ear
   d. audiotoxicity

Pathophysiology of the Eyes

Enter the proper medical term for the phrases below. Some answers require more than one word.

1. movement of the eye   ocular motility

2. drooping (i.e., of the eyelid)   _____

3. agent that dilates the pupil   _____

4. rolling outward of eyelid   _____

5. swelling of the optic disk   _____

6. growing inward of eyelash hairs   _____

7. absence of lens of eye   _____

8. "lazy" eye   _____

9. natural lens replaced with artificial lens   _____

10. lacrimation   _____

11. loss of accommodation in eyes with age   _____

12. involuntary contraction of orbicularis oculi muscle   _____

13. divergent strabismus   _____

14. loss of lens transparency   _____

15. inherited degenerative retinal disorder   _____

16. incision of cornea   _____

17. absence of half of visual field   _____

18. another term for "stye"   _____

19. increased intraocular pressure   _____

20. instrument to measure eye pressure   _____

21. deterioration of retinal macula   _____

22. retinal effects of diabetes mellitus   _____

23. double vision   _____

24. instrument to examine anterior eye structures under microscopic amplification   _____

Pathophysiology of the Eyes, Continued

Fill in the blanks with the correct answers. Some answers may require more than one word.

25. A white or gray band around the margin of the cornea resulting from cholesterol deposition with advancing age is _____ senilis.

26. Bleeding into the anterior chamber of the eye is called _____.

27. Having near and distant vision tested by use of an instrument with many lenses of standard magnification is known as a(n) _____.

28. The normal optic nerve head has a slight central depression; this is known as physiologic _____.

39. Chronic overflow of tears from the lower eyelid onto the cheek is known as _____ .

30. Absence or defect of some ocular tissue is known as _____.

31. A green dye called _____ is sometimes used to delineate structures of the eye and to check for abnormalities.

32. A person who does not see various colors or certain shades of color is said to be _____.

33. The _____ classification is often used to grade funduscopic observations in hypertensive retinopathy.

34. Two types of diabetic retinopathy are _____ and _____.

35. In strabismus, one eye is the fixing eye and the other is the _____ eye.

36. An artificial eye, or _____ , may be inserted to replace a missing eye globe.

37. The standard treatment for hyperopia is _____.

38. _____ is defined as spasm of the eyelid.

39. Keratoconus is a conical bulging of the _____.

40. Two recognized types of glaucoma are _____ and _____ .

41. _____ is continuous, rapid, rhythmic movements of the eyeball.

Pathophysiology of the Eyes, Continued

Choose the correct answer in each of the following multiple-choice questions. Write your answer in the space provided next to the number of the question.

____42. Proliferative diabetic retinopathy is the most common cause of:
a. macular degeneration
b. cataracts
c. vitreous hemorrhage
d. ptyergium

____43. A unilateral inflammation of the cornea of the eye is:
a. conjunctivitis
b. uveitis
c. blepharitis
d. keratitis

____44. The treatment for presbyopia is:
a. prescription eyedrops
b. corrective lenses
c. vision therapy
d. surgical intervention

____45. A patient who sees clearly at 20 feet what a person with good vision can see at 400 feet is:
a. farsighted
b. nearsighted
c. astigmatic
d. hypermetropic

____46. An intraocular malignancy occurring primarily in children, and occurring bilaterally in one-third of cases, is:
a. chorioretinitis
b. hypopyon
c. retrolental fibroplasia
d. retinoblastoma

____47. Flame hemorrhage, cotton wool spots, and copper-wire or silver-wire appearance are terms used to describe:
a. hypertensive retinopathy
b. retinitis pigmentosa
c. macular degeneration
d. glaucoma

____48. Progressive retinal sclerosis, pigmentation, and atrophy are characteristics of:
a. retinal detachment
b. macular degeneration
c. diabetic retinopathy
d. retinitis pigmentosa

Pathophysiology of the Nervous System

Match the terms in the left column with their correct definitions in the right column.

_____ 1. spina bifida

_____ 2. myasthenia gravis

_____ 3. Huntington disease

_____ 4. cerebrovascular accident

_____ 5. meningitis

_____ 6. concussion

_____ 7. shingles

_____ 8. carpal tunnel syndrome

_____ 9. cerebral contusion

_____10. Parkinson disease

_____11. Tourette syndrome

_____12. Charcot-Marie-Tooth disease

_____13. Alzheimer disease

_____14. amyotrophic lateral sclerosis

_____15. epilepsy

_____16. multiple sclerosis

_____17. cerebral palsy

_____18. bovine spongiform encephalopathy

_____19. anencephaly

_____20. Guillain-Barré syndrome

_____21. encephalitis

_____22. migraine

_____23. cluster headache

_____24. transient ischemic attack

_____25. coma

_____26. Bell palsy

A. hypesthesia of thenar eminence

B. congenital defect in spinal column

C. degenerative cerebral disorder manifested by involuntary kinetic movements

D. myelin sheath disease

E. inflammation of peripheral nerves

F. disorder characterized by recurrent seizures

G. congenital absence of cerebral hemispheres

H. recurrent, severe unilateral headache

I. bruising of brain tissue

J. disruption in normal blood supply to brain

K. disease of muscular atrophy

L. degeneration of basal ganglia resulting in tremor

M. disorder of voluntary movement and posture

N. sudden onset of neurologic symptoms that quickly resolve

O. paralysis of facial muscles

P. inflammation of meninges

Q. "mad cow" disease

R. unarousable unconscious state

S. characterized by involuntary movements and use of inappropriate words

T. disease of motor neuron degeneration

U. temporary brain dysfunction after injury

V. relapsing weakness of skeletal muscles

W. progressive degenerative brain disorder character-ized by neurofibrillary tangles and profound dementia

X. recurrent episodes of severe unilateral orbital pain

Y. inflammation of the brain from infection

Z. viral disease of peripheral nerves

Pathophysiology of the Nervous System, Continued

Fill in the blanks with the correct answers. Some answers may require more than one word.

27. The _____ coma scale is a widely used measurment of consciousness.

28. Cranium bifidum, spina bifida, porencephaly, and microcephaly are all examples of _____ defects.

29. Loss of memory, either recent, remote, or total, is called _____.

30. Partial loss of sensation on one or more parts of the body is known as _____.

31. Withdrawal of a specimen of cerebrospinal fluid from the subarachnoid space by inserting a needle between two lower vertebrae is called _____.

32. A patient having a generalized seizure would likely exhibit _____ and _____ contractions of voluntary muscles.

33. The _____ test assesses position sense in the trunk and legs by having the patient stand with feet together, opening and closing the eyes.

34. The _____ reflex, where the sole of the foot is stroked, is normally upgoing in infants and downgoing in adults.

35. A reflex that is present only in neurological disorders is called a _____ reflex.

36. _____ discrimination testing assesses the patient's ability to distinguish two points close together on the skin.

37. Spasm of the facial muscles precipitated by tapping the facial nerve in the region of the parotid gland is known as _____ sign.

38. Amyotrophic lateral sclerosis is commonly called by its more popular, eponymic name, _____ disease.

39. A migraine headache that begins with aura before onset of pain is classified as a _____ migraine.

40. "Brain attack" is another term for _____ .

Pathophysiology of the Nervous System, Continued

Choose the correct answer in each of the following multiple-choice questions. Write your answer in the space provided next to the number of the question.

_____41. Hydrocephalus is:
   a. enlargement of the head
   b. defects in the spinal column
   c. abnormal accumulation of cerebrospinal fluid in the brain
   d. inflammation of the brain

_____42. Meralgia paresthetica is a condition more likely to affect a person who is:
   a. very tall
   b. very short
   c. thin
   d. obese

_____43. Shock-like pain when the volar aspect of the wrist is tapped is known as a positive:
   a. Tinel sign
   b. Phalen sign
   c. Lasegue sign
   d. Hoffmann sign

_____44. Bell palsy, carpal tunnel syndrome, and Lyme disease are all examples of:
   a. mononeuritis
   b. polyneuritis
   c. medial neuritis
   d. lateral neuritis

_____45. A patient exhibiting a series of grand mal seizures without waking intervals is described as being in:
   a. tonic-clonic phase
   b. petit mal
   c. status epilepticus
   d. postictal state

_____46. Inability to extend the knee when the thigh is flexed is a positive:
   a. Kernig sign
   b. Brudzinski sign
   c. Phalen sign
   d. Gaenslen sign

_____47. Which of the following is NOT a type of stroke?
   a. thrombotic
   b. hemorrhagic
   c. embolic
   d. palliative

Pathophysiology of the Nervous System, Continued

____48. General mental decline and deterioration is known as:
   a. dementia
   b. delirium
   c. demyelination
   d. decompensation

____49. A contusion from the brain's impact on the skull opposite the blow is known as a:
   a. concussion
   b. contrecoup injury
   c. contralateral lesion
   d. opposition wound

____50. What is the name of the test used to determine vestibular function by pouring ice-water into the ear canal?
   a. cold pressor test
   b. cold contraction stress test
   c. cold catoptric test
   d. cold caloric test

____51. Which of the following is used to assess coordination?
   a. Romberg test
   b. deep tendon reflexes
   c. heel-to-shin test
   d. proprioception

____52. Which of the following is NOT a treatment for epilepsy?
   a. psychotherapy
   b. medication
   c. avoidance of triggering factor
   d. surgery

____53. An intention tremor occurs:
   a. as an autonomic response
   b. on voluntary movement
   c. when the muscles are at rest
   d. when a patient has lost tactile sensation

____54. A seizure characterized by a sudden momentary break in thought, consciousness, or activity, occasionally with eyelid fluttering but never by flailing or jerking motions, is known as a(n):
   a. partial seizure
   b. absence seizure
   c. pseudoseizure
   d. focal seizure

Pathophysiology of the Nervous System, Continued

_____55. Glioblastoma multiforme is an astrocytoma of grade:
   a. I
   b. III
   c. V
   d. VI

_____56. Huntington disease is BEST classified as:
   a. a mental disorder
   b. a genetic disorder
   c. an acquired disorder
   d. an autoimmune disorder

_____57. Epiloia, which characteristically includes hamartomas of the glial tissues of the brain, is better known as:
   a. cranium bifidum
   b. syringomyelia
   c. wallerian degeneration
   d. tuberous sclerosis

_____58. Poliomyelitis is caused by a virus that enters through the:
   a. gastrointestinal tract
   b. respiratory tract
   c. integumentary system
   d. neurological system

_____59. The signs, symptoms, and course of Creutzfeldt-Jakob disease are much like those of:
   a. hand, foot, and mouth disease
   b. mad cow disease
   c. Parkinson disease
   d. Huntington chorea

_____60. A condition in which there is a defect of the vertebral canal without protrusion of the cord or meninges is:
   a. spina iliaca posterior inferior
   b. spina iliaca anterior superior
   c. spina bifida occulta
   d. spina bifida cystica

_____61. Peripheral neuropathy is a common complication of which disorder?
   a. ulcerative colitis
   b. hepatitis
   c. diabetes mellitus
   d. cystic fibrosis

Pathophysiology of the Immune System

Match the terms in the left column with their correct definitions in the right column. Some definitions match more than one prefix/suffix.

_____ 1. retrovirus

_____ 2. Western blot

_____ 3. Kaposi sarcoma

_____ 4. anaphylaxis

_____ 5. thymoma

_____ 6. Hodgkin disease

_____ 7. infectious mononucleosis

_____ 8. acquired immunodeficiency syndrome

_____ 9. allergen

_____ 10. cytomegalovirus

_____ 11. sarcoidosis

_____ 12. toxoplasmosis

_____ 13. herpes simplex

_____ 14. histoplasmosis

_____ 15. coccidioidomycosis

_____ 16. agammaglobulinemia

_____ 17. candidiasis

_____ 18. tuberculosis

_____ 19. rheumatoid arthritis

_____ 20. systemic lupus erythematosus

_____ 21. Sjögren syndrome

_____ 22. rheumatic fever

_____ 23. carcinoma

_____ 24. adenoma

_____ 25. melanoma

_____ 26. neoplasm

A. profound suppression of immune response from human immunodeficiency virus

B. febrile illness resulting from strep infection, causing connective tissue lesions

C. virus that causes colitis, pneumonitis, and retinitis

D. viral infection with blisters on lips, nose, or genitals

E. systemic granulomatous disease

F. pulmonary infection due to _Mycobacterium_

G. infectious disease characterized by the presence of lymphocytes, monocytes, enlarged lymph nodes

H. autoimmune disorder of exocrine glands

I. inability to form antibodies

J. yeast infection

K. test that detects the presence of HIV in serum

L. autoimmune connective tissue disease affecting the heart, joints, and skin

M. malignant tumor from epithelium

N. malignant tumor of lymph tissue in spleen and lymph nodes

O. sensitizing agent

P. malignant tumor arising from pigment cells

Q. RNA virus that copies itself by using host cell's DNA

R. benign tumor arising from glandular epithelium

S. parasitic infection of lungs and brain

T. exaggerated, severe hypersensitivity reaction

U. new growth or tumor

V. malignant capillary tumor associated with AIDS

W. fungal infection from inhaled contaminated dust; pathogen found in bat and bird droppings

X. San Joaquin valley fever

Y. chronic inflammatory disease of the joints

Z. malignant tumor of thymus gland

Pathophysiology of the Immune System, Continued

Fill in the blanks with the correct answers. Some answers may require more than one word.

27. The Broders classification of squamous cell carcinoma categorizes 75 percent of undifferentiated cells as grade _____.

28. A basic framework used in staging a wide variety of malignancies is classification of tumor, nodal disease, and _____.

29. A procedure that is performed to reduce tumor volume or provide pain relief but is not curative is called a _____ procedure.

30. Treatment of cancer with medications is known as _____.

31. Treatment of cancer with x-ray therapy is known as _____.

32. Treatment of cancer with both medications and x-ray therapy is known as

_____.

33. _____ is the main cause of bronchogenic

carcinoma.

34. Women who have never had children or whose first pregnancy occurs late in childbearing years are at increased risk of _____ cancer.

35. Adenocarcinoma of the _____ is the most common cancer in men and is often treated surgically with a radical _____.

36. _____ cancer, occurring in both men and women, ranks second as a cause of cancer deaths in the U.S.

37. A _____ is a surgically created opening from the colon to the abdominal wall.

38. A patient with a positive RA test and inflammatory changes in joint membranes would likely be diagnosed with _____.

39. A variant of systemic lupus erythematosus in which abnormalities are confined to the skin is

_____.

40. Oral hairy _____ is a shaggy whitish plaque of abnormal oral mucosa commonly seen in patients with AIDS.

Pathophysiology of the Immune System, Continued

Choose the correct answer in each of the following multiple-choice questions. Write your answer in the space provided next to the number of the question.

____41. All of the following are cancer treatments EXCEPT:
a. fibrinolytic therapy
b. radiation therapy
c. chemotherapy
d. mutagenic therapy

____42. Normal cells undergo spontaneous disintegration by a process known as:
a. acrokeratosis
b. hypocytosis
c. coptosis
d. apoptosis

____43. Which of the following is NOT a major classification of cancerous tumors?
a. adenoma
b. carcinoma
c. sarcoma
d. mixed-tissue tumor

____44. A connective tissue disorder in which collagen is deposited in tendons, ligaments, bones, and cartilage is:
a. Chediak-Higashi disease
b. Job syndrome
c. systemic lupus erythematosus
d. Wiskott-Aldrich syndrome

____45. Which of the following is one of cancer's seven warning signals?
a. breast tenderness
b. rectal itching
c. extremely dry skin and hair
d. indigestion

____46. Which of the following cancers is typically far advanced and inoperable when first diagnosed?
a. bronchogenic
b. breast
c. prostatic
d. uterine

____47. Which grading system is used for adenocarcinoma of the prostate?
a. Pauwel
b. Gleason
c. Jewett
d. Kiel

Pathophysiology of the Psyche

Match the terms in the left column with their correct definitions in the right column.

_____ 1. affect

A. manic-depressive illness

_____ 2. compulsion

B. an uncontrollable urge

_____ 3. id

C. obsessive preoccupation

_____ 4. repression

D. lack of interest

_____ 5. psychosis

E. instability

_____ 6. neurosis

F. inability to remember

_____ 7. mutism

G. inability to recognize reality

_____ 8. depression

H. external emotion or emotional response

_____ 9. amnesia

I. inability to experience pleasure

_____10. autism

J. false sensory perception

_____11. lability

K. false belief

_____12. delusion

L. mental confusion, faulty perception, irrational behavior

_____13. schizophrenia

M. inability to speak

_____14. paranoia

N. central coordination branch of the personality

_____15. apathy

O. delusions of persecution

_____16. bipolar disorder

P. loss of memory, judgment, and reasoning

_____17. anhedonia

Q. anxiety and avoidance behavior

_____18. phobia

R. unconscious defense mechanism

_____19. ego

S. emotional withdrawal and retarded language

_____20. dissociative disorder

T. hopelessness

_____21. fugue

U. a sense of having done wrong or not meeting expectations

_____22. delirium

V. irrational fear

_____23. mania

W. amnesic state with flight from reality

_____24. hallucination

X. disturbance of memory, identity, or consciousness

_____25. guilt

Y. major psychotic disorder with disorganized thinking

_____26. dementia

Z. unconscious part of the personality

Pathophysiology of the Psyche, Continued

Fill in the blanks with the correct answers. Some answers may require more than one word.

27. An eating disorder of excess dieting and refusal to maintain a normal body weight is

    _____.

28. _____ is an eating disorder in which the patient

    binge eats and then induces vomiting.

29. Mental illnesses have been precisely defined and classified by the American Psychiatric

    Association in a publication called _____.

30. Biochemical research has established a correlation between certain mental disorders and

    neurotransmitters such as dopamine, norepinephrine, and _____.

31. The patient who is oriented x 3 is aware of time, place, and _____.

32. An intense fear of being alone or being in a public place from which escape might be diffi-

    cult is known as _____ .

33. The two mood swings that are typical of bipolar disorder are _____

    and _____.

34. Withdrawal from alcohol dependence can result in an acute disturbance of brain function

    characterized by confusion and even hallucinations; this condition is called

    _____.

35. Alzheimer disease, Huntington chorea, and Cruetzfeldt-Jakob disease are all examples of

    chronic, progressive deterioration in mental function termed _____.

36. _____ is the term used to describe the invention of

    stories about one's past, often bizarre and complex.

37. According to Freud, the human personality consists of three parts: _____,

    _____, and _____.

38. A type of group therapy in which clients resolve conflicts and distressing emotional states

    by acting out their fantasies and fears is _____.

39. A person who justifies an act or omission through logical reasoning or argument, usually to

    reduce guilt, is said to be _____.

40. Thoughts of committing suicide as a relief from mental distress without actual attempts at

    suicide, is termed suicidal _____.

Pathophysiology of the Psyche, Continued

_____41. Which of the following is NOT part of the mental status examination?
  a. memory
  b. insight
  c. hypnosis
  d. appearance

_____42. Which of the following is characteristic of schizophrenia?
  a. anxiety
  b. depression
  c. hallucination
  d. delirium

_____43. Which of the following is NOT classified as an anxiety disorder?
  a. panic disorder
  b. agoraphobia
  c. social phobia
  d. depression

_____44. For many psychiatric disorders, the most rapid, effective, and predictable mode of treatment is:
  a. drug therapy
  b. group therapy
  c. behavioral therapy
  d. psychotherapy

_____45. Excessive handwashing, repetitive checking of locks, and performance of everyday actions in a ritualized fashion is an example of:
  a. manic-depressive disorder
  b. mood disorder
  c. attention-deficit hyperactivity disorder
  d. obsessive-compulsive disorder

_____46. Which of the following is NOT a type of schizophrenia?
  a. paranoid
  b. panic
  c. catatonic
  d. hebephrenic

_____47. Attention-deficit hyperactivity disorder is how many times more prevalent in boys than in girls?
  a. 1 to 3
  b. 3 to 8
  c. 8 to 15
  d. 15 to 25

_____48. The mechanism by which one refuses to believe, remember, or accept an unpleasant fact or circumstance is known as:
  a. denial
  b. aversion
  c. guilt
  d. sublimation

Section 6.
Surgery

Match the terms in the left column with their correct definitions in the right column. Some definitions fit more than one term.

_____ 1. sponge

_____ 2. asepsis

_____ 3. drape

_____ 4. dorsal recumbent position

_____ 5. Fowler position

_____ 6. Sims position

_____ 7. gurney

_____ 8. prep

_____ 9. bolster

_____ 10. bleeder

_____ 11. dehiscence

_____ 12. pursestring

_____ 13. ligate

_____ 14. nonabsorbable

_____ 15. retention suture

_____ 16. free tie

_____ 17. dressing

_____ 18. hemostasis

_____ 19. electrocautery

_____ 20. clamp

_____ 21. ablation

_____ 22. approximate (verb)

_____ 23. forceps

_____ 24. bur

_____ 25. curette

_____ 26. retractor

_____ 27. reamer

_____ 28. osteotome

_____ 29. probe

_____ 30. tenaculum

_____ 31. scalpel

A. instrument that clasps tissue

B. instrument used to create a hollow area in bone

C. freedom from germs and infection

D. splitting apart of a wound

E. complete removal or destruction

F. bring together by suturing

G. instrument used to cut bone

H. severed vessel

I. reinforcement suture

J. material covering a wound

K. sitting position

L. instrument used for exploration of wound or cavity

M. suture technique

N. fluid-resistant sterile barrier

O. lying on one's side

P. instrument that holds tissue out of the way

Q. electrical current used to control hemorrhage

R. absorbent pad of folded gauze

S. instrument used to drill holes

T. supine position

U. spoon-shaped instrument used for scraping

V. wheeled cot

W. to make ready

X. retention suture tubing

Y. tie

Z. instrument used to make incisions

AA. a length of suture for tying

BB. suture material not absorbed by the body

CC. control of bleeding

General Surgery, Continued

Select one of the following terms that matches the definition.

incisional biopsy   excisional biopsy   brushing
needle biopsy   fine-needle aspiration   smear
washing   frozen section   biopsy
cryostat   curettage   punch biopsy
shave biopsy

32. removal of a plug of skin with a cylindrical punch   _____

33. surgical scraping   _____

34. chilled platform   _____

35. lavage of an organ with fluid, then collection of the fluid for pathologic study   _____

36. whisking of an organ for cell collection   _____

37. surgical removal of an entire lesion from a living person   _____

38. material spread thinly on a slide for microscopic examination   _____

39. removal of tissue from a living person for pathologic examination   _____

40. cells removed by suction with a needle   _____

41. removal of tissue from an organ with the use of a needle   _____

42. thin layer of skin removed with a blade parallel to the surface   _____

43. rapid cryotechnique for reading surgical specimens from a living person   _____

44. surgical removal of part of a lesion from a living person   _____

General Surgery, Continued

Choose the correct answer in each of the following multiple-choice questions. Write your answer in the space provided next to the number of the question.

_____ 45. Among the following, which is the *finest* suture material?
    a. 10-0
    b. #0
    c. #2
    d. 1-0

_____ 46. Which of the following is a type of suture material?
    a. interrupted
    b. figure-of-8
    c. synthetic
    d. pursestring

_____ 47. A trocar is used:
    a. for traction
    b. to puncture a cavity and withdraw fluid
    c. to support and stabilize another surgical instrument
    d. to enable the surgeon to view internal anatomy

_____ 48. Laparoscopy is an example of:
    a. open surgery
    b. minimal access surgery
    c. peripheral vascular surgery
    d. "painless" surgery

_____ 49. How is the Trendelenburg position best described?
    a. head lower than trunk and thighs
    b. head elevated above trunk and legs
    c. hips elevated higher than legs and head
    d. lying on side with lower leg flexed

_____ 50. For which of the following surgeries would the patient be in lithotomy position?
    a. brain surgery
    b. chest surgery
    c. vaginal surgery
    d. knee surgery

_____ 51. Which of the following is a suture technique?
    a. mattress
    b. catgut
    c. chromic
    d. monofilament nylon

_____ 52. Which of the following is a wound dressing material?
    a. Sabreloc
    b. Lembert
    c. Penrose
    d. Kerlix

Anesthesia

Choose the correct answer in each of the following multiple-choice questions. Write your answer in the space provided next to the number of the question.

_____ 1. Which is NOT a type of anesthesia?
   a. endotracheal
   b. spinal
   c. analgesic
   d. topical

_____ 2. Bier block anesthesia would be used for:
   a. cholecystectomy
   b. angioplasty
   c. myringotomy with insertion of ventilation tubes
   d. carpal tunnel release

_____ 3. A "muscle relaxant" is given under general endotracheal anesthesia to:
   a. sedate the patient
   b. paralyze the muscles
   c. keep the patient unconscious
   d. combat postoperative nausea

_____ 4. Which type of anesthesia might be used for cesarean section?
   a. spinal
   b. local
   c. topical
   d. epidural

_____ 5. A patient undergoing laryngoscopy would NOT receive:
   a. intravenous sedation anesthesia
   b. topical anesthesia
   c. general anesthesia
   d. spinal anesthesia

_____ 6. Which of the following phrases BEST describes _general anesthesia with nasotracheal intubation?_
   a. patient unconscious with breathing tube in throat
   b. patient unconscious with breathing tube in nose
   c. patient unconscious with breathing tube in trachea
   d. patient unconscious with breathing tube in esophagus

_____ 7. Epidural anesthesia may be used for certain surgical procedures:
   a. below the spine
   b. below the chest
   c. below the neck
   d. below the head

Surgery on the Integumentary System

Below are plastic surgery procedures that involve the skin. List the anatomic structures or body parts affected by the surgery.

1. blepharoplasty   eyelids

2. rhytidectomy   _____

3. microtia reconstruction   _____

4. rhinoplasty   _____

5. cleft palate repair   _____

6. transverse rectus abdominis
    myocutaneous (TRAM) flap   _____

7. mental implant   _____

8. liposuction   _____

9. mastopexy   _____

10. glomus tumor excision   _____

11. platysmaplasty   _____

Choose the correct answer in each of the following multiple-choice questions. Write your answer in the space provided next to the number of the question.

_____ 12. Debridement is the process of:
     a.   attaching suture material to a needle
     b.   shaving a patient in preparation for surgery
     c.   removing dead skin and debris from a wound
     d.   making a surgical incision

_____ 13. The destruction of tissue by use of a freezing instrument is called:
     a.   sclerosis
     b.   stenosis
     c.   cryocautery
     d.   dermatogenesis

_____ 14. A section of skin that is relocated to an area denuded of skin is known as a:
     a.   transplant
     b.   skin graft
     c.   donor site
     d.   dermatophysis

_____15. The instrument used to take a split-thickness graft is a:
a. dermatome
b. rasp
c. scoop
d. scraper

_____16. Separation of skin and subcutaneous tissue from underlying attachments is called:
a. devitalizing
b. meshing
c. undermining
d. dissection

_____17. Port-wine "birthmark" stains consisting of reddish pink or purple areas are best treated by:
a. surgical excision
b. laser surgery
c. camouflage tattooing
d. chemocautery

_____18. Sanding of the skin with a power-driven abrasive disk is known as:
a. sanding
b. dermabrasion
c. tattooing
d. peeling

_____19. What method of fresh tissue chemosurgery is often performed to remove basal cell carcinoma?
a. Orr
b. Trueta
c. Rebuck
d. Mohs

_____20. Senile keratoses and warts are often removed by application of which liquid?
a. carbolic acid
b. nitrogen
c. povidone-iodine
d. acid alcohol

_____21. A device containing a circulating refrigerant that can be rapidly chilled and can deliver subfreezing temperatures to tissues with precision is a(n):
a. cryoprobe
b. ablator
c. pinpoint wand
d. dissector

Surgery on the Integumentary System, Continued

____ 22. What is the name of the procedure in which small pieces of skin graft are placed randomly over a recipient site?
   a. pinch graft
   b. flap graft
   c. pedicle graft
   d. compression graft

____ 23. An instrument that cuts many tiny slits in graft skin to enlarge the graft is called a skin:
   a. mesher
   b. grille
   c. lattice
   d. reticulator

____ 24. A procedure in which the face is painted with a solution of phenol to burn and erode the area to which it is applied is called:
   a. dermabrasion
   b. cryocautery
   c. autografting
   d. chemical peel

____ 25. An atraumatic surgical needle with the suture already attached by the manufacturer, and used to minimize skin trauma, is known as what kind of needle?
   a. cutting
   b. swaged
   c. eyed
   d. blunt point

____ 26. Malignant nodular melanomas require what type of surgical excision?
   a. wide margin
   b. narrow margin
   c. lateral margin
   d. shallow margin

____ 27. Of the following surgically excised lesions, which represents the most serious health threat to the patient?
   a. actinic keratosis
   b. dermatofibroma
   c. basal cell carcinoma
   d. squamous cell carcinoma

____ 28. A gangrenous body part must be:
   a. incised and drained
   b. biopsied
   c. amputated
   d. reconstructed

Surgery on the Genitourinary System

Complete each statement by filling in the blank with a term from the list below.

Babcock	stent	iliac fossa
cadaver	Young	Retzius
circumcision	subcostal	transurethral resection
flank	suprapubic	Marshall-Marchetti-Kranz
vas deferens	nephrolithotomy	stress urinary incontinence

1. If a kidney stone cannot be removed ureteroscopically or via lithotripsy, an open procedure known as a _____ is performed.

2. A _____ is performed to reduce the size of a prostate gland enlarged due to benign prostatic hyperplasia (BPH).

3. A simple nephrectomy is performed through a _____ incision.

4. When urinary diversion is required for an extended period, a _____ catheter may be surgically placed.

5. Suspension of the bladder neck and urethra to the cartilage of the pubic symphysis is performed to correct _____ in a female patient.

6. One of the operations designed to suspend the bladder neck and urethra in a female patient is called a(n) _____ procedure.

7. Surgical procedures in the pubic area are initiated by entry into structure known as the space of _____.

8. Orchiectomy may be indicated when the testicle has become twisted around the _____.

9. Following dilatation of a ureteral stricture, a _____ may be left in place to keep the ureter open for drainage.

10. A penile epispadias is corrected by formation of a new urethral tube using the technique of _____.

11. A _____ clamp is often used for urological surgery procedures.

12. The surgeon gains access to the retroperitoneal space to perform a nephrostomy using a _____ incision.

13. A kidney for transplantation is taken from either a living donor or from a _____.

14. The donor kidney is placed in the recipient's (anatomy) _____.

15. A _____ is performed to correct phimosis.

Surgery on the Genitourinary System, Continued

Choose the correct answer in each of the following multiple-choice questions. Write your answer in the space provided next to the number of the question.

_____16. What is the medical term for male castration?
  a. penectomy
  b. eunuchization
  c. vasectomy
  d. orchiectomy

_____17. The procedure that brings an undescended testicle into the scrotum is called a(n):
  a. hypospadias repair
  b. hydrocelectomy
  c. orchiopexy
  d. vasectomy

_____18. Surgical removal of the prostate gland in which the bladder is not entered is accomplished via:
  a. suprapubic prostatectomy
  b. retropubic prostatectomy
  c. infrapubic prostatectomy
  d. transvesical prostatectomy

_____19. Sterilization in the male is accomplished by excising a small portion of the:
  a. vas deferens
  b. ejaculatory duct
  c. epididymis
  d. seminal vesicles

_____20. Chordee is:
  a. an abnormal curvature of the penis
  b. insertion of an implant into the penis
  c. an intractable erection
  d. sequential catheterization

_____21. The indwelling urethral catheter used most commonly is the:
  a. straight catheter
  b. Foley catheter
  c. Gibbon catheter
  d. Robinson catheter

_____22. An obturator is a:
  a. hollow fiberglass tube
  b. light cable
  c. telescopic lens
  d. metal rod with round tip

_____23. A lithotrite is:
  a. a calculus that is still within the urinary tract
  b. a calculus that has been retrieved
  c. a stone crusher
  d. a stone basket

Surgery on the Gastrointestinal System

Choose the correct answer by matching the lettered terms with their definitions below. Write your answer in the space provided next to the number of the question.

a. laparotomy
b. sponge
c. incisional hernia
d. catgut
e. retraction
f. deflection

g. transect
h. blunt dissection
i. McBurney
j. gastrostomy
k. pursestring
l. Kock ileal reservoir

m. pop-off
n. cholecystectomy
o. Whipple procedure
p. wedge resection
q. hiatal hernia
r. hemorrhoidectomy
s. partial gastrectomy

____ 1. defect in the phrenoesophageal membrane at the level of the diaphragm

____ 2. weakening in the abdominal wall due to previous surgery

____ 3. removal of a portion of liver to determine presence of metastatic disease

____ 4. separation of tissue planes with an instrument that has no cutting ability

____ 5. absorbable monofilament suture of organic material

____ 6. pouch for the collection of urine following removal of the bladder

____ 7. open exploration of abdominal contents

____ 8. peeling away or retraction of tissue without detaching it

____ 9. incision most often used for an appendectomy

____10. pancreaticojejunostomy

____11. incision made into the stomach to allow insertion of a feeding tube

____12. absorbent pad of gauze or cotton

____13. suture used to close a rounded opening

____14. to cut across an organ or section of tissue

____15. suture separated from the needle with a gentle tug

____16. removal of part of stomach

____17. pulling tissues back or away to expose a structure or another tissue

____18. surgical removal of a diseased gallbladder

____19. excision of painfully dilated veins of the anus and rectum

Surgery on the Gastrointestinal System, Continued

Choose the correct answer in each of the following multiple-choice questions. Write your answer in the space provided next to the number of the question.

_____20. Surgical treatment for esophageal varices includes injecting the varices with a solution of:
   a. saline
   b. denatured alcohol
   c. cartilage emulsion
   d. hydrocortisone

_____21. A loop colostomy is:
   a. excision of part of the ileum
   b. excision of part of the transverse colon
   c. a temporary diversion of the colon
   d. a Whipple procedure

_____22. A GIA instrument is a:
   a. stapler
   b. clamp
   c. reservoir
   d. laser

_____23. A Roux-en-Y anastomosis is performed in which of the following procedures?
   a. inguinal hernia repair
   b. hemorrhoidectomy
   c. gastric bypass
   d. cholecystectomy

_____24. Pyloromyotomy is performed for:
   a. globus hystericus
   b. biliary atresia
   c. pyloric stenosis
   d. esophageal stricture

_____25. Varicose veins of the esophagus are treated with:
   a. vein excision
   b. saline injections
   c. esophagectomy
   d. incision and drainage

_____26. The most common indication for splenectomy is:
   a. bacterial infection
   b. viral infection
   c. parasitic infection
   d. trauma

_____27. An open cholecystectomy is the procedure of choice when:
     a. stones are present in the gallbladder
     b. laparoscopic cholecystectomy is not an option
     c. the cholecystokinin test is positive
     d. the patient is obese

_____28. What substance is used to create a pneumoperitoneum for laparoscopic abdominal surgery?
     a. carbon dioxide
     b. nitrous oxide
     c. sterile water
     d. saline solution

_____29. During laparoscopic abdominal surgery, what instrument is inserted with the trocar?
     a. sleeve
     b. probe
     c. straight grasper
     d. hook scissors

_____30. An esophagogastroduodenoscopy is performed to assess all but the following structure:
     a. esophagus
     b. stomach
     c. duodenum
     d. jejunum

_____31. Which scissors are commonly used for abdominal procedures?
     a. Castroviejo
     b. Metzenbaum
     c. Bellucci
     d. Dean

_____32. Which procedure is commonly performed with vagotomy?
     a. partial gastrectomy
     b. esophagectomy
     c. gastrojejunostomy
     d. pyloroplasty

_____33. End-to-end and end-to-side are types of:
     a. suture techniques
     b. drains
     c. anastomoses
     d. bandages

_____34. An appendectomy that is performed prophylactically during the course of another abdominal surgery is termed:
     a. vermiform
     b. incidental
     c. unnecessary
     d. absolute

Surgery on the Musculoskeletal System

Match the orthopedic surgical devices in the left column with their correct definitions in the right column. Some definitions match more than one device.

_____ 1. cast

_____ 2. nail

_____ 3. saw

_____ 4. knife

_____ 5. rod

_____ 6. depth gauge

_____ 7. awl

_____ 8. armboard

_____ 9. mallet

_____ 10. screwdriver

_____ 11. rasp

_____ 12. reamer

_____ 13. screw

_____ 14. elevator

_____ 15. rongeur

_____ 16. pin

_____ 17. osteotome

_____ 18. curette

_____ 19. clamp

_____ 20. retractor

_____ 21. caliper

_____ 22. hammer

_____ 23. gouge

A. instrument used to scrape, smooth, pierce, or cut bone

B. instrument used to lift periosteum from bone surface

C. an external stabilization device

D. instrument used to hold bone or soft tissue

E. instrument used to drive nails, rods, or screws

F. an internal fixation device

G. a measuring device

Surgery on the Musculoskeletal System, Continued

Choose the correct answer in each of the following multiple-choice questions. Write your answer in the space provided next to the number of the question.

_____ 24. Comminution is the presence of more than how many fracture fragments?
  a. 1
  b. 2
  c. 3
  d. 4

_____ 25. A division of bone to correct angular or rotatory deformity is an:
  a. epiphysectomy
  b. articulotomy
  c. arthrodesis
  d. osteotomy

_____ 26. A lensed fiberoptic telescope inserted into a joint space is:
  a. an arthroscope
  b. an orthoscope
  c. a ventriculoscope
  d. a laparoscope

_____ 27. A meniscal repair is performed for which condition?
  a. greenstick fracture
  b. bowstring deformity
  c. bucket-handle tear
  d. Osgood-Schlatter disease

_____ 28. A Bankart procedure is performed on the:
  a. ankle
  b. wrist
  c. hip
  d. shoulder

_____ 29. In a total hip replacement procedure, the stem of the acetabular prosthesis is inserted into what part of the femur?
  a. glenoid labrum
  b. lateral meniscus
  c. greater trochanter
  d. lesser multangular

_____ 30. Fractures in young children are often complicated by involvement of:
  a. smooth muscles
  b. epiphyseal plates
  c. supporting ligaments
  d. joint spaces

Surgery on the Musculoskeletal System, Continued

____ 31. A patellar shaving procedure is often indicated because of:
   a. chondromalacia patellae
   b. patellofemoral dislocation
   c. patellar tendinitis
   d. bipartite patella

____ 32. Methyl methacrylate is a:
   a. contrast medium
   b. casting material
   c. prosthetic joint
   d. bone cement

____ 33. A Bristow procedure is used for repair of the:
   a. shoulder
   b. cervical spine
   c. wrist
   d. hip

____ 34. Deformity of the finger characterized by flexion of the proximal interphalangeal joint and hyperextension of the distal joint is called:
   a. lobster-claw
   b. boutonnière
   c. swan-neck
   d. crossbar

____ 35. A K-wire, often used for orthopedic fixation, is properly termed:
   a. Kocher wire
   b. Kidner wire
   c. Kirschner wire
   d. Küntscher wire

____ 36. An infolding or tuck of tissue, as in a tuck made in plication, is called:
   a. reefing
   b. reducing
   c. dog-earring
   d. undermining

____ 37. The condition know as talipes equinovarus is also known as:
   a. claw toe
   b. genu valgum
   c. clubfoot
   d. pigeon toes

____ 38. Which of the following is NOT an example of an internal fixation device?
   a. pin
   b. rod
   c. cone
   d. plate

Surgery on the Cardiovascular System

Fill in the blanks with the correct terms. Answers may require more than one word.

1. The goals of carotid endarterectomy are to remove _____ and

   restore _____.

2. Operative repair of an abdominal aortic aneurysm requires replacement of the diseased

   aortic segment with a prosthetic _____.

3. A femoral embolectomy is performed to remove _____

   from the femoral-popliteal system and restore circulation to the limb.

4. A portacaval shunt is anastomosis of the portal vein to the vena cava to treat portal

   _____.

5. Saphenous vein stripping is performed to treat _____

   of the leg.

6. A ventriculotomy is performed to close a hole in the intraventricular septum; this procedure

   is known as closure of a(n) _____.

7. A _____ graft, made of Dacron or Teflon, is used to

   strengthen a suture line or close a defect.

8. A compartment _____ develops when injury causes

   pressure within an osteofascial compartment to rise, leading to impairment of nerve conduc-

   tion and blood flow through the compartment.

9. A solution that is used to stop the heart is called a _____

   solution.

10. Correction of _____ of the thoracic aorta is performed to

    correct congenital stenosis of the thoracic aorta.

11. Cardiopulmonary _____ is the method used to divert blood away

    from the heart and lungs temporarily while surgery on the heart and vessels is performed.

Surgery on the Cardiovascular System, Continued

Choose the correct answer in each of the following multiple-choice questions. Write your answer in the space provided next to the number of the question.

_____12. Which of the following catheters would be inserted in the pulmonary artery to monitor blood pressure in the heart during open heart surgery?
   a. Foley
   b. Hickman
   c. Fogarty
   d. Swan-Ganz

_____13. The lower extremity vessel most often removed for coronary artery bypass graft is the:
   a. femoral artery
   b. saphenous vein
   c. popliteal vein
   d. iliac artery

_____14. Traditional coronary artery bypass graft surgery is done through a median:
   a. sternotomy
   b. thoracotomy
   c. nephrotomy
   d. alveotomy

_____15. A procedure performed to stretch a narrowed coronary artery is:
   a. PTDC
   b. PTMC
   c. PTHC
   d. PTCA

_____16. A material used for arterial bypass grafts is:
   a. Interpore
   b. OpSite
   c. Gore-Tex
   d. Synthaderm

_____17. During cardiac surgery, cardioplegic solution is injected in order to precipitate:
   a. cardiac arrest
   b. adequate hemostasis
   c. mild bradycardia
   d. nodal rhythm

_____18. Which of the following suture materials used in cardiac surgery is nonabsorbable?
   a. PDS
   b. catgut
   c. Dexon
   d. silk

_____19. Repair of a patent ductus arteriosus is done to close the communication between the thoracic aorta and the:
  a. thoracic vein
  b. inframammary artery
  c. pulmonary artery
  d. subclavian vein

_____20. Transvenous and subxiphoid pacemaker implantations do NOT require:
  a. fluoroscopy
  b. thoracotomy
  c. local anesthesia
  d. drains

_____21. Which procedure is used to correct transposition of the great vessels?
  a. Carpentier
  b. Fontan
  c. Shumway
  d. Mustard

_____22. Tiny pieces of felt used along a suture line to reinforce an anastomosis are called:
  a. pledgets
  b. liners
  c. bolsters
  d. wedges

_____23. Mosquito clamps are so named for their:
  a. grip
  b. small size
  c. buzzing sound
  d. winged blades

_____24. During heart catheterization, the procedure is often initiated using which technique?
  a. Seldinger
  b. Sones
  c. Stoney
  d. Sarns

_____25. During thoracotomy, the patient is placed in which position?
  a. lateral
  b. supine
  c. prone
  d. Fowler

_____26. Satinsky and Cooley are types of angled:
  a. drains
  b. scissors
  c. cannulas
  d. clamps

Surgery on the Cardiovascular System, Continued

_____27. Gelpi and Weitlaner are types of:
   a. retractors
   b. sumps
   c. fine-tissue forceps
   d. catheters

_____28. Beaver and Bard-Parker are types of:
   a. metal rings
   b. aortic punches
   c. blades
   d. dilators

_____29. A cardiac pacemaker receives power from the:
   a. ventricles of the heart
   b. pulse generator
   c. subxiphoid electrodes
   d. myocardium

_____30. Cardiopulmonary bypass is also known as:
   a. heart-lung bypass
   b. CABG
   c. cannulation
   d. defibrillation

_____31. On completion of anastomosis of vein graft to coronary artery, what must be removed before decannulation can be achieved?
   a. sutures
   b. air
   c. blood
   d. tissue

_____32. The procedure performed to relieve stricture in the left coronary artery system caused by atherosclerotic plaque is:
   a. valvulotomy
   b. angioplasty
   c. commissurotomy
   d. catheterization

_____33. Porcine prosthetic heart valves are taken from:
   a. cows
   b. cadavers
   c. pigs
   d. monkeys

370

Surgery on the Cardiovascular System, Continued

_____34. Surgical correction of congenital pulmonary valve stenosis is accomplished by which procedure?
   a. pulmonary valve resection
   b. pulmonary valvulotomy
   c. pulmonary valve replacement
   d. pulmonary diversion

_____35. A device used to assist cardiopulmonary bypass for patients who have suffered myocardial infarction is:
   a. intra-aortic balloon catheter
   b. Klein pump
   c. 90/90 wire
   d. Ray threaded fusion cage

_____36. Arteriosclerotic disease of the femoral artery may be surgically treated with:
   a. aortofemoral bypass
   b. femoral endarterectomy
   c. femoral embolectomy
   d. femoral-popliteal bypass

_____37. A "roto-rooter job" is a slang expression for which procedure?
   a. atherectomy
   b. percutaneous transluminal angioplasty
   c. balloon angioplasty
   d. cardiac catheterization

_____38. What type of incision is made to facilitate carotid endarterectomy?
   a. neck incision
   b. supraclavicular incision
   c. subxiphoid incision
   d. submental incision

_____39. The surgical treatment for advanced cardiomyopathy is:
   a. cardiac revascularization
   b. cardiac catheterization
   c. cardiac bypass
   d. heart transplant

_____40. What might the cardiac surgeon require to convert a patient's quivering heart to normal sinus rhythm?
   a. pacemaker
   b. cardioplegic solution
   c. protamine sulfate
   d. defibrillator

Surgery on the Pulmonary System

Fill in the blanks with the correct names of the pulmonary procedures based on the corresponding descriptions.

1. Surgical incision into the thoracic cavity to provide access to organs of the chest

   _____

2. Insertion of chest tube

   _____

3. Excision of a small piece of lung tissue for microscopic examination

   _____

4. Insertion of a lighted instrument into the space in the middle of the chest cavity between the heart and two pleural cavities

   _____

5. Creation of a temporary or permanent opening into the trachea to allow air to enter the bronchi and lungs

   _____

6. Surgical excision of a lung

   _____

7. Insertion of a lighted instrument into the respiratory tree

   _____

8. Insertion of a tube into the trachea to facilitate breathing

   _____

9. Whisking of the bronchi for pathologic examination

   _____

10. Irrigation of the bronchi for pathologic examination

    _____

11. Surgical splitting of sternal bone to allow access to thoracic cavity

    _____

12. Surgical excision of a lobe of the lung

    _____

13. Surgical stapling technique used for removal of emphysematous lung tissue

    _____

14. Replacement of a patient's poorly functioning or nonfunctioning lung with a donor lung

    _____

15. Surgical excision of a rib

    _____

Surgery on the Pulmonary System, Continued

Choose the correct answer in each of the following multiple-choice questions. Write your answer in the space provided next to the number of the question.

_____16. A chest tube may be inserted following thoracic surgery in order to prevent:
  a. lung expansion
  b. lung collapse
  c. rib fractures
  d. flail chest

_____17. Surgical excision of a lung would likely be performed for:
  a. carcinoma
  b. tuberculosis
  c. intractable fungal infection
  d. chronic bronchiectasis

_____18. What procedure might be performed to keep an airway open for more than 36 continuous hours?
  a. intravenous cutdown
  b. Hickman catheter insertion
  c. tracheotomy
  d. intubation

_____19. Of the following, which is NOT a function of bronchoscopy?
  a. extraction of tissue for examination
  b. removal of foreign objects
  c. maintenance of an airway
  d. visualization of the respiratory tree and lungs

_____20. Which of the following is a standard brand of bronchoscope?
  a. Everest
  b. Whitney
  c. Denali
  d. Olympus

_____21. The incision for a mediastinoscopy procedure is made:
  a. above the thyroid cartilage
  b. over the suprasternal notch
  c. between the tracheal rings
  d. below the diaphragm

_____22. A thoracotomy incision divides:
  a. latissimus dorsi, rhomboid, and trapezius muscles
  b. pectoralis major, coracobrachialis, and deltoid muscles
  c. serratus anterior, external oblique, and internal oblique muscles
  d. rectus abdominis, transversus abdominis, and pectoralis minor muscles

Surgery on the Female Reproductive System

Fill in the blanks with the correct terms. Answers may require more than one word.

1. Although more technically difficult for the surgeon, a _____ hysterectomy is less traumatic for the patient and recovery time is shorter.

2. Surgical excision of a _____ fistula is performed because urine escapes through the vagina, causing pain and incontinence.

3. Elective premature removal of the fetus from the uterus through the vagina is known as a(n) _____ abortion.

4. Smooth, sharp, and serrated _____ are used to scrape the interior of the uterus in a D&C procedure.

5. Removal of the viable fetus via abdominal incision into the uterus is known as

    _____.

6. A hysterectomy in which pelvic lymphadenectomy and wide excision of parametrial and vaginal supporting structures is performed is termed a _____ hysterectomy.

7. Surgery to correct a cystocele and rectocele is called a(n) _____ repair.

8. A surgical procedure to reduce the size of abnormally large breasts is called a(n) _____ mammoplasty.

9. Removal of a cone of tissue from the cervix for biopsy is called_____.

10. _____ is the name of the procedure where a needle is inserted into the cul-de-sac and fluid is aspirated.

11. Surgical sterilization can be achieved by means of a laparoscopic _____.

12. A sample of the _____ is taken during amniocentesis.

13. A rectovaginal fistula should be surgically repaired to prevent infection from the passage of _____ through the vagina.

14. The surgical procedure to treat aggressive cancer of the vulva is known as radical

    _____.

Surgery on the Female Reproductive System, Continued

Choose the correct answer in each of the following multiple-choice questions. Write your answer in the space provided next to the number of the question.

_____15. An incision often used for abdominal hysterectomy, made horizontally just above the symphysis with the convexity curving downward, is the:
   a. McBurney
   b. Rockey-Davis
   c. Pfannenstiel
   d. Maylard

_____16. When an ectopic pregnancy lodges in the fallopian tube, it is necessary to perform:
   a. a hysteroscopy
   b. a salpingectomy
   c. an oophorectomy
   d. a gonioscopy

_____17. Prior to dilatation and curettage, the depth of the uterine cavity is determined by inserting a:
   a. caliper
   b. catheter
   c. clamp
   d. sound

_____18. In which position is a patient placed for vaginal hysterectomy?
   a. lithotomy
   b. recumbent
   c. decubitus
   d. prone

_____19. Which surgical procedure does NOT preserve the breast?
   a. mastectomy
   b. lymph node sampling
   c. lumpectomy
   d. radiation therapy

_____20. Which needle is commonly used to establish pneumoperitoneum during a laparoscopic procedure?
   a. Veress
   b. Verres
   c. Verre
   d. Vernes

_____21. A cerclage procedure used for correction of an incompetent cervix is:
   a. McGill
   b. McDuff
   c. McIndoe
   d. McDonald

Surgery on the Female Reproductive System, Continued

_____22. A common tubal ligation procedure is named for:
   a. Douglas
   b. Salpinx
   c. Pomeroy
   d. Hunter

_____23. Which is NOT usually an indication for elective hysterectomy?
   a. cervical cancer
   b. irregular menstrual periods
   c. painful endometriosis
   d. leiomyomata uteri

_____24. Which condition requires that a baby be delivered by cesarean section?
   a. footling breech
   b. amniotic fluid leak
   c. previous cesarean section
   d. cephalopelvic disproportion

_____25. The Bartholin gland may require surgery when it:
   a. shrinks
   b. becomes cystic
   c. is callused
   d. secretes mucus

_____26. During a dilatation and curettage procedure, the cervix is grasped with a:
   a. clamp
   b. tenaculum
   c. dilator
   d. hemostat

_____27. A total hysterectomy is defined as:
   a. complete removal of the uterus
   b. complete removal of the uterus and cervix
   c. complete removal of the uterus, cervix, and fallopian tubes
   d. complete removal of the uterus, cervix, fallopian tubes, and ovaries

_____28. After the baby has been removed by cesarean section, the placenta is then removed using which technique?
   a. forceps
   b. vacuum
   c. manual
   d. vaginal

_____29. Suspicious cervical lesions requiring biopsy are identified using:
   a. colposcopy
   b. laparoscopy
   c. amnioscopy
   d. gonioscopy

Surgery on the Ears, Nose, and Throat

Fill in the blanks with the correct answers. Answers may require more than one word.

1. A _____ procedure is carried out to visualize the vocal cords and take biopsies.

2. Adenoidectomy is rarely carried out on adults because the adenoids in most adult patients are _____.

3. When a patient's sense of smell has been obliterated, or if the patient's airway is obstructed from the edematous outgrowths of sinus tissue in the middle meatus, a nasal _____ procedure is often done.

4. Insertion of collar-button tubes is done in a _____ procedure.

5. Repair of _____ palate is done when the child is one or two years of age.

6. Excision of _____ is necessary when these cystlike collections of skin cells and cholesterol cause tympanic perforation.

7. The most common site of facial trauma is the _____ .

8. A relatively new and controversial device called a _____ , which allows the deaf to understand spoken words, is surgically placed under the skin near the mastoid process above and behind the ear.

9. Removal of the third ossicle of the middle ear is called a(n) _____.

10. Nasal antrostomy entails drilling a hole through the nasal antrum for the purpose of facilitating _____.

11. Some cases of gum disease are so severe that a _____ (excision of part of the gums) is necessary to remove pockets of pus and allow new tissue to form.

12. Surgical removal of the stapes and replacement with an artificial stapes is the treatment for _____.

Surgery on the Ears, Nose, and Throat, Continued

Choose the correct answer in each of the following multiple-choice questions. Write your answer in the space provided next to the number of the question.

_____13. Ablation by radiosurgery or surgical excision is carried out to remove acoustic neuromas arising from this cranial nerve:
  a. third
  b. eighth
  c. ninth
  d. twelfth

_____14. The classification system for maxillary fractures is:
  a. Malgaigne
  b. Delbet
  c. Salter
  d. LeFort

_____15. A Caldwell-Luc procedure is performed because of a diagnosis of:
  a. tonsillitis
  b. hearing loss
  c. chronic sinusitis
  d. nasal fracture

_____16. A bobbin is a type of:
  a. aural speculum
  b. drainage tube
  c. suction device
  d. suture passer

_____17. Myringotomy is indicated for a diagnosis of:
  a. deviated nasal septum
  b. dental malocclusion
  c. chronic otitis media
  d. nerve deafness

_____18. Which incision would likely be used for a radical mastoidectomy?
  a. postauricular
  b. intra-auricular
  c. preauricular
  d. submandibular

_____19. A stapedectomy re-establishes linkage between the:
  a. incus and oval window
  b. acoustic meatus and tympanic membrane
  c. vestibule and round window
  d. cochlea and eustachian tube

____20. The initial incision for a nasal septal reconstruction is made through the:
   a. columella
   b. maxillary antrum
   c. mucoperichondrium
   d. parotid duct

____21. Nasal polyps are removed with the use of a(n):
   a. aspirator
   b. snare
   c. rongeur
   d. osteotome

____22. Repair of mandibular fractures includes fixation with a(n):
   a. arch bar
   b. stent
   c. plaster cast
   d. splint

____23. Endoscopic ethmoidectomy with nasal antrostomy procedure may be indicated for a diagnosis of:
   a. broken nose
   b. mastoiditis
   c. deviated nasal septum
   d. sinusitis

____24. En bloc removal of lymphatic chains and all nonvital structures of the neck is a:
   a. parotidectomy
   b. polypectomy
   c. radical neck dissection
   d. tracheal exteneration

____25. Most head and neck procedures are carried out with the operating table in a slight:
   a. Trendelenburg position
   b. reverse Trendelenburg position
   c. Fowler position
   d. Sims position

____26. A rhinoplasty is usually carried out:
   a. within the nose
   b. through the roof of the mouth
   c. following the natural lines and creases on the outside of the nose
   d. through the sinuses

____27. A procedure performed on patients who have repeated epistaxis is:
   a. temporary closure of the nostril with sutures
   b. excision of the bleeding vessels
   c. suturing of nasal packing to the nose
   d. cauterization of the bleeding vessels

Surgery on the Eyes

Complete the following statements; answers may be more than one word.

1. Corneal incisions spreading outward from a common center characterize a procedure called

   _____.

2. Cataract extraction and intraocular lens implantation produce what is called a

   pseudo-_____ in the eye.

3. A(n) _____ suture is used to provide traction in

   ophthalmic surgery.

4. Surgery to correct strabismus requires either recession or resection of the

   _____ muscles of the eye.

5. Indications for _____ of an eye include intraocular

   malignancy and penetrating ocular wound.

6. During a(n) _____ procedure, an ultrasonic

   probe fragments the lens of the eye and reduces it to a liquid material that can be aspirated

   from the eye.

7. The greater the number of zeros in a suture size, such as that used in ophthalmic surgery,

   the _____ the suture material.

8. The purpose of a filtering procedure in glaucoma is to provide a channel for

   _____ of aqueous humor from within the eye.

9. An incision into the iris of the eye is called a(n) _____.

10. The _____ allows the surgeon to operate on

    structures too small to be viewed effectively with the naked eye.

11. Creation of a new, larger opening between the lacrimal sac and the nasal sinus is called

    a(n) _____.

12. Entropion repair is done to prevent rubbing of the _____

    on the cornea.

13. Following corneoplasty, the surgeon fills the anterior chamber of the eye with

    _____ salt solution.

Surgery on the Eyes, Continued

Choose the correct answer in each of the following multiple-choice questions. Write your answer in the space provided next to the number of the question.

____14. During a cataract operation, incision is made into which part of the eye?
   a. iris
   b. sclera
   c. pupil
   d. lens

____15. Surgical instruments are often placed on what kind of stand?
   a. Cleveland
   b. Lahey
   c. Meninger
   d. Mayo

____16. What is the name of the suture in which one needle is attached to each end of a suture length?
   a. bivalve
   b. multi-tip
   c. double-armed
   d. bird-leg

____17. Prep for surgery on the eye extends from the hairline to the mouth and:
   a. from one ear to the other ear
   b. from the nose to the ear
   c. from the chin to the neck
   d. from jaw to jaw

____18. Which instrument is used to help isolate the eye from its surrounding structures so that anesthesia can be instilled?
   a. eye trocar
   b. eye speculum
   c. eye scissors
   d. eye forceps

____19. After repair of entropion, the surgeon dresses the eye with a(n):
   a. hypoallergenic bolster
   b. cotton eye patch
   c. Kerlix bandage
   d. absorbable sponge

____20. Eye muscle surgery is performed to correct a condition called:
   a. strabismus
   b. nystagmus
   c. diplopia
   d. enucleation

____21. A procedure in which a portion of the eye muscle is excised and the severed end is
reattached at the original point of insertion is known as:
   a. anterior rectus resection
   b. lateral rectus resection
   c. medial rectus recession
   d. posterior rectus recession

____22. Repair of ectropion provides for proper drainage of:
   a. pus
   b. blood
   c. tears
   d. mucus

____23. Dacryocystorhinostomy is performed to:
   a. unblock the tearduct
   b. prepare the eye for cataract extraction
   c. create a passageway between the inner canthus of the eye and the sinus
   d. correct a drooping eyelid

____24. Excision of a circular portion of the cornea in preparation for transplant is called:
   a. marsupialization
   b. skeletization
   c. trephination
   d. arborization

____25. A scleral buckle procedure is performed to correct:
   a. strabismus
   b. detached retina
   c. vitreous leakage
   d. macular degeneration

____26. A cataract is usually extracted when:
   a. it is first discovered
   b. the patient becomes blind
   c. it becomes "ripe"
   d. the lens of the eye decays

____27. What is the treatment for diabetic retinopathy?
   a. laser photocoagulation
   b. scleral buckle
   c. vitrectomy
   d. keratoplasty

____28. The purpose of radial keratotomy is to:
   a. treat corneal abrasion
   b. prevent retinal detachment
   c. restore vision as close to 20/20 as possible
   d. prepare the cornea for transplant

Surgery on the Nervous System

Choose the correct answer by matching the lettered terms with their definitions below. Write your answer in the space provided next to the number of the question.

a. myelography
b. pneumoencephalography
c. ventriculography
d. echoencephalography
e. computed axial tomography
f. neurorrhaphy
g. ventriculoperitoneal shunt
h. rhizotomy

i. sympathectomy
j. laminectomy
k. anterior cervical fusion
l. craniotomy
m. cranioplasty
n. repair of aneurysm
o. evacuation of subdural hematoma

p. cordotomy
q. bur hole
r. decompression
s. cerebral revascularization
t. excision of AV malformation
u. excision of acoustic neuroma
v. ventriculoatrial shunt

_____ 1. diversion of cerebrospinal fluid away from ventricle to atrium

_____ 2. anastomosis of extracranial artery to intracranial artery to bypass stricture

_____ 3. interruption of cranial or spinal nerve root

_____ 4. opening made in the skull to expose the brain and structures

_____ 5. ultrasound study performed to identify brain abscess, tumor, or hematoma

_____ 6. interruption of lateral spinothalamic tract of spinal cord

_____ 7. direction of cerebrospinal fluid away from ventricle to peritoneal cavity

_____ 8. surgical interruption of sympathetic nerve fibers

_____ 9. removal of accumulation of blood in the space below the dura of the brain

_____10. incision of the scalp, tissue, and creation of hole in the skull

_____11. injection of contrast into spinal canal, followed by x-rays to delineate structures

_____12. replacement of area of bone in the skull with a plate or graft

_____13. injection of air into subarachnoid space with x-rays taken to delineate structures

_____14. pictorial radiographs that outline brain structures

_____15. excision of herniated cervical intervertebral disks and placement of bone grafts

_____16. surgical removal of abnormal communication between artery and vein

_____17. substitution of air or contrast for cerebrospinal fluid, followed by x-rays

_____18. removal of ear tumor extending into posterior fossa of cranial cavity

_____19. release of pressure on cranial nerves

_____20. peripheral nerve repair

_____21. excision of outpouching of internal carotid or middle cerebral artery

_____22. creation of opening in the lamina to remove herniated disk, tumor, or aneurysm

Surgery on the Nervous System, Continued

Choose the correct answer in each of the following multiple-choice questions. Write your answer in the space provided next to the number of the question.

_____23. A craniotome is a:
  a. nerve ending
  b. drill
  c. tissue fragmenter
  d. suction/irrigation tool

_____24. Hemostasis following creation of a bur hole in the skull is often achieved with the use of:
  a. methyl methacrylate
  b. Gelfoam and cotton pledgets
  c. Kerlix pressure bandage
  d. bone wax

_____25. A surgical loupe is used to:
  a. magnify small structures
  b. tie off a very fine suture
  c. round out a small hole
  d. wrap one structure around another

_____26. Cranial expansion and reconstruction is a common surgical treatment for:
  a. subdural hematoma
  b. residual surgical defects
  c. decompression of cranial nerves
  d. cranial synostosis

_____27. In what position is the patient usually placed for anterior cervical spine procedures?
  a. prone
  b. Trendelenburg
  c. supine
  d. reverse Trendelenburg

_____28. A lumbar laminectomy is performed to:
  a. remove a herniated nucleus pulposus
  b. relieve arterial spasm due to vascular disease
  c. anastomose a severed nerve
  d. graft gaping intervertebral disks

_____29. What is the name of the procedure that surgically rejoins individual severed nerve fibers?
  a. decompression
  b. funicular repair
  c. epineural repair
  d. neural fusion

_____30. Which instrument is used to bite off protruding bony spinous processes?
   a. drill
   b. mallet
   c. rongeur
   d. dermatome

_____31. The surgical approach for cervical disk herniation is:
   a. lateral or ventral
   b. superior or inferior
   c. cephalad or caudal
   d. anterior or posterior

_____32. A depressed skull fracture where part of the skull has been removed would likely require what additional surgical procedure?
   a. craniotomy
   b. cranioplasty
   c. craniectomy
   d. craniostomy

_____33. Congenital hydrocephalus is treated by what surgical technique?
   a. bur holes
   b. shunting
   c. fusion
   d. excision

_____34. Carpal tunnel syndrome may be surgically treated by:
   a. decompression of the ulnar nerve
   b. release of the entrapped cutaneous nerve
   c. excision of the median nerve
   d. division of the carpal ligament

_____35. A hypophysectomy is performed to treat a tumor of the:
   a. meninges
   b. glia
   c. pituitary
   d. arachnoid space

_____36. Resection of the vagus nerve is done to:
   a. control bleeding
   b. eliminate nerve pain
   c. slow the spread of metastatic disease
   d. decrease the amount of gastric juice

_____37. Resection of a tumor of the pituitary gland is approached through the:
   a. mouth
   b. back of the head
   c. frontal hairline
   d. ear canal

Section 7.
Laboratory

General Laboratory

Match the terms in the left column with their correct definitions in the right column.

____ 1. hemoglobin

____ 2. leukocyte

____ 3. urinalysis

____ 4. ferritin

____ 5. folic acid

____ 6. creatinine

____ 7. panel

____ 8. antinuclear antibody

____ 9. hematocrit

____ 10. differential

____ 11. culture and sensitivity

____ 12. alanine aminotransferase

____ 13. postprandial glucose

____ 14. lactic dehydrogenase

____ 15. electrolytes

____ 16. erythrocyte

____ 17. lymphocyte

____ 18. occult blood

____ 19. smear

____ 20. stain

____ 21. wet mount

____ 22. uric acid

____ 23. specific gravity

____ 24. titer

____ 25. lipoprotein

____ 26. triglycerides

A. principal form in which iron is stored in the body

B. waste product of protein metabolism

C. enzyme elevated in certain liver diseases

D. blood sugar taken after a meal

E. translucent layer of specimen spread thinly on a glass slide for microscopic examination

F. weight of a substance per unit of volume compared to pure water

G. specimen examined without drying or staining

H. non-phagocyte leukocyte

I. oxygen-carrying complex of iron and protein in red blood cells

J. another name for "red blood cell"

K. isoenzyme found in heart muscle.

L. dye used to color tissue samples

M. another name for "white blood cell"

N. organism grown on antibiotic-laden disks to determine resistance to antibiotic

O. concentration or activity of substance in a specimen

P. group of tests performed on a urine specimen

Q. B vitamin essential in red blood cell formation

R. breakdown product of purine metabolism

S. antibody detected in patients with rheumatoid arthritis

T. determination of six types of white blood cells normally found in peripheral blood

U. chemical substances with positively or negatively charged ions

V. blood in too small a concentration to be seen by the naked-eye

W. group of blood chemistry tests done by automation

X. proteins that bind and transport fat materials

Y. level of fat in the serum

Z. percentage of blood sample consisting of cells

General Laboratory, Continued

Test your knowledge of blood cells, platelets, blood groups, and clotting factors. Fill in the blanks with the correct answers from the list below.

27. Another name for *red blood cell* is _____.

28. The percentage of red blood cells per unit of blood volume is known as

_____.

29. The iron-containing substance responsible for the red color of blood is

_____,

30. *Leukocyte* is another word for a(n) _____.

31. A white blood cell _____ count determines the

relative number of each type of white blood cell.

32. White blood cell count elevation above 10,000 is termed _____.

33. A depressed white blood cell count is called _____.

34. Platelets are formed in the _____.

35. _____ is a blood fluid consisting mostly of water, electrolytes,

proteins, nutrients, and dissolved gases.

36. Another word for a thrombocyte is a(n) _____.

37. The process of blood clotting is known as _____.

38. A prothrombin time may be ordered when a(n) _____

disorder is suspected.

39. The ABO blood typing system includes types _____, _____,

_____, and _____.

40. The two main types of Rh antibodies are _____ and

_____.

General Laboratory, Continued

Choose the correct answer in each of the following multiple-choice questions. Write your answer in the space provided next to the number of the question.

_____ 41. All of the following are different types of white blood cells EXCEPT:
  a. eosinophils
  b. granulocytes
  c. basophils
  d. erythrocytes

_____ 42. _Poikilocytosis_ refers to blood cells that are:
  a. irregular in shape
  b. oval
  c. round
  d. sickle-shaped

_____ 43. Antigens are:
  a. agents that destroy harmful bacteria
  b. foreign substances often toxic to the body or cells
  c. similar to antibodies
  d. produced in the spleen

_____ 44. Which of the following is NOT another name for _polymorphonuclear leukocytes?_
  a. segs
  b. basos
  c. neutrophils
  d. polys

_____ 45. The substance called albumin:
  a. helps fight infections
  b. helps maintain proper water balance
  c. produces antibodies
  d. produces antigens

_____ 46. A test for ova and parasites is performed on:
  a. sputum
  b. urine
  c. blood
  d. feces

_____ 47. AST was formerly known as:
  a. GGTP
  b. SGPT
  c. SGOT
  d. GGT

General Laboratory, Continued

_____ 48. Which of the following is NOT an electrolyte?
   a. chloride
   b. potassium
   c. calcium
   d. aluminum

_____ 49. An increase in lymphocytes in the blood is termed:
   a. lymphotemia
   b. lymphopenia
   c. lymphosis
   d. lymphocytosis

_____ 50. A deficiency of hemoglobin results in:
   a. thrombocytopenia
   b. leukemia
   c. hemophilia
   d. anemia

_____ 51. Hemoglobin transports:
   a. iron
   b. oxygen
   c. potassium
   d. erythrocytes

_____ 52. The function of a phagocyte is to:
   a. engulf and destroy foreign material
   b. coagulate red blood cells to stop bleeding
   c. maintain the normal red blood count
   d. transport nutrients to other cells

_____ 53. Another name for granulocyte is:
   a. monocyte
   b. polymorphonuclear leukocyte
   c. reticulocyte
   d. megakaryocyte

_____ 54. An eosinophil functions and responds in:
   a. bacterial infection
   b. allergy
   c. viral infection
   d. coagulation

_____ 55. Mean corpuscular hemoglobin is the:
   a. average concentration of hemoglobin in red blood cells
   b. determination of the relative proportions of white blood cells
   c. average weight of hemoglobin per red blood cell
   d. average size of red blood cells

General Laboratory, Continued

_____ 56. The mean corpuscular volume is:
   a. average concentration of hemoglobin in red blood cells
   b. determination of the relative proportions of white blood cells
   c. average weight of hemoglobin per red blood cell
   d. average size of red blood cells

_____ 57. A specialized coagulation test to identify deficient clotting factors is:
   a. activated partial thromboplastin time
   b. clotting time
   c. sedimentation rate
   d. sickle test

_____ 58. A test that analyzes various hemoglobins, normal and abnormal, in the patient's blood is:
   a. glycosylated hemoglobin
   b. mean corpuscular hemoglobin
   c. hemoglobin electrophoresis
   d. mean corpuscular hemoglobin concentration

_____ 59. Which of the following is NOT a vitamin?
   a. calcium
   b. retinol
   c. folic acid
   d. vitamin K

_____ 60. Which of the following are the only WBCs NOT produced in bone marrow?
   a. eosinophils
   b. lymphocytes
   c. monocytes
   d. neutrophils

_____ 61. The blood levels of virtually all known hormones can be determined by obtaining a(n):
   a. RAST
   b. A/G ratio
   c. cytogenic study
   d. radioimmunoassay

_____ 62. Creatinine is a breakdown product of:
   a. creatine
   b. ammonia
   c. uric acid
   d. bilirubin

_____ 63. To avoid a false-positive drug test, which substance should NOT be ingested within several days of testing?
   a. caffeine
   b. Italian squash
   c. poppy seeds
   d. herbal teas

General Pathology

Fill in the blanks with the correct answers.

1. An autopsy specimen is taken from a patient who is _____.

2. A(n) _____ is a fluid that stops the decomposition of a specimen and is used to prepare it for microscopic study.

3. _____ is the division of anatomy concerned with the microscopic study of tissues.

4. A(n)_____ uses a stream of electrons instead of a beam of visible light to magnify a specimen.

5. A(n) _____ is a physician with postdoctoral training and certification by the American Board of Pathology.

6. _____ wax is used to set up specimens for examination.

7. Cytology is the study of _____.

8. The term "post" is another word for _____.

9. Formalin is made from bubbling _____ gas through water.

Circle the correct choice.

10. During an autopsy, the pathologist removes organs one by one and subjects them to an immediate (microscopic, gross) examination.

11. (Microscopic, Gross) examination of certain kinds of surgical specimens may be routinely omitted, such as pathologic examination of a (gallbladder, tooth).

12. The size of a solid specimen is usually dictated in (metric, English) units of measure.

13. Fluid volumes are usually recorded in (metric, English) units of measure.

14. The dictation of a gross examination always begins with the (description, identification) of the specimen.

15. A biopsy is taken from a person who is (alive, dead).

General Pathology, Continued

Choose the correct answer in each of the following multiple-choice questions. Write your answer in the space provided next to the number of the question.

_____ 16. Which of the following statements would be found under the microscopic description of a pathology report?
  a. "The specimen is submitted in formalin."
  b. "Sections of the specimen show hyperkeratosis without atypical changes."
  c. "The gallbladder measures 8 x 4 x 4 cm."
  d. "The specimen consists of an ellipse of grayish-tan, irregular-shaped tissue."

_____ 17. A mordant is used to:
  a. render tissues chemically more receptive to staining
  b. decolorize the tissue
  c. allow counterstaining of tissues
  d. chemically bind two stains

_____ 18. The gross findings and microscopic findings of a tissue specimen are usually dictated:
  a. an hour apart
  b. a day apart
  c. a week apart
  d. two weeks apart

_____ 19. The pathologist looks at tissue specimen slides with the aid of a:
  a. light microscope
  b. Withrow lens
  c. Barlow lens
  d. magnifying glass

_____ 20. The most commonly used combination of stains for routine histopathology work is:
  a. hematoxylin and eosin
  b. acetic acid and alcohol
  c. carbolfuchsin and methylene blue
  d. crystal violet and Darrow red

_____ 21. In most laboratories, prepared slides of tissue are available for the pathologist's examination:
  a. immediately
  b. 6 to 8 hours after removal from the body
  c. 12 to 24 hours after removal from the body
  d. 24 to 72 hours after removal from the body

_____ 22. On a transcribed pathology report, the gross description is usually located above:
  a. the patient's name
  b. the clinical diagnosis
  c. the name of the tissue specimen
  d. the microscopic description

General Radiology

Choose the correct answer in each of the following multiple-choice questions. Write your answer in the space provided next to the number of the question.

_____ 1. An x-ray study of bones and soft tissue without contrast or special apparatus is specifically termed a(n):
    a. radiograph
    b. ionization
    c. roentgenogram
    d. plain film

_____ 2. A study in which a radioactive substance is given and emits positrons to create a cross-sectional image is a:
    a. nuclear medicine study
    b. CT scan
    c. PET scan
    d. MRI scan

_____ 3. A study in which a material is injected to delineate surrounding tissue is called a:
    a. CT scan
    b. SPECT scan
    c. nuclear medicine study
    d. contrast study

_____ 4. A study in which a fluorescent screen is used to derive a visual image from the x-rays that pass through the patient is called:
    a. ultrasound
    b. fluoroscopy
    c. tomography
    d. MRI scan

_____ 5. A study which employs high-frequency, inaudible sound waves that bounce off body tissues and are then recorded is termed:
    a. roentgenography
    b. CT scan
    c. PET scan
    d. sonography

_____ 6. A study in which a series of x-ray pictures are taken layer by layer, slice by slice is called:
    a. tomography
    b. PET scan
    c. MRI scan
    d. fluoroscopy

General Radiology, Continued

____ 7. A study in which single-photon emission is used to construct a three-dimensional image from a composite of many views is called a:
   a. PET scan
   b. SPECT scan
   c. CT scan
   d. MRI scan

____ 8. A study in which ionizing x-rays pass through a patient at multiple angles around a specific section of the body, then are relayed to a computer to determine absorption capacities of body tissues, is called a:
   a. CT scan
   b. MRI scan
   c. nuclear medicine study
   d. digital subtraction angiography

____ 9. A study that does not use x-rays or contrast but instead is based on magnetic imaging of nuclei is called a:
   a. nuclear medicine study
   b. SPECT scan
   c. sonogram
   d. MRI scan

____ 10. A procedure that traces the amounts of radioactive substances in the body to evaluate or image an organ is termed:
   a. tomography
   b. nuclear medicine study
   c. roentgenography
   d. sonography

____ 11. A study in which an x-ray image of contrast-injected blood vessels is produced by taking two x-rays, the first without contrast, and using a computer to eliminate the shadows, is called a:
   a. digital subtraction angiography
   b. radioisotope study
   c. nuclear medicine study
   d. fluoroscopy

____ 12. A study in which an image of veins is taken after injecting intravenous contrast is termed:
   a. venography
   b. echocardiography
   c. angiography
   d. bronchography

Integumentary System Lab

Choose the correct answer in each of the following multiple-choice questions. Write your answer in the space provided next to the number of the question.

_____ 1. A screening test is performed on a patient who is:
   a. sick
   b. well
   c. immunocompromised
   d. unable to communicate

_____ 2. An ultraviolet lamp under which certain fungi of the skin or hair fluoresce is called a:
   a. Tyndall light
   b. polarized light
   c. cold quartz light
   d. Wood light

_____ 3. Which of the following is NOT a skin test method?
   a. sniff
   b. patch
   c. intradermal injection
   d. scratch

_____ 4. Fungal material can be cultured from the skin and identified with a prep of:
   a. H&E
   b. PTAH
   c. KOH
   d. GMS

_____ 5. Which one of the following is done to detect viral infection from vesicular or bullous diseases?
   a. Papanicolaou test
   b. Gram stain
   c. Tzanck smear
   d. fluorescent antibody test

_____ 6. Which of the following is a skin test for detecting tuberculosis?
   a. tine
   b. ring
   c. skin window
   d. fern

_____ 7. Which of the following body fluids is used to culture for cellulitis?
   a. urine
   b. feces
   c. sputum
   d. blood

Integumentary System Lab, Continued

_____ 8. A small flat piece of clear glass or plastic that is pressed firmly against the skin to distinguish capillary dilatation from other causes is called a:
   a. diascope
   b. stethoscope
   c. dermatoscope
   d. Wood light

_____ 9. Microscopic examination of scrapings from scabies lesions may show:
   a. fungi
   b. mites
   c. spores
   d. rods

_____ 10. Radioallergosorbent testing can identify specific:
   a. yeast forms
   b. antibodies
   c. viruses
   d. phagocytes

_____ 11. Tinea versicolor is caused by the pathogen:
   a. *Candida albicans*
   b. *Sarcoptes scabiei*
   c. *Pediculus corporis*
   d. *Malassezia furfur*

_____ 12. Ringworm of the body is caused by a:
   a. yeast
   b. parasite
   c. bacterium
   d. fungus

_____ 13. Herpesvirus type 2 causes:
   a. genital herpes
   b. fever blisters
   c. chickenpox
   d. shingles

_____ 14. What virus is responsible for warts?
   a. Epstein-Barr virus
   b. herpesvirus
   c. human papillomavirus
   d. RNA virus

_____ 15. A pathogen that commonly causes wound and burn infections is:
   a. *Streptobacillus moniliformis*
   b. *Pseudomonas aeruginosa*
   c. *Coxiella burnetii*
   d. *Cryptococcus neoformans*

Genitourinary System Lab

Choose the correct answer in each of the following multiple-choice questions. Write your answer in the space provided next to the number of the question.

_____ 1. The organism that causes syphilis is:
   a. *Neisseria gonorrhoeae*
   b. *Treponema pallidum*
   c. *Chlamydia trachomatis*
   d. *Staphylococcus aureus*

_____ 2. The purpose of the PSA test is to screen for:
   a. venereal disease
   b. urinary tract infection
   c. prostate cancer
   d. kidney stones

_____ 3. Fluorescent antibody testing is done to diagnose:
   a. bladder cancer
   b. benign prostatic hyperplasia
   c. sexually transmitted diseases
   d. diabetes mellitus

_____ 4. Urinalysis cannot detect:
   a. pollakiuria
   b. glycosuria
   c. ketosis
   d. albuminuria

_____ 5. Which of the following methods of urine collection avoids contamination?
   a. catheter
   b. clean-catch
   c. midstream
   d. bagged

_____ 6. Which system is NOT outlined on KUB x-ray?
   a. bladder
   b. ureter
   c. ovaries
   d. kidney

_____ 7. Many cases of acute cystitis are caused by the pathogen:
   a. *H. pylori*
   b. *H. flu*
   c. *S. aureus*
   d. *E. coli*

Genitourinary System Lab, Continued

____ 8. Which one of the following values is abnormal on urinalysis?
   a. specific gravity 1.018
   b. color straw
   c. 0 white blood cells
   d. 3-5 red blood cells

____ 9. A normal urinalysis would be negative for:
   a. casts
   b. crystals
   c. glucose
   d. mucus

____ 10. Which radiographic study might be performed to rule out urinary tract stone?
   a. IVP
   b. IVC
   c. CT
   d. ERCP

____ 11. The FTA-ABS test is used to identify the organism that causes:
   a. syphilis
   b. herpes
   c. gonorrhea
   d. chlamydia

____ 12. Screening tests for the presence of *Chlamydia trachomatis* are positive in what percent of sexually active, asymptomatic women?
   a. 1 percent
   b. 3 percent
   c. 5 percent
   d. 10 percent

____ 13. Which pathogen has been implicated in cervical dysplasia and carcinoma?
   a. herpesvirus
   b. human papillomavirus
   c. *Candida albicans*
   d. *Gardnerella vaginalis*

____ 14. A voiding cystourethrogram (the act of voiding with contrast medium in the urine) is performed with the female patient in the:
   a. lithotomy position
   b. recumbent position
   c. sitting position
   d. standing position

Genitourinary System Lab, Continued

____ 15. The normal level of uric acid in the serum is:
   a. 3.4 to 7 mg/dL
   b. 8.4 to 16.2 mg/dL
   c. 18.5 to 30 mg/dL
   d. 42 to 52.4 mg/dL

____ 16. Urine pH is very alkaline at:
   a. 5
   b. 6
   c. 7
   d. 8

____ 17. Which of the following colors is abnormal for urine?
   a. yellow
   b. amber
   c. orange
   d. straw-colored

____ 18. Acid phosphatase is found in high concentrations in:
   a. the prostate
   b. bladder tissue
   c. nephrons
   d. the kidneys

____ 19. The high normal for blood urea nitrogen is:
   a. 10 mg/dL
   b. 25 mg/dL
   c. 40 mg/dL
   d. 60 mg/dL

____ 20. Which of the following findings is of little significance on urinalysis?
   a. epithelial cells
   b. casts
   c. protein
   d. bilirubin

____ 21. Which of the following is NOT a urine electrolyte?
   a. sodium
   b. phosphorus
   c. chloride
   d. potassium

____ 22. A 24-hour urine is:
   a. a specimen that has been refrigerated for 24 hours before examination
   b. collection of one urine specimen in each 24-hour period
   c. a test to determine what pathogens will grow in a urine specimen for 24 hours
   d. all urine passed by one patient in 24 hours

Gastrointestinal System Lab

Match the disease with the description of the diagnostic findings by filling in the blank with the correct letter.

a. hepatitis C
b. irritable bowel syndrome
c. appendicitis
d. gastroesophageal reflux disease

e. chronic pancreatitis
f. Crohn disease
g. acute peritonitis
h. adynamic ileus

_____ 1. Patient has recurrent bouts of left upper quadrant pain. Sugar is elevated in both urine and blood as a result of diabetes mellitus due to slow destruction of pancreatic tissue. Pancreatic lipase and amylase are elevated. Abdominal x-ray shows widening of the curve of the duodenum due to pancreatic edema.

_____ 2. Abdominal x-ray shows distended loops of small bowel and fluid levels. Bowel sounds are absent.

_____ 3. Patient gives a long history of pyrosis. Imaging studies confirm reflux of swallowed barium from the stomach, with ulceration and stricture. Endoscopy gives visual proof of inflammation.

_____ 4. Patient gives history of being hit violently in the abdomen with resultant acute abdominal pain. WBC is elevated; blood studies show electrolyte imbalance and anemia. Fluid obtained via paracentesis shows amylase or lipase. Imaging identifies intra-abdominal catastrophe.

_____ 5. Carriers of this chronic disease are identified by serologic testing.

_____ 6. Patient gives history of bowel urgency and diarrhea after meals, worse with caffeine ingestion. Stool exams, barium enema, colonoscopy, and blood studies are all negative.

_____ 7. Patient gives history of recurrent crampy abdominal pain and fatty stools. WBC and ESR are elevated. Barium enema shows "string sign." Endoscopy shows inflammation and "skip" areas.

_____ 8. Patient has exquisite right lower quadrant pain. WBC is elevated with shift to the left. Abdominal imaging shows opacity in the appendiceal lumen. Barium per rectum fails to fill the appendix.

Gastrointestinal System Lab, Continued

Choose the correct answer in each of the following multiple-choice questions. Write your answer in the space provided next to the number of the question.

_____ 9. In hepatitis A infection, which antibody appears early in the course of the disease and then disappears; which develops later and persists indefinitely?
   a. IgE appears early; IgM appears later
   b. IgM appears early; IgE appears later
   c. IgM appears early; IgG develops later
   d. IgE appears early; IgG develops later

_____10. The presence of HB_SAg after the acute phase of which illness suggests chronic infection?
   a. hepatitis A
   b. hepatitis B
   c. hepatitis C
   d. hepatic cirrhosis

_____11. Which of the following is NOT a pathogen?
   a. Protozoa
   b. fungi
   c. toxins
   d. viruses

_____12. Infestation with the pathogen *Campylobacter* is known to cause severe diarrhea, fever, nausea, and vomiting. By which route is this pathogen transmitted?
   a. fecal-oral
   b. airborne
   c. sexual
   d. droplet

_____13. The pathogen *Giardia lamblia,* which causes vomiting and diarrhea and can disseminate in persons with AIDS, is a:
   a. bacterium
   b. parasite
   c. fungus
   d. yeast

_____14. Stool for ova and parasites would be ordered for suspicion of:
   a. hepatitis C
   b. peptic esophagitis
   c. GERD
   d. amebiasis

_____15. What food should be avoided to prepare for occult blood test of the stool?
   a. fibrous vegetables
   b. milk products
   c. meat
   d. nuts and seeds

Gastrointestinal System Lab, Continued

____ 16. In which gastrointestinal disorder is the AST likely to be elevated?
   a. hemorrhoids
   b. pancreatitis
   c. hernia
   d. gastroesophageal reflux

____ 17. Lactic dehydrogenase, which is elevated in some gastrointestinal disorders, is normally below:
   a. 110 U/L
   b. 150 U/L
   c. 180 U/L
   d. 200 U/L

____ 18. The low normal for the ALT enzyme is:
   a. 8
   b. 80
   c. 180
   d. 280

____ 19. The alkaline phosphatase level is normally:
   a. undetectable in children
   b. undetectable in adults
   c. lower in children than adults
   d. higher in children than adults

____ 20. Significant change in the serum amylase level is diagnostic of a disorder of which organ?
   a. liver
   b. gallbladder
   c. bile duct
   d. pancreas

____ 21. Which of the following is an abnormal finding on microscopic examination of stool?
   a. helminths
   b. bacteria
   c. muscle fibers
   d. fat

____ 22. A finding of excessive fat in the feces on stool specimen suggests:
   a. starvation
   b. intestinal bleeding
   c. malabsorption
   d. peptic ulcer disease

Musculoskeletal System Lab

Choose the correct answer in each of the following multiple-choice questions. Write your answer in the space provided next to the number of the question.

_____ 1. What organism causes Lyme disease?
  a. *Leptospira icterohemorrhagiae*
  b. *Borrelia burgdorferi*
  c. *Legionella pneumophila*
  d. *Mycobacterium leprae*

_____ 2. To test bone density, rays are passed through bones and a machine measures how well the rays penetrate the bones. This test is known as a(n):
  a. bone scan
  b. ultrasound
  c. photon absorptiometry
  d. tomography

_____ 3. Osteomyelitis is caused by:
  a. parasites
  b. fungi
  c. viruses
  d. bacteria

_____ 4. A disease in which urate crystals are present in synovial fluid and the serum uric acid level and erythrocyte sedimentation rate is generally elevated is:
  a. degenerative joint disease
  b. gout
  c. osteoporosis
  d. chondromalacia patellae

_____ 5. Rheumatoid arthritis can be confirmed by a:
  a. positive RA latex test
  b. sed rate greater than 20 mm/hr.
  c. C-reactive protein greater than 820 ng/mL
  d. positive CEA test

_____ 6. An x-ray that demonstrates osteophyte formation shows:
  a. nodular deposits in the joints
  b. swiss-cheese-type holes in the periosteum of the bone
  c. outgrowths from the surface of bone
  d. calcium layering at a fracture site

_____ 7. A person is considered to be deficient in calcium, an important building block for bones, if the total serum calcium level falls below:
  a. 9.2 mg/dL
  b. 10.2 mg/dL
  c. 10.8 mg/dL
  d. 11 mg/dL

Cardiovascular System Lab

Choose the correct answer in each of the following multiple-choice questions. Write your answer in the space provided next to the number of the question.

_____ 1. A diagnostic procedure in which a tube is introduced into a peripheral vein or artery and advanced into the heart to measure pressures and oxygen saturation in the great vessels and cardiac chambers is:
   a. balloon angioplasty
   b. thallium treadmill test
   c. ventilation-perfusion test
   d. cardiac catheterization

_____ 2. ST segment depression and flattened or inverted T waves found on electrocardiogram are indicative of:
   a. subacute bacterial endocarditis
   b. cor pulmonale
   c. primary pulmonary hypertension
   d. myocardial ischemia

_____ 3. What naturally occurring entity is used to produce an echocardiogram?
   a. ultraviolet light
   b. infrared waves
   c. sound waves
   d. heat

_____ 4. A Holter monitor is used to obtain:
   a. arterial wedge pressures
   b. radionuclide angiography
   c. myocardial perfusion study
   d. 24-hour electrocardiogram

_____ 5. Which of the following is not an EKG wave?
   a. P
   b. Q
   c. U
   d. X

_____ 6. Kerley B lines on chest x-ray are diagnostic of:
   a. pulmonary venous congestion
   b. myocardial ischemia
   c. left ventricular enlargement
   c. mitral valve prolapse

_____ 7. Which creatine kinase isoenzymes are elevated in myocardial infarction?
   a. MB bands
   b. MM bands
   c. BB bands
   d. amylase

_____ 8. The highest acceptable fasting serum level of cholesterol is generally considered to be less than:
   a. 120 mg/dL
   b. 150 mg/dL
   c. 180 mg/dL
   d. 200 mg/dL

_____ 9. Which of the following is NOT a lipoprotein?
   a. HDL
   b. LDL
   c. VDRL
   d. VLDL

_____ 10. The term *triglyceride* is a chemical designation for animal:
   a. protein
   b. carbohydrates
   c. fat
   d. glucose

_____ 11. A preponderance of low-density lipoproteins is associated with:
   a. obesity
   b. severe malnutrition
   c. a lower risk for atherosclerosis
   d. a higher risk for atherosclerosis

_____ 12. Which procedure is used to confirm, localize, and quantify venous obstruction by recording variations in blood supply?
   a. color Doppler study
   b. impedance plethysmography
   c. echocardiogram
   d. MRI of the chest

_____ 13. A person is considered to have hypertriglyceridemia when the fasting triglyceride level is elevated above:
   a. 160 mg/dL
   b. 100 mg/dL
   c. 60 mg/dL
   d. 30 mg/dL

_____ 14. Acute rheumatic fever is caused by which pathogen?
   a. *Corynebacterium diphtheriae*
   b. *Streptococcus pyogenes*
   c. *Haemophilus influenzae*
   d. *Pseudomonas aeruginosa*

Pulmonary System Lab

Match the disease with the description of the diagnostic findings by filling in the blank with the correct letter.

A. acute bronchitis	E. pneumonia
B. chronic bronchitis	F. pulmonary tuberculosis
C. bronchiectasis	G. pneumoconiosis
D. emphysema	H. pulmonary embolism

_____ 1. Patient presents with history of cystic fibrosis and chronic cough. Imaging studies show lung cysts and fibrous cuffing around affected bronchi.

_____ 2. Patient has cough and bloody sputum. Sputum contains acid-fast organisms. Skin test is positive. Chest x-ray shows calcified primary focus, hilar lymphadenopathy, infiltrates, pleural effusion, and cavitation.

_____ 3. Patient presents with history of HIV infection and cough. WBC count is elevated. Sputum culture shows *Pneumocystis carinii.* Chest x-ray shows evidence of infiltrate.

_____ 4. Patient presents with chest pain and shortness of breath. Arterial O_2 tension is diminished. ECG shows right axis deviation. Chest x-ray shows atelectasis and wedge-shaped zone of opacification. Ventilation-perfusion scan is positive. Imaging studies confirm the source of obstruction.

_____ 5. Patient has cough and low fever. Blood studies are normal. Sputum smear and culture indicate no bacterial infection. Chest x-ray shows increased bronchial markings.

_____ 6. Patient presents with shortness of breath and long smoking history. Chest x-ray shows hyperinflation of the chest cavity and hyperlucency of lung tissue; also shows bullae and blebs. ABGs show diminished PO_2. PFTs show increased total lung capacity but reduced vital capacity and air exchange.

_____ 7. Chest x-ray shows diffusely scattered fibrotic changes in lungs and findings of asbestosis. PFTs show reduced vital capacity and flow rates. Arterial O_2 and PO_2 are reduced.

_____ 8. Patient presents with long smoking history, chronic cough, and shortness of breath. The hematocrit is slightly elevated from diminished oxygen exchange in the lungs. Arterial blood gases show reduction of oxygen and increased carbon dioxide. Chest x-ray shows increased bronchopulmonary markings. EKG shows right axis deviation and P pulmonale.

Pulmonology System Lab, Continued

Choose the correct answer in each of the following multiple-choice questions. Write your answer in the space provided next to the number of the question.

_____ 9. The normal partial pressure of oxygen in arterial blood is approximately:
- a. 10 to 25 torr
- b. 25 to 50 torr
- c. 50 to 75 torr
- d. 75 to 100 torr

_____ 10. Hypercapnia occurs when the partial pressure of carbon dioxide rises above:
- a. 45 torr
- b. 30 torr
- c. 20 torr
- d. 10 torr

_____ 11. Which of the following is an arterial blood gas test?
- a. Na
- b. O_2
- c. Cl
- d. K

_____ 12. Concentrations of chloride and sodium in sweat are increased in which disorder?
- a. mucoviscidosis
- b. Goodpasture syndrome
- c. pulmonary tuberculosis
- d. Legionella pneumonia

_____ 13. The arterial pH is a determination of blood:
- a. acidity
- b. volume
- c. viscidity
- d. fluidity

_____ 14. Pulmonary infiltrates on radiographic study are diagnostic of:
- a. bronchiectasis
- b. tuberculosis
- c. pneumonia
- d. pneumoconiosis

Endocrine System Lab

Choose the correct answer in each of the following multiple-choice questions. Write your answer in the space provided next to the number of the question.

_____ 1. Skull x-rays in a patient with acromegaly may show enlargement of the:
  a. pituitary gland
  b. cerebral hemispheres
  c. sella turcica
  d. bony skeleton

_____ 2. Albuminuria is the presence of what substance in the urine?
  a. urobilinogen
  b. occult blood
  c. myoglobulin
  d. protein

_____ 3. A diagnosis of diabetes mellitus is made when the fasting blood sugar is consistently over:
  a. 100
  b. 140
  c. 180
  d. 200

_____ 4. Similarly, a diagnosis of diabetes mellitus is made when random blood sugars are consistently elevated above:
  a. 100
  b. 140
  c. 180
  d. 200

_____ 5. What diagnosis would likely be made in the face of elevated T3 and T4, depression of TSH, and increased RAI uptake?
  a. hyperthyroidism
  b. hyperadrenalism
  c. hyperglycemia
  d. Addison disease

_____ 6. Which of the following is NOT a blood test that can determine relatively long-term glucose control in diabetic patients?
  a. glucose-6-phosphatase
  b. glycosylated hemoglobin
  c. hemoglobin A_{1C}
  d. HgA_{1C}

_____ 7. Which of the following would NOT be present in the urine of a diabetic patient in acidosis?
  a. bilirubin
  b. acetone
  c. glucose
  d. ketones

Female Reproductive System Lab

Choose the correct answer in each of the following multiple-choice questions. Write your answer in the space provided next to the number of the question.

_____ 1. Interpretation of the Pap smear is usually reported according to what system?
   a. Bethesda system
   b. SI system
   c. IU system
   d. Breslow system

_____ 2. The presence of human chorionic gonadotropin on laboratory testing indicates:
   a. pregnancy
   b. miscarriage
   c. fetal damage
   d. hydatidiform mole

_____ 3. Irregularity of one X chromosome, short stature, infertility, and possible cardiac abnormalities in the female are indicative of the developmental disorder:
   a. pseudohermaphroditism
   b. Brenner tumor
   c. DES exposure
   d. Turner syndrome

_____ 4. Examination of cervical mucus may be tested by this procedure, which in German means "ability to be drawn out into a string":
   a. mittelschermz
   b. spinnbarkeit
   c. leishmanin
   d. Lundh

_____ 5. Hemolytic disease of the newborn is caused by:
   a. failure of marrow production of red blood cells
   b. Rh incompatibility
   c. rupture of the placental barrier
   d. sickled cells

_____ 6. *Gardnerella vaginalis* is diagnosed by the presence, on microscopic examination, of
   a. ferning
   b. clue cells
   c. stippled white cells
   d. giant leukocytes

_____ 7. The single most useful laboratory test in the clinical evaluation of ectopic pregnancy is the:
   a. beta hCG assay
   b. chorionic villi test
   c. CEA test
   d. rabbit test

Female Reproductive System Lab, Continued

____ 8. An indirect Coombs test is positive in the mother of an infant with:
   a. hyaline membrane disease
   b. PKU
   c. erythroblastosis fetalis
   d. hyperbilirubinemia

____ 9. Down syndrome can be confirmed by the presence of an abnormality on which chromosome?
   a. 11
   b. 13
   c. 17
   d. 21

____ 10. Pap smear is taken from the:
   a. ureterovesical junction
   b. squamocolumnar junction
   c. vaginoperineal junction
   d. intercellular junction

____ 11. Which test is always part of an evaluation for dysfunctional uterine bleeding?
   a. beta hCG
   b. PKU
   c. HDL
   d. GnRH

____ 12. A breast malignancy is NOT diagnosed with:
   a. ultrasound
   b. fine needle biopsy
   c. frozen section
   d. endometrial biopsy

____ 13. Squamous cell carcinoma of the cervix has been linked to infection with:
   a. human immunodeficiency virus
   b. *Candida albicans*
   c. genital wart virus
   d. *Giardia lamblia*

____ 14. Human chorionic gonadotropin is produced by the:
   a. maternal pituitary gland
   b. placenta
   c. developing embryo
   d. maternal ovaries

____ 15. Lactation that occurs long after breast-feeding has ceased is due to:
   a. high FSH level
   b. high prolactin level
   c. hypothalamic production of GnRH
   d. abnormally low LH level

Otorhinolaryngology Lab

Choose the correct answer in each of the following multiple-choice questions. Write your answer in the space provided next to the number of the question.

_____ 1. A rapid slide test for beta-hemolytic streptococci in pharyngeal secretions is the:
   a. Tzanck smear
   b. strep screen
   c. litmus test
   d. Umber test

_____ 2. The normal human ear can detect sounds ranging in pitch from 20 to 20,000:
   a. hertz
   b. megahertz
   c. decibels
   d. octaves

_____ 3. Bacterial pathogens causing throat infections can be identified on:
   a. blood test
   b. urinalysis
   c. nasal smear
   d. throat culture

_____ 4. A hearing test that utilizes tuning forks positioned near the pinna to test for air conduction and bone conduction is:
   a. Valsalva maneuver
   b. Rinne test
   c. Weber test
   d. pneumotympanometry

_____ 5. Which test is performed by placing a tuning fork against the head at the midline to send vibrations through the bones of the skull to check if sounds are heard equally on both sides?
   a. Valsalva maneuver
   b. Rinne test
   c. Weber test
   d. Cohn test

_____ 6. On nasal smear, which leukocytes are likely to be elevated in response to severe nasal allergy?
   a. eosinophils
   b. neutrophils
   c. lymphocytes
   d. monocytes

_____ 7. On nasal smear, which leukocytes are likely to be elevated in response to infection?
   a. eosinophils
   b. neutrophils
   c. lymphocytes
   d. monocytes

Ophthalmology Lab

Choose the correct answer in each of the following multiple-choice questions. Write your answer in the space provided next to the number of the question.

_____ 1. Visual field examination of the interior eye is called:
    a. slit-lamp examination
    b. tonometry
    c. fluorescein angiography
    d. ophthalmoscopy

_____ 2. Which protozoan parasite can cause keratitis in contact lens wearers?
    a. *Aspergillus*
    b. *Acanthamoeba*
    c. *Arachnia*
    d. *Actinomyces*

_____ 3. Visual field testing is often done using:
    a. two-point discrimination
    b. Jaeger chart
    c. Snellen chart
    d. Amsler grid

_____ 4. Gonococcal conjunctivitis is confirmed with what test?
    a. culture
    b. blood test
    c. urine culture and sensitivity
    d. fluorescein angiography

_____ 5. An eye chart commonly used to test vision is:
    a. Baylor chart
    b. Jaeger chart
    c. Snellen chart
    d. Amsler grid

_____ 6. An exam that assesses peripheral vision by testing the subject's ability to discern moving objects or flashing lights at the extreme periphery of the visual fields is called a:
    a. tonometry examination
    b. funduscopic examination
    c. perimetry examination
    d. slit-lamp examination

_____ 7. A test of tear production in which a piece of filter paper is inserted over the conjunctival sac of the lower lid is the:
    a. Schirmer test
    b. Schiller test
    c. Schaffer test
    d. Scherer test

Nervous System Lab

Choose the correct answer in each of the following multiple-choice questions. Write your answer in the space provided next to the number of the question.

_____ 1. Prenatal diagnosis of neural tube defect can be made by the elevated finding of which substance in the amniotic fluid after 16 weeks' gestation?
   a. alpha fetoprotein
   b. beta hCG
   c. lymphocytes
   d. surfactant

_____ 2. What finding is diagnostic of multiple sclerosis on MRI of the brain and spinal cord?
   a. loss of motor nerve supply to affected areas
   b. plaque deposition
   c. neurofibrillary tangles
   d. areas of hemorrhage or infarction

_____ 3. A diagnostic test to determine trauma, local nerve compression, or nerve entrapment, and often performed with nerve conduction velocity studies, is:
   a. electroencephalogram
   b. electromyography
   c. electrobioscopy
   d. electrokymography

_____ 4. Viral meningitis is caused by:
   a. _Neisseria meningitidis_
   b. _H. influenzae_ or beta strep
   c. herpesvirus or Epstein-Barr
   d. echovirus or coxsackievirus A

_____ 5. What is the cause of the debilitating neuromuscular disorder myasthenia gravis?
   a. exposure to _Haemophilus influenzae_
   b. formation of autoantibody to cholinergic receptors
   c. pre-existing systemic lupus erythematosus diagnosed by anti-DNA antibody
   d. various viruses transmitted by mosquitoes and ticks

_____ 6. What test is used to diagnose and classify idiopathic epilepsy?
   a. roentgenogram
   b. lumbar puncture
   c. electroencephalogram
   d. blood and urine studies

_____ 7. What procedure can be performed to remove autoantibody to myelin for patients with Guillain-Barré syndrome?
   a. plasmapheresis
   b. frequent blood donations
   c. kidney dialysis
   d. pulse oximetry

Immune System, Oncology, & Genetics Lab

Choose the correct answer in each of the following multiple-choice questions. Write your answer in the space provided next to the number of the question.

_____ 1. The parasitic organism that can cause pneumonia in immunocompromised people is:
   a. *Pneumocystis carinii*
   b. *Mycobacterium avium*
   c. *Histoplasma capsulatum*
   d. *Haemophilus influenzae*

_____ 2. Infectious mononucleosis is caused by the:
   a. Newcastle virus
   b. Yale SK virus
   c. Epstein-Barr virus
   d. Norwalk virus

_____ 3. Which type of white cell is elevated and atypical in the infectious disease mononucleosis?
   a. monocytes
   b. lymphocytes
   c. eosinophils
   d. polymorphonuclear leukocytes

_____ 4. The LE cell prep is positive in:
   a. Wegener granulomatosis
   b. Reiter syndrome
   c. rheumatoid arthritis
   d. disseminated lupus erythematosus

_____ 5. Which of the following is NOT an immunoglobulin?
   a. IgL
   b. IgA
   c. IgG
   d. IgD

_____ 6. All of the following are different types of T cells EXCEPT:
   a. suppressor cells
   b. killer cells
   c. cytotoxic cells
   d. plasma cells

_____ 7. In Hodgkin disease, lymph node biopsy is positive for:
   a. Niemann-Pick cells
   b. Leydig cells
   c. Reed-Sternberg cells
   d. Hürthle cells

____ 8. A disease in which the plasma level of factor IX is deficient is:
  a. hemophilia
  b. AIDS
  c. Von Willebrand disease
  d. Christmas disease

____ 9. In which disorder is the Philadelphia chromosome present?
  a. non-Hodgkin lymphoma
  b. chronic myelogenous leukemia
  c. multiple myeloma
  d. thrombasthenia

____ 10. The presence of hemoglobin S is diagnostic of:
  a. hemolytic anemia
  b. sickle cell disease
  c. polycythemia vera
  d. leukemia

____ 11. Pernicious anemia is due to a deficiency of vitamin:
  a. A
  b. B_{12}
  c. D
  d. E

____ 12. In a patient with Cushing syndrome, what happens to the elevated serum level of cortisol after administration of dexamethasone?
  a. it falls to near zero
  b. it diminishes somewhat
  c. it stays the same
  d. it rises dramatically

____ 13. A serum level of phenylalanine greater than 121 is diagnostic of:
  a. Reye syndrome
  b. phenylketonuria
  c. Marfan syndrome
  d. acute intermittent porphyria

____ 14. Hemophilia is caused by a deficiency of factor:
  a. III
  b. V
  c. VIII
  d. X

Section 8.
Pharmacology

General Pharmacology

Choose the correct answer in each of the following multiple-choice questions. Write your answer in the space provided next to the number of the question.

_____ 1. A generic drug name is transcribed:
   a. completely in capital letters
   b. initial capital letters only
   c. underlined and boldfaced
   d. in all lower case letters

_____ 2. Drugs administered via the oral route may include:
   a. tablets, topicals, and creams
   b. elixirs, caplets, and liquids
   c. capsules, tablets, and sublinguals
   d. sublinguals, lozenges, and suspensions

_____ 3. A drug idiosyncrasy is:
   a. a drug that doesn't work as it was intended
   b. a drug reaction that is not common
   c. an allergic reaction
   d. an immune reaction

_____ 4. Drugs approved for marketing are known by the following three names:
   a. brand name, trade name, and generic name
   b. chemical name, generic name, and trade name
   c. brand name, trade name, and chemical name
   d. generic name, brand name, and nickname

_____ 5. _In vivo_ refers to a drug which:
   a. has undergone rigorous evaluation
   b. utilizes recombinant DNA technology
   c. has been analyzed in animals and/or people
   d. has not yet received FDA approval

_____ 6. It is the job of the Food and Drug Administration to:
   a. review and evaluate the safety of drugs
   b. ensure that orphan drug research is carried out
   c. regulate the manufacturing and dispensing of dangerous drugs
   d. regulate prescription drugs only

_____ 7. Over-the-counter drugs are:
   a. not subject to regulation by the FDA
   b. generally considered safe for consumers
   c. schedule drugs
   d. available by prescription only

419

Integumentary System Drugs

The following dermatologic drugs are listed by brand name. In the space provided, list the corresponding generic name and short description of the drug.

1. Neosporin ointment   polymyxin, neomycin, bacitracin—topical antibiotic

2. Propecia   _____

3. Benzagel   _____

4. Zostrix   _____

5. Pernox   _____

6. Aristocort A   _____

7. Decadron Phosphate   _____

8. Lidex   _____

9. Diflucan   _____

10. Cortisporin Otic   _____

11. Terazol   _____

12. Loprox   _____

13. Hibiclens   _____

14. Benadryl   _____

15. Kenalog   _____

16. Synalar   _____

17. Depo-Medrol   _____

18. Lotrimin cream   _____

19. Atarax   _____

20. Oxy 10   _____

21. Periactin   _____

22. Cleocin T   _____

23. Elocon   _____

24. Topicort   _____

25. Zovirax ointment   _____

Integumentary System Drugs, Continued

Choose the correct answer in each of the following multiple-choice questions. Write your answer in the space provided next to the number of the question.

_____ 26. Which of the following descriptions is best applied to the drug Silvadene?
   a. used internally for itching
   b. used topically as a moisturizer
   c. used internally for fungal infections
   d. used topically for burns

_____ 27. A person undergoing allergy testing is told to refrain from taking which type of medication for 72 hours prior to testing?
   a. any medication
   b. antibiotics
   c. decongestants
   d. antihistamines

_____ 28. What anxiolytic agent is also prescribed for acute urticaria?
   a. Atarax
   b. Valium
   c. Librium
   d. Xanax

_____ 29. The generic name for Hismanal is:
   a. cetirizine
   b. astemizole
   c. terconazole
   d. terfenadine

_____ 30. Retin-A was originally approved by the FDA as a treatment for:
   a. wrinkles
   b. "liver spots" and other lesions of the face
   c. acne
   d. freckles

_____ 31. This drug is often prescribed with birth control pills because of its teratogenic effect on the developing fetus:
   a. Accutane
   b. Benadryl
   c. Eucerin
   d. Tinactin

_____ 32. A drug commonly prescribed to treat ringworm of the body is:
   a. diphenhydramine
   b. benzoyl peroxide
   c. triamcinolone
   d. griseofulvin

Integumentary System Drugs, Continued

____ 33. Seborrheic dermatitis of the scalp is often treated with shampoo containing:
   a. nondetergent cleansers
   b. coal tar extract
   c. selenium
   d. hydrocortisone

____ 34. Most cases of impetigo can be successfully treated with topical:
   a. penicillin
   b. tetracycline
   c. mupirocin
   d. cefazolin

____ 35. Cellulitis is best treated with:
   a. topical antibiotics
   b. topical steroids
   c. systemic antibiotics
   d. systemic steroids

____ 36. A person infected with herpesvirus type 2 may obtain symptomatic relief by treatment with:
   a. Kantrex
   b. Valtrex
   c. Entex
   d. Nimbex

____ 37. Which of the following is NOT used to kill the organism that causes scabies?
   a. permethrin
   b. hydrocortisone
   c. lindane
   d. crotamiton

____ 38. A common treatment for patients with vitiligo and psoriasis is:
   a. PUFA
   b. PABA
   c. PUMA
   d. PUVA

____ 39. Which drug is taken orally to treat male pattern baldness?
   a. Rogaine
   b. Propecia
   c. Formula 405
   d. Nor-Tet

____ 40. A drug used to treat fungal skin infections is:
   a. Bactroban
   b. Valisone
   c. Diprolene
   d. Nizoral

Genitourinary System Drugs

The following genitourinary drugs are listed by brand name. In the space provided, list the corresponding generic name and short description of the drug.

1. Lasix   furosemide—diuretic

2. Viagra   _____

3. Macrobid   _____

4. Vicodin   _____

5. K-Dur   _____

6. Klor-Con   _____

7. Bactrim   _____

8. Pyridium   _____

9. Septra DS   _____

10. Caverject   _____

11. Vibramycin   _____

12. Cipro   _____

13. Micro-K   _____

14. Keflex   _____

15. Ecotrin   _____

16. Tylenol   _____

17. Proscar   _____

18. Hytrin   _____

19. Cardura   _____

20. Bicillin   _____

21. Ery-Tab   _____

22. Achromycin   _____

23. Rocephin   _____

24. Vasomax   _____

25. Maxzide   _____

Genitourinary System Drugs, Continued

Choose the correct answer in each of the following multiple-choice questions. Write your answer in the space provided next to the number of the question.

_____ 26. Which of the following drugs is a diuretic?
    a. hydrochlorothiazide
    b. nifedipine
    c. atenolol
    d. flecainide

_____ 27. Diuretics are used to treat:
    a. urinary tract infections
    b. chronic renal failure
    c. hypertension
    d. impotence

_____ 28. Which of the following is NOT a diuretic?
    a. diazepam
    b. Maxzide
    c. Lasix
    d. hydrochlorothiazide

_____ 29. Diuretics are used to increase the natural excretion of:
    a. potassium
    b. protein
    c. calcium
    d. sodium

_____ 30. Loop diuretics act at the proximal and distal tubules, as well as at the loop of:
    a. Henle
    b. Biebl
    c. Cordonnier
    d. Roeder

_____ 31. The excess loss of potassium can cause:
    a. urinary frequency
    b. cardiac arrhythmia
    c. bladder spasms
    d. swelling of the extremities

_____ 32. The dosage of potassium supplements is measured in:
    a. micrograms
    b. decaliters
    c. milliequivalents
    d. grams

Genitourinary System Drugs, Continued

_____ 33. Which of the following drugs are used to treat urinary tract infections but are not true antibiotics because they only *inhibit* the growth of bacteria?
   a. sulfonamides
   b. cephalosporins
   c. aminoglycosides
   d. corticosteroids

_____ 34. Flavoxate, L-hyoscyamine, and bethanechol are prescribed for:
   a. hypertension
   b. urinary tract irritation
   c. urinary tract infection
   d. chronic renal failure

_____ 35. Which of the following drugs changes the urine to ammonia and formaldehyde to exert a killing effect on bacteria?
   a. furosemide
   b. triamterene
   c. methanamine
   d. sulfamethoxazole

_____ 36. Dietary sources are not sufficient to replace diuretic-induced loss of:
   a. potassium
   b. sodium
   c. magnesium
   d. albumin

_____ 37. Which of the following drugs would likely be used to treat a urogenital infection with the sexually transmitted pathogen *Chlamydia trachomatis?*
   a. alendronate
   b. acetazolamide
   c. acetaminophen
   d. azithromycin

_____ 38. Bladder spasms associated with acute cystitis are often treated with the urinary tract analgesic:
   a. Pyridium
   b. Dyrenium
   c. Uricult
   d. Mestinon

_____ 39. Doxycycline, Septra DS, and Bactrim are prescribed for:
   a. hypertension
   b. urinary tract irritation
   c. urinary tract infection
   d. chronic renal failure

Gastrointestinal System Drugs

The following gastrointestinal drugs are listed by brand name. In the space provided, list the corresponding generic name and short description of the drug.

1. Tagamet   cimetidine—H$_2$ antagonist

2. Torecan _____

3. Donnatal _____

4. Ethamolin _____

5. Anusol-HC suppository _____

6. Mylanta _____

7. Phenergan _____

8. Tigan suppository _____

9. Mylicon _____

10. Lomotil _____

11. Propulsid _____

12. Reglan _____

13. Dulcolax tablets _____

14. Azulfidine _____

15. Surfak _____

16. Carafate _____

17. Metamucil _____

18. Axid _____

19. Prevacid _____

20. Prilosec _____

21. Pepcid AC _____

22. Di-Gel _____

23. Transderm Scop _____

24. Maalox _____

25. Zantac _____

Gastrointestinal System Drugs, Continued

Choose the correct answer in each of the following multiple-choice questions. Write your answer in the space provided next to the number of the question.

____ 26. H$_2$ blockers work by:
    a. neutralizing stomach acid
    b. preventing the release of stomach acid
    c. slowing peristalsis
    d. inhibiting the formation of prostaglandins

____ 27. An example of a laxative is:
    a. Gaviscon
    b. Prilosec
    c. Tagamet
    d. Senokot

____ 28. A common therapeutic gastrointestinal side effect of opiate drugs is:
    a. gastroesophageal reflux
    b. diarrhea
    c. constipation
    d. coffee grounds emesis

____ 29. Scopalamine is NOT used to treat:
    a. esophageal varices
    b. motion sickness
    c. stomach distress
    d. irritable colon

____ 30. Aluminum, magnesium, and calcium salts are active ingredients in:
    a. antiemetics
    b. antacids
    c. anthelmintics
    d. antidiarrheals

____ 31. The active ingredient in a Fleet enema is:
    a. barium
    b. sodium phosphates
    c. potassium
    d. aspidium

____ 32. Tucks pads are used for:
    a. cleansing the perianal area
    b. colostomy covering
    c. wound dressing
    d. truss padding

____ 33. The active ingredient in Preparation H rectal suppositories is:
    a. witch hazel
    b. lidocaine
    c. benzocaine
    d. shark liver oil

Gastrointestinal System Drugs, Continued

_____ 34. Which of the following is NOT an indication for Pepto-Bismol?
   a. constipation
   b. nausea and vomiting
   c. indigestion
   d. traveler's diarrhea

_____ 35. Compazine is indicated for:
   a. constipation
   b. diarrhea
   c. nausea and vomiting
   d. indigestion

_____ 36. Gastrointestinal infestation with *Giardia lamblia* may be treated with:
   a. Vermox
   b. Flagyl
   c. Biaxin
   d. Azulfidine

_____ 37. Treatment of Crohn's disease includes low-fiber diet, specific anti-inflammatory drugs, and medication to:
   a. reduce intestinal motility
   b. increase intestinal motility
   c. stop gastroesophageal reflux
   d. prevent vomiting

_____ 38. Which drug may be administered in an attempt to dissolve gallstones?
   a. loperamide
   b. paromomycin
   c. chenodiol
   d. ranitidine

_____ 39. An example of a bulk-producing laxative is:
   a. Phillips Milk of Magnesia
   b. Dulcolax tablets
   c. Citrucel
   d. Ex-Lax

_____ 40. The active ingredient in Tums antacid is:
   a. sodium
   b. calcium carbonate
   c. magnesium
   d. aluminum

_____ 41. In which doses are Propulsid tablets available?
   a. 1 and 2 mg
   b. 10 and 20 mg
   c. 100 and 200 mg
   d. 1 and 2 g

Musculoskeletal System Drugs

The following musculoskeletal drugs are listed by brand name. In the space provided, list the corresponding generic name and short description of the drug.

 1. Daypro   oxaprozin—nonsteroidal anti-inflammatory

 2. Anaprox   _____

 3. Lorcet   _____

 4. Soma   _____

 5. Flexeril   _____

 6. Tylenol with Codeine No. 3 _____

 7. Darvocet-N   _____

 8. Fiorinal   _____

 9. Tylenol   _____

10. Motrin   _____

11. Aleve   _____

12. Nalfon   _____

13. Lodine   _____

14. Naprosyn   _____

15. Oruvail   _____

16. Relafen   _____

17. Advil   _____

18. Toradol   _____

19. Voltaren   _____

20. Valium   _____

21. Feldene   _____

22. Percodan   _____

23. Tolectin DS   _____

24. Fosamax   _____

25. Ben-Gay   _____

Musculoskeletal System Drugs, Continued

Choose the correct answer in each of the following multiple-choice questions. Write your answer in the space provided next to the number of the question.

_____ 26. What is the name of the papaya extract used for lumbar disk injection?
    a. papaverine
    b. papain
    c. chymotrypsin
    d. chymopapain

_____ 27. Which chemical element is a therapeutic treatment for rheumatoid arthritis?
    a. copper
    b. gold
    c. silver
    d. zinc

_____ 28. The chemical name for aspirin is:
    a. lysergic acid
    b. naproxcn sodium
    c. acetylsalicylic acid
    d. acetylglucosamine

_____ 29. Which chemotherapy drug is sometimes used to treat rheumatoid arthritis?
    a. methotrexate
    b. doxorubicin
    c. cyclophosphamide
    d. actinomycin

_____ 30. The oldest drug to treat arthritis is:
    a. aspirin
    b. ibuprofen
    c. naproxen
    d. codeine

_____ 31. The generic name for Zyloprim is:
    a. allobarbital
    b. alfentanil
    c. allopurinol
    d. allantoin

_____ 32. A common treatment for bursitis and other inflammatory conditions is injection directly into the site with a:
    a. nonsteroidal anti-inflammatory agent
    b. corticosteroid
    c. smooth muscle relaxant
    d. saline solution

Musculoskeletal System Drugs, Continued

____ 33. Alendronate sodium is used to treat:
    a. inflammatory muscle conditions
    b. muscle spasm
    c. joint pain
    d. osteoporosis

____ 34. Paget disease may be treated with:
    a. calcipotriene
    b. calciferol
    c. caldiamide
    d. calcitonin

____ 35. Colchicine and probenecid are used in treatment of:
    a. bursitis
    b. gout
    c. muscle pain
    d. bone cancer

____ 36. When aspirin is prescribed in grains, it is prescribed according to which system of weights and measures?
    a. metric
    b. U.S. Standard
    c. apothecary
    d. British Standard

____ 37. Of the following drugs, which pain reliever is least likely to cause stomach upset?
    a. acetaminophen
    b. ibuprofen
    c. naproxen
    d. aspirin

____ 38. Which of the following drugs is spelled correctly?
    a. indomethocin
    b. carisoprodol
    c. etodilac
    d. diazapam

____ 39. Of the following musculoskeletal drugs, which functions as an antiprostaglandin?
    a. cyclobenzaprine
    b. carisoprodol
    c. aspirin
    d. alendronate

____ 40. Of the following musculoskeletal drugs, which functions as a skeletal muscle relaxant?
    a. orphenadrine
    b. prednisone
    c. dexamethasone
    d. ketoprofen

Cardiovascular System Drugs

The following cardiovascular drugs are listed by brand name. In the space provided, list the corresponding generic name and short description of the drug.

1. Cardizem — diltiazem—antianginal

2. Lescol _____

3. Calan _____

4. Minipress _____

5. Catapres _____

6. Lopressor _____

7. Nitro-Bid _____

8. Tonocard _____

9. Inderal _____

10. Coumadin _____

11. Capoten _____

12. Pravachol _____

13. Lanoxicaps _____

14. Quinidex _____

15. Isordil _____

16. Persantine _____

17. Procardia _____

18. Accupril _____

19. Adalat _____

20. Mevacor _____

21. Calan SR _____

22. Cardura _____

23. Cozaar _____

24. Dilacor XR _____

25. Lanoxin _____

Cardiovascular System Drugs, Continued

Choose the correct answer in each of the following multiple-choice questions. Write your answer in the space provided next to the number of the question.

_____ 26. Which of the following categories best describes the drug morphine?
  a. general anesthetic
  b. stimulant
  c. analgesic
  d. anti-inflammatory

_____ 27. Which of the following categories best describes heparin?
  a. vasodilator
  b. vasoconstrictor
  c. cardiotonic
  d. anticoagulant

_____ 28. Of the following drugs, which is prescribed as a cholesterol-lowering agent?
  a. Zocor
  b. Monopril
  c. Vasotec
  d. Norvasc

_____ 29. Nitrostat is administered:
  a. transdermally
  b. sublingually
  c. rectally
  d. intramuscularly

_____ 30. Which of the following drugs contains more than one active ingredient?
  a. Altace
  b. Zestril
  c. Prinivil
  d. Dyazide

_____ 31. Of the following drugs, which is used as a "clot buster" (thrombolytic agent) for patients with acute myocardial infarction?
  a. pentoxifylline
  b. alteplase
  c. nitroglycerin
  d. atenolol

_____ 32. What is the generic name for Zestril?
  a. lisinopril
  b. guanfacine
  c. verapamil
  d. reserpine

434

____ 33. The generic drug benazepril hydrochloride is also known by the brand name:
   a. Wyamine
   b. Wytensin
   c. Lotensin
   d. Lozol

____ 34. Ziac is indicated for:
   a. shock
   b. high cholesterol
   c. high blood pressure
   d. blood clots

____ 35. Of the following drugs, which is given to prevent or relieve angina pectoris?
   a. Nitrol
   b. Nicobid
   c. Nitropress
   d. Nicotrol

____ 36. Which of the following drugs is misspelled?
   a. Quinalan
   b. Tenex
   c. Prevalite
   d. Verilan

____ 37. Which of these drugs is indicated for intermittent claudication?
   a. Transderm-Nitro
   b. Trental
   c. Tridil
   d. Toprol XL

____ 38. Quinaglute is an:
   a. antithrombolytic
   b. antiarrhythmic
   c. antihypertensive
   d. antianginal

____ 39. Nitro-Bid ointment is prescribed by the:
   a. gram
   b. ounce
   c. cc (cubic centimeter)
   d. inch

____ 40. Pronestyl-SR is a long-acting form of:
   a. acebutolol
   b. sotalol
   c. pentoxifylline
   d. procainamide

Pulmonary System Drugs

The following respiratory system drugs are listed by brand name. In the space provided, list the corresponding generic name and short description of the drug.

1. Alupent   metaproterenol—bronchodilator

2. Theo-Dur   _____

3. Suprax   _____

4. Proventil aerosol   _____

5. Solu-Cortef   _____

6. Bricanyl   _____

7. Marax   _____

8. Isoclor liquid   _____

9. Ventolin aerosol   _____

10. Intal aerosol   _____

11. Bronkometer   _____

12. Vanceril AQ   _____

13. Slo-bid   _____

14. Atrovent   _____

15. Azmacort   _____

16. Hycotuss   _____

17. Serevent   _____

18. Slo-phyllin   _____

19. Adrenalin Chloride   _____

20. Deltasone   _____

21. Floxin   _____

22. Lorabid   _____

23. Brethaire   _____

24. Actifed   _____

25. Flovent   _____

Pulmonary System Drugs, Continued

Choose the correct answer in each of the following multiple-choice questions. Write your answer in the space provided next to the number of the question.

_____ 26. Which of the following drugs is an anticholinergic/bronchodilator?
    a. pseudoephedrine
    b. triamcinolone
    c. ipratropium
    d. fluoroquinolone

_____ 27. The successful treatment of non-drug-resistant pulmonary tuberculosis entails medicating the patient over an extended period of time with:
    a. three or four bactericidals
    b. two or more adrenal suppressants
    c. several cephalosporin antibiotics
    d. combination steroidal and antiinflammatory drugs

_____ 28. In what form is the bronchodilator drug Theo-Dur administered?
    a. sublingual absorption
    b. aerosol for inhalation
    c. sustained-release tablets
    d. intramuscular and intravenous administration only

_____ 29. The generic name for Azmacort is:
    a. flunisolide
    b. fluticasone
    c. triamcinolone
    d. beclomethasone

_____ 30. A brand name for the generic drug salmeterol is:
    a. Flovent
    b. Serevent
    c. Proventil
    d. Ventolin

_____ 31. The active ingredient in Primatene mist is:
    a. epinephrine
    b. theophylline
    c. albuterol
    d. isoetharine

_____ 32. Suprax, which is indicated for patients with an *S. pneumoniae* respiratory infection, should be taken:
    a. q.o.d. or q.d.
    b. q.d. or b.i.d.
    c. b.i.d. or t.i.d.
    d. q.i.d. or q.i.d.

Pulmonary System Drugs, Continued

_____ 33. The medication in an Atrovent inhaler is dispensed in:
   a. milliequivalents
   b. milliliters
   c. milligrams
   d. micrograms

_____ 34. The prophylactic allergic medication nedocromil is also known by the brand name:
   a. Talacen
   b. Tegopen
   c. Teladar
   d. Tilade

_____ 35. The active ingredient in Aquaphyllin, Elixophyllin, and Quibron-T is:
   a. bethamethasone
   b. theophylline
   c. isoproterenol
   d. ephedrine

_____ 36. The medication in an Isuprel inhaler is categorized as:
   a. an adrenergic agonist agent
   b. a beta blocker
   c. an anticholinergic
   d. an adrenal corticosteroid

_____ 37. In what form is Solu-Medrol administered?
   a. orally
   b. transdermally
   c. I.M. or I.V.
   d. via inhaler

_____ 38. Prednisone may be indicated in the treatment of:
   a. pulmonary tuberculosis
   b. emphysema
   c. severe asthma
   d. pleural effusion

_____ 39. Of the following drugs, which would NOT be used to help dissolve or prevent a pulmonary embolus?
   a. heparin
   b. prednisolone
   c. warfarin
   d. streptokinase

Endocrine System Drugs

The following endocrine system drugs are listed by brand name. In the space provided, list the corresponding generic name and short description of the drug.

1. Synthroid   levothyroxine—thyroid hormone

2. Lente L _____

3. Cytomel _____

4. Ultralente _____

5. Humulin 70/30 _____

6. Glucotrol _____

7. NPH Iletin I _____

8. Micronase _____

9. Glucophage _____

10. Lupron Depot _____

11. Glynase _____

12. Levoxyl _____

13. DiaBeta _____

14. Thyrolar _____

15. Regitine _____

16. Triostat _____

17. PTU _____

18. Nutropin AQ _____

19. Cytadren _____

20. Glucotrol XL _____

21. Tapazole _____

22. Sandostatin _____

23. Precose _____

24. Novolin L _____

25. Amaryl _____

Endocrine System Drugs, Continued

Choose the correct answer in each of the following multiple-choice questions. Write your answer in the space provided next to the number of the question.

_____ 26. Thyroid supplements may be synthetically manufactured or obtained from:
   a. desiccated fetal tissue
   b. ground bone fragments
   c. cadaveric donations
   d. dried animal glands

_____ 27. Which one of the following drugs is used to treat hyperthyroidism?
   a. liothyronine
   b. methimazole
   c. glimepiride
   d. levothyroxine

_____ 28. Which one of the following drugs is used as replacement therapy for decreased growth hormone?
   a. propylthiouracil
   b. somatropin
   c. betamethasone
   c. molgramostim

_____ 29. Low levels of ADH may be treated with:
   a. vasopressin
   b. Lopressor
   c. Catapres
   d. lutrelin

_____ 30. Which of the following is NOT an oral antidiabetic agent?
   a. Dymelor
   b. Glucophage
   c. Novolin
   d. Micronase

_____ 31. The therapeutic action of insulin can be lengthened by the addition of:
   a. protamine
   b. proadifen
   c. probenecid
   d. profenamine

_____ 32. Insulins are classified according to how quickly they act, which depends on the:
   a. size of the dose
   b. frequency of administration
   c. size of the insulin crystal
   d. time of injection

Endocrine System Drugs, Continued

_____ 33. Which of the following is a trade name for the generic drug triamcinolone?
    a. Decadron
    b. Solu-Cortef
    c. Kenalog
    d. Azulfidine

_____ 34. Of the following drugs, which is an oral corticosteroid?
    a. methylphenidate
    b. methylaminopterin
    c. methylnaltrexone
    d. methylprednisolone

_____ 35. In patients with Addison disease, fludrocortisone is used to treat low levels of:
    a. parotin
    b. aldosterone
    c. estrone
    d. erythropoietin

_____ 36. What does the letter R stand for in the drug Humulin R?
    a. regulated
    b. regular
    c. (slow) release
    d. recombinant

_____ 37. Type 1 diabetics must take:
    a. biguanides
    b. sulfonylureas
    c. insulin
    d. corticosteroids

_____ 38. A brand name for the generic drug metformin is:
    a. Glucophage
    b. Glucagon
    c. Glynase
    d. Glucotrol

_____ 39. Insulin is measured in:
    a. milligrams
    b. ounces
    c. micrograms
    d. units

_____ 40. Which diabetic drug does not usually produce hypoglycemia in diabetics?
    a. insulin
    b. glipizide
    c. glyburide
    d. metformin

Female Reproductive System Drugs

The following female reproductive system drugs are listed by brand name. In the space provided, list the corresponding generic name and short description of the drug.

1. Ortho-Novum 7/7/7   norethindrone, ethinyl estradiol—oral contraceptive

2. Flagyl _____

3. Triphasil _____

4. RhoGAM _____

5. Provera _____

6. Premarin _____

7. Parlodel _____

8. Vibramycin _____

9. Claforan _____

10. Gyne-Lotrimin _____

11. Prempro _____

12. Feosol _____

13. Cycrin _____

14. Demulen _____

15. Norplant _____

16. Estrace _____

17. Estraderm _____

18. Genora _____

19. Loestrin Fe _____

20. Lo/Ovral _____

21. Ortho-Cept _____

22. Ortho-Tri-Cyclen _____

23. Terazol 3 _____

24. Tri-Levlen _____

25. Desogen _____

Choose the correct answer in each of the following multiple-choice questions. Write your answer in the space provided next to the number of the question.

_____ 26. A solution applied to the cervix to highlight zones of abnormal tissue is:
    a. Lugol
    b. Shohl
    c. Monsel
    d. Burow

_____ 27. Which drug is a cervical ripening agent to terminate pregnancy?
    a. levonorgestrel
    b. dinoprostone
    c. magnesium sulfate
    d. saline solution

_____ 28. This androgen is prescribed for women with fibrocystic breast disease and pelvic pain from endometriosis:
    a. Arrestin
    b. Android
    c. Danocrine
    d. Virilon

_____ 29. Which drug inhibits milk production and breast engorgement in the nonlactating woman?
    a. Duvoid
    b. Lamictal
    c. Tace
    d. Parlodel

_____ 30. Menotropins are manufactured from:
    a. menstrual blood
    b. placental remnants
    c. urine of pregnant mares
    d. urine of postmenopausal women

_____ 31. Progestasert is a birth control method in which the contraceptive is:
    a. surgically inserted under the skin of the upper arm for five years
    b. placed into the uterine cavity for a period of a year
    c. placed over the cervix up to 12 hours before each sexual encounter
    d. injected intramuscularly every three months

_____ 32. Oxytocin is given to the pregnant woman in labor to:
    a. ease pain
    b. relax the uterus
    c. induce or speed up labor
    d. separate the symphysis pubis to facilitate delivery

Female Reproductive System Drugs, Continued

____ 33. Of the following drugs, which is NOT a local treatment for vaginal infection with *Candida albicans?*
   a. miconazole
   b. terconazole
   c. clotrimazole
   d. ketoconazole

____ 34. Dysmenorrhea is often treated with:
   a. antiprostaglandins
   b. antiinfectives
   c. antifungals
   d. antivirals

____ 35. What type of oral contraceptive is Ortho-Novum 7/7/7?
   a. aphasic
   b. monophasic
   c. biphasic
   d. triphasic

____ 36. The oral contraceptive Triphasil contains:
   a. ethinyl estradiol, levonorgestrel, and norgestimate
   b. ethinyl estradiol and levonorgestrel
   c. ethinyl estradiol and norethindrone
   d. ethinyl estradiol, norgestimate, and norethindrone

____ 37. Conjugated estrogens (but not combined with other drugs) are often prescribed for:
   a. birth control
   b. primary ovarian failure
   c. symptoms of menopause
   d. osteoporosis

____ 38. Of the following drugs, which are likely to be prescribed to treat an infection with *Gardnerella vaginalis?*
   a. danazol or progesterone
   b. leuprolide or nafarelin
   c. metronidazole or clindamycin
   d. clomiphene or synthetic estrogen

____ 39. Which of the following is classified as an ovulation stimulator?
   a. Climara
   b. Clomid
   c. Depo-Estradiol
   d. Estratab

Otorhinolaryngology Drugs

The following otorhinolaryngology drugs are listed by brand name. In the space provided, list the corresponding generic name and short description of the drug.

1. Claritin   loratadine—antihistamine

2. Beconase AQ _____

3. Flonase _____

4. Nasalide _____

5. Ocean Mist _____

6. Synalgos-DC _____

7. Amoxil _____

8. Augmentin _____

9. Duricef _____

10. Principen _____

11. Sumycin _____

12. Trimox _____

13. Zyrtec _____

14. Hismanal _____

15. Nasacort _____

16. Vancenase AQ _____

17. Antivert _____

18. Entex LA _____

19. Orabase _____

20. Otobiotic drops _____

21. Otosporin _____

22. Rhinocort Aqua _____

23. Auralgan Otic _____

24. Tympagesic _____

25. Cepastat _____

Otorhinolaryngology Drugs, Continued

Choose the correct answer in each of the following multiple-choice questions. Write your answer in the space provided next to the number of the question.

_____ 26. The initials DM in the trade name of a drug usually indicates the ingredient:
   a. Deconamine
   b. diphenhydramine
   c. Diamine
   d. dextromethorphan

_____ 27. Decongestants act in the tissues of the nose and respiratory tract by:
   a. opening the sinuses
   b. vasodilation
   c. vasoconstriction
   d. increasing the flow of mucus

_____ 28. An effective treatment for the common cold is the use of:
   a. dopamine receptor agonists
   b. antimicrobials
   c. decongestants
   d. antibiotics

_____ 29. Clotrimazole, ketoconazole, and nystatin are used to treat:
   a. thrush
   b. cold sores
   c. fever blisters
   d. gingivitis

_____ 30. Which of the following suppress the cough center in the brain?
   a. antiinfectives
   b. antiinflammatories
   c. antitussives
   d. analgesics

_____ 31. Some of the newer antihistamines do not cause drowsiness because they do not cross:
   a. the venous system
   b. the blood-brain barrier
   c. the heart
   d. the arterial system

_____ 32. Cerumenex is used to treat:
   a. itchy eyes
   b. stuffy nose
   c. sore throat
   d. ear wax

_____ 33. Refractory epistaxis may be treated medically with topical:
  a. clindamycin
  b. phenylpropanolamine
  c. sulfa
  d. silver nitrate

_____ 34. A patient who experiences vertigo resulting from acute labyrinthitis might be treated with:
  a. chlorpheniramine maleate
  b. prednisone
  c. meclizine
  d. cefazolin

_____ 35. Which of the following would NOT be given to treat swimmer's ear?
  a. antibiotics
  b. hydrocortisone
  c. analgesics
  d. antivirals

_____ 36. Otitis media caused by *Streptococcus pneumoniae* or *Haemophilus influenzae* might be treated with:
  a. Antivert
  b. Augmentin
  c. Arlidin
  d. Aquaphor

_____ 37. Nasal polyps and severe vasomotor rhinitis may be treated with beclomethasone and dexamethasone, which are:
  a. metabolites
  b. corticosteroids
  c. stimulants
  d. enzymes

_____ 38. The active ingredient in Flonase nasal spray is:
  a. oxymetalazone
  b. saline solution
  c. silver nitrate
  d. fluticasone

_____ 39. Chloraseptic throat spray works by:
  a. delivering a topical antibiotic
  b. counteracting inflammation with topical steroid
  c. anesthetizing the throat
  d. inducing asepsis

Ophthalmology Drugs

The following ophthalmology drugs are listed by brand name. In the space provided, list the corresponding generic name and short description of the drug.

1. Cyclogyl   cyclopentolate—cycloplegic, mydriatic

2. Sodium Sulamyd _____

3. Timoptic Ocumeter _____

4. Trusopt _____

5. Epifrin _____

6. Humorsol Ocumeter _____

7. Garamycin drops _____

8. Opti-Soft _____

9. Optigene _____

10. Healon _____

11. Neosporin ophthalmic _____

12. Botox _____

13. TobraDex _____

14. Ilotycin _____

15. NeoDecadron Ocumeter _____

16. Blephamide _____

17. Betopic-S _____

18. Terra-Cortril _____

19. Viroptic _____

20. Ocuflox _____

21. Alomide _____

22. Acular _____

23. Lacrisert _____

24. Alphagan _____

25. Cetapred _____

Ophthalmology Drugs, Continued

Choose the correct answer in each of the following multiple-choice questions. Write your answer in the space provided next to the number of the question.

_____ 26. Silver nitrate is often applied to the eyes of newborn infants to prevent possible infection from:
    a. gonorrhea
    b. meconium
    c. streptococcus
    d. candidiasis

_____ 27. A yellow water-based dye that is used to outline corneal abrasions is:
    a. floxuridine
    b. fludarabine
    c. fluorescein
    d. fludrocortisone

_____ 28. Drugs to treat glaucoma act by:
    a. decreasing the aqueous humor
    b. toughening the inner eye structures
    c. shrinking the overall size of the eyeball
    d. releasing microdroplets of antibiotic

_____ 29. A drug used commonly in eye surgery to keep the anterior chamber expanded is:
    a. Isopto Cetamide
    b. Viroptic
    c. Amvisc
    d. Betimol

_____ 30. A drug that constricts the pupil is called a:
    a. mimetic
    b. mydriatic
    c. microtia
    d. miotic

_____ 31. Which of the following drugs is NOT used to treat open-angle glaucoma?
    a. levobunolol
    b. metipranolol
    c. propranolol
    d. timolol

_____ 32. A brand name for the combination drug sulfacetamide sodium and phenylephrine is:
    a. Vasosulf
    b. FML-S
    c. Bleph-10
    d. Vasocidin

Ophthalmology Drugs, Continued

_____ 33. The generic name for Mydriacyl is:
   a. tropicamide
   b. scopolamine
   c. atropine
   d. apraclonidine

_____ 34. Adsorbonac is used to:
   a. paralyze the eyelid
   b. constrict the pupil
   c. dilate the pupil
   d. reduce corneal edema

_____ 35. An intraocular irrigant of physiologic saline solution used during eye surgery to irrigate and protect the eye is:
   a. IOP
   b. BSS
   c. AZT
   d. IOL

_____ 36. Liquifilm is used for:
   a. rehydrating dry eyes
   b. intraocular pressure reduction
   c. topical anesthesia
   d. controlling diabetic retinopathy

_____ 37. Superficial infections of the cornea, conjunctiva, eyelid, and tear duct are often treated with:
   a. topical corticosteroids
   b. topical antivirals
   c. topical anesthetics
   d. topical antibiotics

_____ 38. Mydriatics block the action of:
   a. sorbitol
   b. aqueous humor
   c. acetylcholine
   d. histamine

_____ 39. Botox works by:
   a. lysing fibers which hold the lens in place
   b. preventing contraction of the pupil during surgery
   c. lubricating the lacrimal glands
   d. paralyzing muscle fibers

Nervous System Drugs

The following nervous system drugs are listed by brand name. In the space provided, list the corresponding generic name and short description of the drug.

1. Dilantin   phenytoin—anticonvulsant

2. Tegretol _____

3. Sinemet CR _____

4. Tensilon _____

5. Pamelor _____

6. Diamox _____

7. Ambien _____

8. BuSpar _____

9. Depakote _____

10. Effexor _____

11. Klonopin _____

12. Paxil _____

13. Prozac _____

14. Risperdal _____

15. Ritalin _____

16. Tranxene-SD _____

17. Asendin _____

18. Xanax _____

19. Zoloft _____

20. Enlon _____

21. Lortab ASA _____

22. Imitrex _____

23. Propacet 100 _____

24. Roxicet _____

25. Stadol NS _____

Nervous System Drugs, Continued

Choose the correct answer in each of the following multiple-choice questions. Write your answer in the space provided next to the number of the question.

_____ 26. Which of the following of routes of administration best describes injection of a drug into the meninges of the spinal column?
    a. subcutaneous
    b. intrathecal
    c. intracavitary
    d. intradermal

_____ 27. Which of the following medications is the drug of choice for treating adults with tonic-clonic seizures?
    a. diazepam
    b. phenytoin
    c. selegiline
    d. tacrine

_____ 28. Which of the following drugs is classified as a hydantoin?
    a. Mestinon
    b. Metrodin
    c. Metasome
    d. Mesantoin

_____ 29. Drug therapies for Parkinson disease act to restore the natural balance between dopamine and:
    a. acetylcholine
    b. cholinesterase
    c. histamine
    d. prostaglandin

_____ 30. Nonbarbiturate hypnotics include:
    a. flurazepam
    b. clozapine
    c. thiothixene
    d. desipramine

_____ 31. Nonbarbiturate over-the-counter sleep aids commonly contain which active ingredient?
    a. decongestant
    b. antihistamine
    c. acetaminophen
    d. aspirin

_____ 32. Severe attention deficit disorder in children is often treated with:
    a. hypnotics
    b. barbiturates
    c. amphetamines
    d. hydantoins

Nervous System Drugs, Continued

_____ 33. This drug is used exclusively to treat the symptoms of manic-depressive illness:
  a. clozapine
  b. haloperidol
  c. lithium
  d. chlorpromazine

_____ 34. Which of the following drugs is prescribed for alcoholics who wish to stop drinking?
  a. fluoxetine
  b. disulfiram
  c. molindone
  d. carisoprodol

_____ 35. Phenothiazines are just as effective as barbiturates in treating psychosis but produce much less:
  a. anxiety
  b. dizziness
  c. central nervous system stimulation
  d. central nervous system depression

_____ 36. Minor tranquilizers exert a specific therapeutic action in treating:
  a. obsessive-compulsive disorder
  b. schizophrenia
  c. neurosis
  d. bipolar disorder

_____ 37. Benzodiapezines are categorized as which schedule drugs?
  a. I
  b. II
  c. III
  d. IV

_____ 38. The treatment of psychosis involves the use of antipsychotic drugs, also called:
  a. anxiolytics
  b. neuroleptics
  c. hypnotics
  d. succinimides

_____ 39. Migraine headaches can be treated successfully in most people with:
  a. imipramine
  b. sertraline
  c. sumatriptan
  d. amitriptyline

_____ 40. Which drug is used to treat myasthenia gravis?
  a. edrophonium
  b. zolpidem
  c. alprazolam
  d. paroxetine

453

Immune System and Oncology Drugs

The following immune system drugs are listed by brand name. In the space provided, list the corresponding generic name and short description of the drug.

1. Zovirax   acyclovir—antiviral

2. Solu-Medrol _____

3. Cytovene _____

4. Cytoxan _____

5. Adriamycin _____

6. Platinol _____

7. Zithromax _____

8. Abelcet _____

9. DaunoXome _____

10. Marinol _____

11. Epogen _____

12. Crixivan _____

13. Procrit _____

14. Neupogen _____

15. Hivid _____

16. Zerit _____

17. Leukine _____

18. Invirase _____

19. Pentam 300 _____

20. Megace _____

21. Epivir _____

22. Alferon N _____

23. Foscavir _____

24. Imuran _____

25. Oncovin _____

Immune System and Onology Drugs, Continued

Choose the correct answer in each of the following multiple-choice questions. Write your answer in the space provided next to the number of the question.

____ 26. Which of the following is a cancer chemotherapy drug?
    a. Gantrisin
    b. Cytoxan
    c. Amoxil
    d. Keflex

____ 27. Gamimune N is used in the treatment of which autoimmune disorder?
    a. systemic lupus erythematosus
    b. multiple sclerosis
    c. acquired immunodeficiency syndrome
    d. rheumatoid arthritis

____ 28. The chemotherapy protocol MOPP is an abbreviation for the drugs:
    a. mechlorethamine, doxorubicin, prednisone, cisplatin
    b. nitrogen mustard, vincristine, procarbazine, prednisone
    c. vincristine, methotrexate, cyclophosphamide, bleomycin
    d. methotrexate, vincristine, cisplatin, prednisone

____ 29. For anorexia associated with weight loss in patients with AIDS, which medication is given to stimulate appetite?
    a. Alferon N
    b. Dexedrine
    c. Marinol
    d. Foscavir

____ 30. Saquinavir mesylate is categorized as:
    a. an antiviral agent
    b. a chemotherapy drug
    c. an adrenergic agonist agent
    d. an antiemetic

____ 31. Which of these drugs is used to treat cytomegalovirus in patients with AIDS?
    a. megestrol acetate
    b. azithromycin
    c. clindamycin
    d. foscarnet

____ 32. DaunoXome is a medication that may be prescribed for patients with AIDS in an attempt to treat:
    a. progressive CMV infection
    b. advanced HIV-related Kaposi sarcoma
    c. intractable anorexia and cachexia
    d. severe neutropenia

Immune System and Oncology Drugs, Continued

_____ 33. The generic name for Retrovir is:
   a. sargramostim
   b. zalcitabine
   c. zidovudine
   d. indinavir

_____ 34. *Mycobacterium avium* complex can often be prevented in persons with AIDS using:
   a. Alferon N
   b. Crixivan
   c. Zithromax
   d. Combivir

_____ 35. Which of the following drugs would be prescribed for a person suffering from oro-pharyneal and esophageal candidiasis and cryptococcal meningitis?
   a. Diflucan
   b. Epivir
   c. Epogen
   d. Abelcet

_____ 36. Of the following, which is NOT prescribed as a preventative for *Pneumocystis carinii* pneumonia?
   a. penicillin
   b. atovaquone
   c. pentamidine
   d. trimethoprim-sulfamethaxazole

_____ 37. Avonex and Betaseron are used in the treatment of:
   a. Hodgkin disease
   b. hairy cell leukemia
   c. recurring genital or venereal warts
   d. multiple sclerosis

_____ 38. Interferon gamma-1b is known by the trade name:
   a. Roferon-A
   b. Pentam 3000
   c. Actimmune
   d. Ambisome

_____ 39. Acute rheumatic fever, an autoimmune disease that affects the heart, joints, and the skin, must be treated immediately with:
   a. amphotericin B lipid complex
   b. penicillin or similar antibiotic
   c. GM-CSF or G-CSF
   d. prednisone or similar corticosteroid

Anesthesia Drugs

The following anesthesia drugs are listed by brand name. In the space provided, list the corresponding generic name and short description of the drug.

1. Phenergan   promethazine—antihistamine, antiemetic

2. Epifoam

3. Marcaine

4. Fluothane

5. Xylocaine Viscous

6. Versed

7. Suprane

8. Diprivan

9. Duranest

10. Naropin

11. Nesacaine

12. Americaine

13. Ophthetic

14. Cetacaine

15. Dyclone

16. Emla

17. Pramoxine HC

18. Adrenalin Chloride

19. Pentothal

20. Novocain

21. Anectine

22. Pontocaine

23. Sensorcaine

24. Fluori-Methane

25. ProctoFoam NS

457

Anesthesia Drugs, Continued

Choose the correct answer in each of the following multiple-choice questions. Write your answer in the space provided next to the number of the question.

_____26. Which type of anesthesia produces loss of consciousness?
 a. general
 b. regional
 c. local
 d. spinal

_____27. Which of the following drugs is a tranquilizer used occasionally during surgery because of its postoperative amnesiac effect?
 a. Valium
 b. Versed
 c. Restoril
 d. Xanax

_____28. The most widely used topical, local, regional, and spinal anesthetic is:
 a. Xylocaine
 b. Marcaine
 c. Novocain
 d. Hurricaine

_____29. Which of the following is NOT a method by which anesthesia is obtained in the trunk and lower extremities?
 a. spinal
 b. caudal
 c. epidural
 d. regional

_____30. Why is atropine often administered preoperatively?
 a. to relax the patient
 b. for prophylaxis against wound infections
 c. to decrease mouth and upper airway secretions
 d. to reduce blood loss

_____31. What drug classification includes mephentermine, metaraminol, and methoxamine?
 a. antidote
 b. antiarrhythmic
 c. vasopressor
 d. osmotic

_____32. What substance is often included in local anesthetic injections to act as a vasoconstrictor to decrease blood flow to the area of surgery?
 a. curare
 b. epinephrine
 c. prednisone
 d. acetylcysteine

____ 33. How is anesthesia obtained in a single, whole body part such as an extremity?
   a. regional nerve block
   b. subarachnoid injection
   c. intravenous injection
   d. subcutaneous local injection

____ 34. What type of analgesics bind with opiate receptors in the brain to block pain and maintain unconsciousness?
   a. salicylates
   b. steroids
   c. barbiturates
   d. narcotics

____ 35. What is the trade name for the IV barbiturate thiopental?
   a. Thioplex
   b. Pentothal
   c. Thorazine
   d. Pentazine

____ 36. Neuromuscular blocking agents are administered during general anesthesia to:
   a. prevent immediate postoperative pain
   b. induce skeletal muscle relaxation
   c. provide an extra measure of anesthesia
   d. reduce blood loss

____ 37. What diagnosis creates the need for the administration of dantrolene during an operative procedure?
   a. epilepsy
   b. drug addiction
   c. malignant hyperthermia
   d. antibiotic allergy

____ 38. How is anesthesia obtained on the skin surface?
   a. topical application
   b. subcutaneous local injection
   c. Bier block
   d. intravenous infusion

____ 39. Halothane, which was developed from technology involved with research on uranium during World War II, is known by what brand name?
   a. Haldol
   b. Fluothane
   c. Halcion
   d. Emetine

Radiology Drugs

The following radiologic drugs are listed by brand name. In the space provided, list the corresponding generic name and short description of the drug.

1. Gastrografin   diatrizoate meglumine, diatrizoate sodium—contrast radiopaque agent

2. Cardiolite   _____

3. Hexabrix   _____

4. Renovue-65   _____

5. Ethiodol   _____

6. Reno-M-Dip   _____

7. Tomocat   _____

8. Technescan Q-12   _____

9. ProstaScint   _____

10. Amipaque   _____

11. Conray   _____

12. Baro-cat   _____

13. Omnipaque   _____

14. Angiovist   _____

15. Cholebrine   _____

16. Hypaque   _____

17. Magnevist   _____

18. Isovue   _____

19. Kinevac   _____

20. Liquipake   _____

21. Lymphazurin   _____

22. Myoscint   _____

23. Oragrafin Sodium   _____

24. Cystografin   _____

25. Baroflave   _____

Radiology Drugs, Continued

Choose the correct answer in each of the following multiple-choice questions. Write your answer in the space provided next to the number of the question.

____ 26. Gadolinium (gd) is used for contrast enhancement for which of the following studies?
    a. computerized tomography
    b. magnetic resonance imaging
    c. Doppler ultrasound imaging
    d. radionuclide scan

____ 27. What type of CT contrast is used in order to avoid contrast reactions?
    a. radionuclide
    b. nonsteroidal
    c. iodinated
    d. nonionic

____ 28. Of the following, which is used for transrectal ultrasound of the prostate?
    a. EchoGen
    b. Magnevist
    c. Reno-M-Dip
    d. Conray

____ 29. The abbreviation for technetium is:
    a. Tm
    b. Tn
    c. Tc
    d. tM

____ 30. Most radioisotopes are administered in:
    a. millijoules
    b. milligrams
    c. milliroentgens
    d. millicuries

____ 31. Contrast material for a myelogram is injected into the:
    a. subdural space
    b. intervertebral disks
    c. nerve roots
    d. subarachnoid space

____ 32. What medication is administered to ease bowel spasm or motion so that clear images can be obtained on radiography?
    a. barium
    b. phenobarbital
    c. glucagon
    d. normal saline solution

Radiology Drugs, Continued

____ 33. Hypaque-Cysto is an imaging agent often used to visualize the:
    a. bladder
    b. gallbladder
    c. esophagus
    d. uterine structures

____ 34. Contrast agents for computed tomography and magnetic resonance scans are administered:
    a. orally
    b. subcutaneously
    c. intravenously
    d. via mask

____ 35. Of the following technetium radioactive agents, which is used for cardiac imaging?
    a. teboroxime
    b. bicisate
    c. medronate
    d. succimer

____ 36. For which of these studies would barium sulfate be used?
    a. CT scan of the sinuses
    b. plain films of the abdomen
    c. ultrasound of the uterus
    d. upper GI series

____ 37. Which of the following radioactive agents is spelled correctly?
    a. penitate
    b. pryophosphate
    c. sulesomab
    d. furfosmin

____ 38. Technetium 99m mertiatide is a radioactive agent used as a diagnostic aid for:
    a. labeling red blood cells
    b. renal function testing
    c. brain imaging
    d. infectious lesions

____ 39. Diethylenetriaminepentaacetic acid, a diagnostic aid that is often bound to technetium for radiographic imaging, is abbreviated:
    a. DTPA
    b. DNPA
    c. DMPA
    d. DLPA

The Authors

The Medical Transcription Workbook was written and developed by the editorial staff of Health Professions Institute (HPI), Modesto, California.

Linda Campbell, CMT, Director of Education and Product Development, has been with HPI since 1987. In this capacity she coordinated the development of *The SUM Program for Medical Transcription Training* and its *Student Syllabus* and *Teacher's Manual.* In addition, she helped to develop the training course, *Medical Transcription Fundamentals & Practice,* published by Prentice Hall, as well as *Module 4, Medical Transcription,* of the Independent Study Program in Medical Record Technology, published by the American Health Information Management Association (AHIMA). She has been in the medical transcription field for over twenty years, having worked as a medical transcriptionist for hospitals, transcription companies, and in self-employment. She has written and edited many articles and books and presented seminars and workshops for medical transcription teachers and practitioners. She works with medical facilities and educational institutions to implement medical transcription training programs and advises individuals in self-directed study.

Diane S. Heath, CMT, Associate Editor of Health Professions Institute since May 1997, has worked in the medical transcription field for over thirty years, working for physician offices, hospitals, and transcription services. She was transcription supervisor for a major medical imaging center for seven years and has also been an independent contractor. She served as Director of Transcription Practices at the American Association for Medical Transcription (AAMT) for five years prior to joining the HPI editorial staff. She has written and edited many articles published in the *Journal of AAMT* and in the HPI quarterly magazine, *Perspectives on the Medical Transcription Profession.*

Sally C. Pitman, M.A. (English), is editor and publisher of Health Professions Institute, Modesto, California. She has published over thirty books (including seven editions of Vera Pyle's *Current Medical Terminology*) and numerous periodicals, including the quarterly *Perspectives on the Medical Transcription Profession,* now in its eighth year. She published *The SUM Program for Medical Transcription Training* and numerous other educational materials for medical transcriptionists, teachers, supervisors, and business owners. She owned a medical transcription service for ten years (until 1982), having previously taught English in a community college for five years. She was a founding director of AAMT (1978-1984), editor and publisher of all AAMT publications for eight years (until September 1986), author of *The eMpTy Laugh Book* (AAMT, 1981), and co-author of the *Style Guide for Medical Transcription* (AAMT, 1985). She was also the founder and first executive director of the Medical Transcription Industry Alliance (MTIA), a membership association for medical transcription businesses. Since 1985 she has owned and operated Health Professions Institute (formerly Prima Vera Publications), serving the medical transcription educational market through publications, seminars, and conferences for teachers, supervisors, business owners, and transcriptionists.